UNDER THE GENERAL EDITORSHIP OF

JESSE W. MARKHAM

Princeton University

HOUGHTON MIFFLIN
ADVISER IN ECONOMICS

ELEMENTS OF

MATHEMATICAL ECONOMICS

A. Kooros
RUTGERS UNIVERSITY

HOUGHTON MIFFLIN COMPANY · BOSTON
NEW YORK · ATLANTA · GENEVA, ILL. · DALLAS · PALO ALTO

To Angela

Editor's Introduction

The present state of the economics profession illustrates the "two cultures" lamented so forcefully and justifiably by the eminent scientist and novelist, C. P. Snow. In one culture are the economists who are versed in the language of traditional economics; in the other culture are the economists versed in the language of mathematical economics.

With *Elements of Mathematical Economics*, Professor Kooros has attempted to make it easier for undergraduates, graduates, and professionals working in the field of economics and untrained in mathematical analysis to learn the language and to master the tools employed by the mathematical economists. Professor Kooros begins his text with a treatment of college algebra and trigonometry (which, for many students, may serve as a review). He then takes the student through the calculus, differential and difference equations, and through vector and matrix analysis. His treatment will be welcomed especially by teachers who find it necessary to teach mathematics to economics students in far less time than allowed by the usual mathematics curriculum.

Unfortunately, but understandably, most mathematics texts are written by mathematicians for mathematicians, all of whom share the same culture and speak the same language. Mindful of the problem of language, Professor Kooros goes far beyond the conventional textbook in providing verbal explanations. And he has related mathematics to the relevant areas of economic inquiry—to demand elasticity, production functions, growth models, systems of stable competitive equilibrium, linear programming, game theory, and activity analysis. In this way he has succeeded in lowering the linguistic barrier between the non-mathematical and the mathematical economist and thereby he has helped to join the two cultures.

JESSE W. MARKHAM
Princeton University

Preface

The role of mathematics in economics has been recognized by a host of economists: economics departments offer courses in mathematical analysis and econometrics; economic journals publish mathematically oriented articles. This recognition has been forthcoming not only because mathematical methods are powerful analytical tools, but also because they simplify exposition. Indeed, many of today's economists and students regard mastery of mathematical methods as essential to their professional advancement.

Elements of Mathematical Economics has evolved from my teaching of mathematical economics and econometrics at Rutgers University and the University of Southern California. In general the students whom I have encountered have had only sketchy backgrounds in pure mathematics. And even the rare students with fuller backgrounds have tended to be unfamiliar with mathematical tools and concepts frequently used in mathematical economics.

This text is addressed to serious undergraduates, as well as to graduate students. My primary purpose has been to demonstrate to students that there are a few basic mathematical models and theorems underlying a great majority of the problems in macroeconomics and microeconomics. I have endeavored to demonstrate this by covering four fundamental areas in the following four parts: *Introduction*—elementary mathematical economics confined to the fields of college algebra and trigonometry (which may be omitted by the advanced student); *Differential and Integral Calculus*—its relation to the concepts of elasticity and production functions; *Differential and Difference Equations*—employment in growth models of Harrod, Hicks, Duesenberry, and Samuelson, and in models of stable competitive equilibrium; *Vector and Matrix Analysis*—application to linear programming, games theory, and activity analysis.

Like most books, this one has been several years in the making. Consequently, the obligations I have incurred to friends and colleagues who discussed its subject matter with me are truly too numerous to specify in full. Obviously, my intellectual debt is to those masters who put economics on a mathematical basis: Alfred Marshall, John M. Keynes, Irving Fisher, Leon Walras, William S. Jevons, Michael Kalecki and Paul Samuelson, to name a few. I am also grateful to my former students, for they have taught me to communicate with my present students, who come to economics with little previous knowledge of mathematics, but with a fund of enthusiasm about learning mathematical economics and econometrics. I also wish to express my gratitude to Professor Jesse W. Markham, editorial adviser in economics for Houghton Mifflin Company; to Professor Kenneth K. Kurihara of Rutgers University for his sincere interest and suggestions; to Professor Stephen Goldfeld of Princeton University for his constructive criticism; and to the editorial staff of Houghton Mifflin Company, particularly Mr. Hugh E. Joyce, Jr. and Miss Saba L. Foster for their invaluably helpful suggestions.

The completion of this book was made possible by a summer fellowship from the Rutgers Research Council. I wish to express my debt of gratitude to the Council.

Finally, my debt to my patient and inspiring wife, to whom I have dedicated this book, extends far beyond these pages.

A. Kooros
Rutgers University

Contents

PART III: Differential and Difference Equations

PART IV: Programming, Games, and Activity Analysis

ELEMENTS OF
MATHEMATICAL ECONOMICS

PART I

Introduction

VARIABLES, FUNCTIONS, AND EQUATIONS

1.1 Introduction

Mathematics is a postulational and deductive discipline. By this it is meant that mathematical conclusions are obtained *a la* certain *a priori* assumptions. One very famous example in view is Euclid's Theorem, "Through a point P not on a line L there can be drawn exactly one line parallel to L," which depends on a certain postulate. From a different postulate, Labachevski and Polyai proved that "Through a point P not on a line L there can be drawn infinitely many different lines parallel to L."

Those branches of systematic sciences which have been steadily progressing toward a universal system of theories develop principles that are strict, and for that purpose mathematics has been indispensable. Indeed, in sciences such as physics, mathematics has been applied with great success; they can hardly proceed without the aid of mathematics. It is believed[1] that Jevons was the first to declare: "I have long thought that as [Economics] deals throughout with quantities, it must be a mathematical science in matter if not in language."[2] Furthermore, he contended that "it is clear that Economics, if it is to be a science at all, must be a mathematical science."[3] That is, if economics is to be systematized at all, so that one can deduce certain logical conclusions, it is to be based on mathematical laws and foundations.

In the latter part of the nineteenth century, there were many economists, actually mathematicians, such as Cournot, Jevons and Marshall, who endeavored to mathematize economics — putting economics into mathematical dimensions — in order to: (1) elaborate their visions with precise logical proofs, (2) make the definitions and assumptions explicit and

---

[1] J. Schumpeter, "The Common Sense of Econometrics," *Econometrica*, 1933, p. 8.
[2] W. S. Jevons, *The Theory of Political Economy*, 3rd Ed., London, 1888, p. vii.
[3] *Ibid.*, p. 3.

3

rigorous at each stage of reasoning process so that the mathematization of a theory may bring out lucidly the limitations and possibilities of the theory while avoiding the digression of vague argumentation. A vivid classical illustration of the above dichotomy is a letter by A. Marshall to Colson, a French economist. Marshall wrote:[4] "Briefly — I read Mill's *Political Economy* in 1886 or '7, while I was teaching advanced mathematics: and, as I thought much more easily in mathematics at that time than in English, I tried to translate him into mathematics before forming an opinion as to the validity of his work. I found much amiss in his analysis, and especially in two matters. . . . At that time and for long after I knew very little of the realities of economic life. But I worked at what I regard as the central problem of distribution and exchange. Before 1871 when Jevons' *very important* Theory of Political Economy appeared, I had worked out the whole skeleton of my present system [*Principles of Economics*] in mathematics though not in English. My mathematical Note xxi concentrated my notions: but the greater part of the earlier notes and especially Notes xiv–xx were evolved in substance about the same time."

From Marshall's letter it is apparent that mathematics can be, and has been, used in two ways. In fact, mathematical economics has been developed in two directions in the twentieth century. One recent example of the first kind is the rigorous mathematical proof of the stability of competitive equilibrium.[5] An example of the second kind is the translation of Keynes' *General Theory* into mathematical terms.[6] Whatever route an economist selects, whether one employs mathematics to expound one's conception or to use mathematics as a translator of one's views, a mathematical economist must be cognizant of a set of mathematical tools with which he can maneuver.

All mathematical tools are abstract in nature and deal with symbols of various kinds. Mathematics defines, in a scientific way, the relationships which exist between these symbols. By and large, mathematics is composed of three categories: mathematical analysis, geometry, and trigonometry. Mathematical analysis is the logical system of the theorems of

---

[4]This letter was reprinted in the *Econometrica*, 1933, pp. 221–22.

[5]T. Negishi, "The Stability of a Competitive Economy: A Survey Article," *Econometrica*, 1962, pp. 635–669. The list of the references at the end of the article gives the names of those who have contributed to the discussion of stability of equilibrium.

[6]J. E. Meade, "A Simplified Model of the Keynes' System," *Review of Economic Studies*, 1936. J. R. Hicks, "Mr. Keynes and the 'Classics'; A Suggested Interpretation," *Econometrica*, 1937. Samuelson has suggested straightforwardly that, "I must confess that my own first reaction to the General Theory was not at all like that of Keats on first looking into Chapman's Homer. No silent watcher, I, upon a peak in Darien. My rebellion against its pretensions would have been complete except for an uneasy realization that I did not at all understand what it was about. And I think I am giving away no secrets when I solemnly aver — upon the basis of vivid personal recollection — that no one else in Cambridge, Massachusetts, really knew what it was about for some 12 to 18 months after its publication. Indeed, until the appearance of the mathematical models of Meade, Lange, Hicks, and Harrod there is reason to believe that Keynes himself did not truly understand his own analysis," in "Lord Keynes and the General Theory," *Econometrica*, 1946, pp. 187–88.

algebra and calculus which are deduced *independently* of the graphical method. It deals with variables, parameters, constants, functional equations and the relationships between the variables of a given mathematical statement.   In being concerned with spatial relationships and graphs, geometry studies the properties of points and all spaces and the relationships of graphs within spaces, including the three-dimensional one in which we live. The conclusions of geometrical investigations are presented in terms of a system of axioms. Trigonometry is a bridge between mathematical analysis and geometry in the sense that it is the extension of mathematical analysis to spatial configurations of geometry.

In this book, we are primarily involved in the application of the rules of mathematical analysis to mathematical economics with references to geometrical and trigonometrical analyses. Nearly all economic issues are presented with the aid of graphical illustrations.

1.2 Variables

Variables are the basic raw materials of mathematical analysis. Variables are letters and other symbols which are used to represent numbers of various nature. As a direct consequence of the introduction of letters and symbols, the rules of arithmetic are replaced by the general statements of analysis. *A variable is a symbol which during a discussion may assume different values or a set of admissible values.* On the other hand, a symbol whose value remains fixed during the discussion is called a *constant*. A particular number or object which can be represented by a variable is called a *value*.

Let us suppose that there are three stores in a small town and that the price of sugar in those stores includes 10, 15, and 20 cents per pound. If we assign p to the price of sugar in all the stores, then p will be our *variable* and 10, 15, 20 are the *values* which p can take on. If the price of sugar were fixed at 15 cents in all three stores, p would be a *constant* mathematically. In the first example, p varies from 10 to 20 cents. Ten and 20 are referred to respectively as the lower and upper bounds of the range of values that p takes on. Thus, a *range* is the set of all possible values of a variable. The lower value of the range is called the lower bound and its upper value is referred to as the upper bound of the range.

For the sake of uniformity, in pure mathematics usually the first letters of the alphabet are used to represent constants, while the letters at the end of the alphabet are used to express variables. There are many exceptions to this rule in mathematical economics where a variable is often represented by the first letter of its name. For example, the symbol for investment is generally I, for savings S, for price P, for quantity Q, and so forth.

A variable may be either continuous or discrete. A *continuous* variable is one which may take on any value within a specified range, where the range is either the whole set of real numbers or any interval of the set.

When values are ranked as to weight, successive values in this case may differ by infinitesimal increments. A *discrete* variable, on the other hand, takes only a discrete range; values of such a variable, ranked in order, change only by definite amounts. The curve of the underlying values of a discrete variable is not smooth as it is for a continuous variable. Employment, shown by N, is commonly considered discrete, while income, investment, savings, prices, and utilities are considered continuous.

1.3 Functions and Their Graphic Representation

Any student who has taken an introductory course in economics has definitely been introduced to two basic concepts: the macroconcept of the consumption function and the micronotions of demand and supply functions. The consumption function is usually an upward sloping curve in a two-dimensional diagram where income is measured along the vertical axis and consumption expenditure along the horizontal one. Similarly, in a two-dimensional diagram, a demand function is illustrated by a downward sloping curve with price and quantity being measured along the vertical and horizontal axes. The consumption function is generally shown by $C = C(Y)$ or specifically by $C = a + bY$, where Y stands for income and C for consumption expenditure. Likewise, a demand function is described by $q = q(p)$ or by $q = a + bp$.

In both cases, one is encountered with the idea of functionality which is basic in mathematics and quantitative economics. The consumption function indicates that there is a definite relationship between C and Y, since to each value assigned to Y there corresponds a definite value of C, given a and b. We express the fact that there is such a correspondence, not *causation*, by stating that consumption expenditure is a *function* of income meaning that the value of consumption expenditure depends on the value of income. Thus, the following definition: If two variables are so related that to each definite value assigned to one of the variables there correspond one or more definite values of the other variable, then the second variable is said to be a function of the first one. For instance, in the case of a demand function, we are assuming that there is a definite relationship between the quantity demand and the price of a given commodity.

Of the two variables, the one to which values are assigned is called the *independent variable*, and the one for which corresponding values are determined is referred to as the *dependent variable*. From our previous examples we gather that, in the first example, income is the independent variable whereas consumption is the dependent variable. The reader can find many other examples in economics, such as the savings function, the investment function, etc.

According to my own experience, one thing over which the student frequently stumbles is the problem of functional notations. The fact that the quantity of a commodity demanded depends on its price is conveniently expressed in symbolic form by the functional notation $q = f(p)$ or, more generally, by $q = q(p)$. Either statement is read, "q is a function of p," and it calls attention to the fact that q for its value depends on the value of p. In any one discussion, the same functional symbol, such as $q(p)$, indicates the same law of correspondence and dependence between the dependent variable, the quantity demanded, and its independent variable price. Generally, if different functional relationships occur in the same discussion, different prefixed letters are to be employed in order to distinguish between them, or one can use different numerical subscripts for the letter preceding the parenthesis. For instance, demand and supply are two distinct functional relationships within one context. Then, $q = q_1(p)$ and $q = q_2(p)$, where the first statement is the demand function and the second one stands for the supply function. Many writers prefer $q = q(p)$ to $q = f(p)$ for the former economizes the letters for the variables and also it directly combines the dependent variable with its independent variable. Of course, Greek letters also can be used for functional notations, e.g., $q = \varphi(p)$.

A functional relation of the form $C = C(Y)$ or $q = q(p)$ is said to define C or q as an *explicit function* of Y or p, since the dependent variables are given explicitly in terms of the independent variables. If, however, two variables C and Y are related by a statement of the form $\varphi(C, Y) = 0$ in which neither variable is expressed explicitly in terms of the other, then each of the two variables is said to be an implicit function of the other. The functional relationship between C and Y is given implicitly by the relation $\varphi(C, Y) = 0$. In explicit functions the value of one variable is made to depend, in some definite form, on the value arbitrarily assigned to one or more other variables. On the other hand, an implicit function describes a mutual relationship between two or more variables, with either variable determining the other. One concrete economic example of implicit functions is the relation between investment and income which can be expressed by $X(Y, I) = 0$. This states that there is a mutual correspondence between the levels of investment and income. That is, under certain conditions investment depends on income and under other conditions income depends on investment, or mathematically, $Y = Y(I)$ and $I = I(Y)$. More generally, an implicit function gives rise to at least two explicit functions. The explicit functions obtained thereby are called the *inverse functions*. Specifically, $I = I(Y)$ is called the inverse of $Y = Y(I)$ and vice versa.

If to each assumed value of the independent variable of an explicit function there corresponds one and only one value of the dependent variable, the given function is called *single-valued*. If, however, to each assumed value of the independent variable of an explicit function corresponds more than one value of the dependent variable, the given variable is called *multi-valued*. Let us suppose that the particular form of a demand function is shown by $q = 100 - 3p$. Further, assume that p takes on the values 10, 15, 20. If we substitute these values in our demand function for each value of price, there will be only one value for quantity. If, however, the demand curve is expressed by $q^2 = 4 + p$ and p takes on the values 5, 12, and 21, the corresponding values for q will be ± 3, ± 4 and ± 5, respectively. This demonstrates that there correspond two values of q to each unique value of p which renders the particular demand function $q^2 = 4 + p$ a two-valued function.

In our example $q = 100 - 3p$, we observed that as the price increased from 10 to 15 and 20, the quantity decreased from 70 to 55 and 40. A function of this nature is referred to as a decreasing one. More generally, if an object or variable y, (e.g., quantity demanded) is a function of a continuous variable or object x, (e.g., price), and if y increases as x decreases or y decreases as x increases, the given function is called a *decreasing* function of x. If, on the other hand, a dependent variable increases as the independent variable of a continuous function increases or if both variables decrease at the same time, the assumed function is said to be an *increasing* function of x. An apt illustrative example of an increasing function in macroeconomics is the consumption function. Usually, increasing and decreasing functions together are named *monotonic functions*. Monotonic functions do not change their directions within the range; if they are increasing or decreasing, they will remain that way for all admissible values of their independent variables.

In order to visualize the shape of a function, it is sometimes found desirable to represent a function with its graph. Commonly, the graphical representation of a function is called the *graph* or *locus* of the function, and the process of drawing the graph is referred to as graphing or plotting the function. For a function consisting of two variables, the rectangular coordinates is usually used for graphing a given function. And a three-dimensional diagram is used for plotting a function composed of three variables. Of course, an n-dimensional diagram belongs to an n-variable function. Anything beyond the three dimensional falls in the field of mathematical analysis; it is abstract and will be dealt with in abstraction.

The system of the rectangular coordinates is composed of two axes intersecting at right angles at the point 0 called the origin of the system. Conventionally, the horizontal axis is assigned to the independent variable and the vertical one to the dependent variable. The intersection of the axes provides for four quadrants which are shown in Figure 1.1. The values of X and Y are positive in the first quadrant. X is negative and Y positive in the second quadrant. Both X and Y are negative in the third quadrant. Finally, X is positive and Y negative in the fourth quadrant. Generally, the first quadrant is called the positive one, and economists would meaningfully choose this section since no sensible economist cares to operate with negative values.

In graphing a two-variable continuous function, one should only assign different admissible values to the independent variable and thus obtain the corresponding values of the dependent variable. Then, the obtained points are to be plotted on the diagram. Statisticians call the plotted points the *scatter diagram*. A point of a two-dimensional plane is represented by a parenthesis encircling two letters, the first of which refers to the horizontal axis and the second letter to the vertical axis. In joining the plotted points, one must proceed from one point to another so that the values of the independent variable are taken in order of magnitude. Then, one ought to draw a smooth curve through the points. Of course, if the reader is in doubt about the nature of the curve between two plotted points, he should determine other points in the interval.

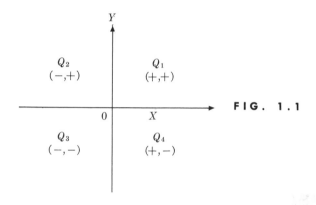

FIG. 1.1

As an example, we graph the demand function $q = 10 - 2p$. In allotting 0, 1, 2, 3, 4, and 5 to p, the following values are found for q: 10, 8, 6, 4, 2, and 0. These points are plotted on Figure 1.2 and are connected with a smooth line which gives the demand *curve*. Our demand function is linear and is one example of the general *linear function* $y = a + bx$. It is necessary to note here that to each function there corresponds a curve.

As another example, let us suppose that the cost function of a firm is shown by $y = x^2$ where x is the independent variable and y, the cost, is the dependent variable. We notice that y will be 0, 1, 4, 9, ... if x takes on 0, ±1, ±2, ±3, ... That is, the curve has two branches: one on the positive side, the other on the negative side. The graph of this function is called the *parabola*, and the function itself is named the explicit quadratic function. The given function shown in Figure 1.3 is one example of the general explicit *quadratic function*

$$y = ax^2 + bx + c.$$

Our last example is taken from utility analysis. Let us suppose that the utility that one gets from purchasing a commodity can be approximated by $uq = 2$. The unique utility curve related to the function is obtained by assigning positive values to q and getting the corresponding values for u. Figure 1.4 depicts the given graph. If we allot negative values to q, we can have another branch in the third quadrant. The graph of our utility function is called the *rectangular hyperbola,* and is one example of the general form of the explicit hyperbola

$$xy = a.$$

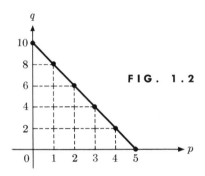

FIG. 1.2

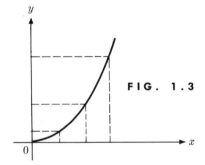

FIG. 1.3

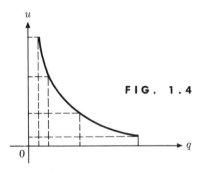

FIG. 1.4

1.4 Equations and Their Graphic Representation

It should be noted that in this section we only consider and study a polynomial which is a formal algebraic expression

$$y = f(x) = a_0x^n + a_1x^{n-1} + \cdots + a_n$$

where n is a positive integer. There are many kinds of equations some of which will be examined in Parts III and IV.

When one variable is said to be a function of the other, the exact way in which one depends on the other is not *par avance* known. An equation expresses the exact way in which one variable depends on the other. An equation is a statement that two expressions are equal, the two expressions being called *members* or *sides* of the equation. Equations are of two kinds: *identical equations* or simply *identities,* and *conditional equations* or briefly *equations.*

If the two sides of an equation are equal for *all* values of the variables for which the sides are defined, the equality is called an *identity*. An example of an identity is

$$(x + y)(x + y) \equiv x^2 + y^2 + 2xy.$$

It is obvious that for any value allotted to x and y, the equality would hold. *Remember! an identity does not represent functionality.* It is very important to remember this warning. An identity is simply a truism. An economic example of an identity is the now familiar investment-savings identity in the accounting sense. We will have two examples in Chapter 3 on the identity concept.

If the two sides of an equality are only equal for *certain* admissible values of the variables involved but not for all values, the equality is called a conditional equality or simply an *equation*. The demand function, cost function, and utility function graphed in the previous section are actually equations of a different nature; they are exact functional relationships. Conventionally, the sign $=$ is used for an equation whereas the sign $\equiv$ is used for an identity. *Remember! an equation conveys functionality.* To this extent an equation is superior to an identity. An identity can be promoted to the status of an equation under certain assumptions which will be explained later.

An equation is comprised of symbols. Certain symbols represent variables, while others may stand for known numbers or values. The former, usually expressed by the letter at the end of the alphabet and in economics by any letter like Y, I, S, C, p or q for income, investment, savings, consumption, price, or quantity, are called the *unknowns* or variables. The latter, commonly indicated by the first letters of the alphabet, are called *constants* or *parameters*. For instance, in $q = a + bp$, q and p are the unknown variables and a and b are the parameters or constants. The constants which are attached to variables, such as b which belongs to p in our example, are often referred to as *coefficients*. It is of cardinal importance to recognize exactly when a symbol like a or b should be called a constant and when a parameter. This distinction will be made clear when the graph of equations is explained.

Degree of An Equation. An equation is composed of terms. In $q = a + bp$, there are three terms q, a, and bp. It is conventional to gather all independent variables on the right-hand side and dependent variables on the left-hand side. The degree of a term of an equation in certain variables is the sum of the exponents of those variables. If the cost function of a firm is approximated by $K = aN^2 + bN + c$ where K stands for cost, N for the aggregate factors which make up the cost and a, b, and c the constants or parameters, we notice that the cost function consists of four terms and two variables one of which is independent and the other is dependent. Since the sum of the exponents of the variables of the first term is 2, the degree of that term is 2. Likewise, the degree of the second term, bN, is unity. The degree of an equation in certain variables is the degree of the term, or terms, that are highest in those variables. Thus, the cost equation given above is of the second degree in N, since the highest degree of that equation is 2. The demand equation $q = a + bp$ is the first degree, or linear, in p, since the degree of the highest term in that equation is one.

The equations in two variables, one dependent and one independent variable, are usually classified according to the degree of the term which is highest in the independent variable. Equations of the first, second, third, fourth, ..., and finally nth degree are called respectively *linear*, *quadratic*, *cubic*, *quartic*, ..., and finally *nth degree* equations. The general form of an explicit linear equation in one independent variable is $y = a + bx$ or $y = ax + b$. And the general form of an implicit linear equation in two variables is $ax + by + c = 0$ which, of course, can be reduced to two explicit linear functions $y = \left(-\dfrac{a}{b}\right)x + \left(-\dfrac{c}{b}\right)$ and $x = \left(-\dfrac{b}{a}\right)y + \left(-\dfrac{c}{a}\right)$ with their coefficients expressed in terms of the constants of the implicit linear function.

The general form of an explicit quadratic equation in one independent variable is given by $y = ax^2 + bx + c$ where x is the independent variable and a, b, and c are the constant parameters. Finally, the nth degree equation is

$$y = a_0 x^n + a_1 x^{n-1} + \cdots + a_{n-1}x + a_n,$$

where n is a positive integer. Since we suggested that equations express functionality, one may wish to express the functional relationships directly with an equation. Thus we wrote:

Equations	General Explicit Form
Linear	$y = y(x) = a + bx,$
Quadratic	$y = y(x) = ax^2 + bx + c,$
Cubic	$y = y(x) = ax^3 + bx^2 + cx + d,$
. . . . .	. . . . ,
nth degree	$y = y(x) = a_0 x^n + a_1 x^{n-1} + \cdots + a_n.$

The implicit form of the above equations is given by

Equations	General Implicit Form
Linear	$f(y, x) = a + bx - y = 0,$
Quadratic	$f(y, x) = ax^2 + by + c - y = 0,$
Cubic	$f(y, x) = ax^3 + bx^2 + cx + d - y = 0,$
. . . . .	. . . . ,
nth degree	$f(y, x) = a_0 x^n + a_1 x^{n-1} + \cdots + a_n - y = 0.$

Mathematical economists and econometricians are interested in the solutions or roots of an assumed equation. Any value of one variable, or set of values of the variables, of an equation is called the *solution* of the equation if the value of the variable substituted in the equation makes its two sides equal. Let the equation be arranged explicitly so that the dependent variable appears on the left and the independent variable(s) on the right. Any value, or a set of values, of the independent variable for which the right-hand side is made equal to zero is called the root of the equation.

The root of a linear equation $y = a + bx$ is $x = -\dfrac{a}{b}$ and the roots of a quadratic equation $y = ax^2 + bx + c$ are

$$x = \frac{-b \mp \sqrt{b^2 - 4ac}}{2a},$$

for if we substitute these values in the assumed equation, we will obtain $y = 0$. Hence, the way to find the root(s) of an equation is to set it equal to zero and solve for the independent variable. It is easy to solve a linear equation and less easy to solve a quadratic one, but the equations higher than the quadratic ones are involved and are not treated here. Suppose that the supply function of a firm is approximated by $q = 3p - 2$. Putting the equation equal to zero, we find out that $p = \frac{2}{3}$. Economically, when the price is $\frac{2}{3}$, the quantity sold is zero. On the other hand, if the cost function of a firm is given by $K = 12N^2 - 7N - 10$, the roots are $-\frac{2}{3}$ and $\frac{5}{4}$. Again economically, when the composite factor cost takes on these values, the total cost will be equal to zero.

If the coefficients a, b, and c are real numbers, then

The roots of $ax^2 + bx + c = 0$ are	when
real and unequal	$b^2 - 4ac > 0$
real and equal	$b^2 - 4ac = 0$
not real	$b^2 - 4ac < 0$

Systems of Linear Equations. We have just concluded that a linear equation in two variables, one independent and the other one dependent, has one root but unlimited solutions. Similarly, a quadratic equation may have two roots but infinite solutions. And so on. This is so because from a specified range of values for the variables, one can find unlimited values of the variables which can *satisfy* the supposed equation. However, economists often desire to find a *unique* solution for a set of equations.

Now, let us consider two equations in two unknowns

$$\begin{cases} a_1x + b_1y + c_1 = 0, \\ a_2x + b_2y + c_2 = 0. \end{cases}$$

These two equations, linear in x and y, are said to form a *system of simultaneous linear equations* when each unknown represents the same number in both equations. A solution of a system of two simultaneous linear equations in two unknowns, x and y, is a pair of corresponding values of x and y which satisfy both of these equations at the same time. To solve such a system is to find all its solutions.

We have just noticed that each of these two equations or both of them may have unlimited solutions under certain conditions. At this stage these conditions are not interesting. However, it is interesting to examine the condition for which these two lines, equations, have only *one* point in common, a solution which satisfies both equations at the same time and is the solution of the system. Such a solution is called *unique*.[7] There are two conditions which must be met in order to be able to obtain a unique solution. First, the equations of the system must be consistent and independent — one equation is not a multiple or a fraction of the other equation(s) of the system. Secondly, there must be as many consistent and independent equations as variables in the system.

A system of equations which does not contain as many equations as the contained variables is called *indeterminate*. For a system of consistent and independent equations we have:

Condition	System
No. of equations $=$ No. of variables	determinate
No. of equations $>$ No. of variables	overdeterminate
No. of equations $<$ No. of variables	underdeterminate

Alfred Marshall, a great mathematical economist, reminded us that if we want to have a determinate market system we must have two independent and consistent equations, a pair of scissors, demand and supply.[8]

If there are as many consistent and independent equations as variables, the unique solution for the variables can be found in many ways, *e.g.*, the method of elimination and determinants. The latter method will be analyzed in detail in Chapter 11 of Part IV. However, as an example we take the two equations for the demand and supply:

$$q = -2 + 3p \qquad \text{(supply)}$$
$$q = 10 - 2p \qquad \text{(demand)}$$

---

[7]The uniqueness of the solutions will be taken up again and will be dealt with comprehensively in Chapter 11.

[8]In the letter which we quoted above, Marshall wrote, "[Mill] did not seem to have a sufficient responsibility — I know I am speaking to a mathematician — for keeping the number of his equations equal to the number of his variables, neither more nor less. Since then I have found similar matters not quite to my taste in the economic work of nearly all those who have had no definite scientific training."

the solution of which via the method of elimination is $p = \frac{12}{5}$, $q = \frac{26}{5}$. Algebraically, the system is being solved by *eliminating* one of the two unknowns between the two equations and solving the resulting equation in the other unknown. The corresponding value of the unknown which was eliminated then was found by substituting the value of the unknown obtained in either of the equations. These two values satisfy both equations *simultaneously*. Hence, the process of finding the unique solution of a consistent system of equations is called simultaneous solution of the system.

Graph of Equations. An equation can be displayed the same way as a function as illustrated in Section 1.3. It is proved, in analytic geometry, that the locus (graph) of any linear function in two variables is a straight line. Therefore, any two points are sufficient to determine the graph of a linear equation in two variables. In practice, the line can be more accurately drawn through two plotted points if they are not too close together. The intercepts on the coordinate axes are usually convenient, too. To plot a linear equation, let us consider a demand relation for sugar in the United States estimated by Henry Schultz:[9]

$$q = 70.62 - 2.26p,$$

where p stands for the deflated wholesale price in cents of a pound of sugar and q for the per capita consumption of sugar in the U.S. in any year. Here q is the dependent variable and p the independent variable.

Mention was made that the easiest way to plot a straight line is to find the intercepts on the coordinate axes. To obtain these intercepts, let $p = 0$ and find q which, according to the demand equation, is 70.62; then let $q = 0$ for which $p = 31.25$. We may now plot these points and then connect them. Of course, a third point should be always used as a check. The graph of the function is given in Figure 1.5. This graph, and in general all graphs of linear equations, have two basic properties: the slope of the curve and its intercept with the axis allotted to the dependent variable. The slope of an equation, and its curve, is the amount of rise or fall of the dependent variable per unit of the independent variable. It is the rate of change of the dependent variable per unit change of the independent variable.

The slope of a curve indicates the degree of responsiveness of the dependent variable with respect to one unit change of the independent variable. If the rate of change is positive, the slope is called positive; if, however, the rate of change is negative, the slope is also negative. A curve with a positive slope belongs to an increasing function and the curve of a decreasing function has a negative slope. By examining the graph of Figure 1.5, it is obvious that the slope of the curve is constant since the rate

---

[9]H. Schultz, *The Theory and Measurement of Demand*, Chicago: University of Chicago Press, 1938, p. 196.

of change of the dependent variable per unit change of the independent variable is constant. Intuitively, we can conclude that the slope of all linear equations with two variables is always constant. The slope of a linear equation is the coefficient of the independent variable. In the demand equation for sugar, the numerical slope is -2.26.

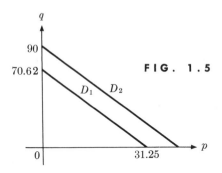

FIG. 1.5

If we move D_1 of Figure 1.5 parallel to itself to a new position D_2, the new curve will have the same slope since the rate of change of the dependent variable per unit change of the independent variable remains constant. Nevertheless, in this *shift* the q-intercept increases from 70.62 to 90. Let us transform our demand equation into the general form $q = a + bp$ and utilize the above analysis. If one is interested in the shape and position of a curve of the linear equation; *i.e.*, where p and q are the important phenomena to be considered, a and b are called *constants*. If, however, there is a shift in the curve and we want to compare the new position with the old one, a and b are called *parameters*. Thus, parameters cause the *shift* in the curve. This is a result of significant importance which will be used in Chapter 3.

By now we know how to chart the curve of a linear equation. Sometimes, we want to obtain an equation from a diagram. The equation of the line passing through the two fixed points (p_1, q_1), (p_2, q_2) is

(1.4.1)
$$q - q_1 = \frac{q_2 - q_1}{p_2 - p_1}\,(p - p_1).$$

Also, the equation of the line passing through a fixed point (p_1, q_1) with slope m is

(1.4.2)
$$q - q_1 = m(p - p_1).$$

Hence, if two points or one point and one slope are given, an equation can be readily written. From (1.4.1) and (1.4.2) we can deduce that the slope can be written as [10]

---

[10] Δ is a symbol used commonly for an "incremental change." Δq is the incremental change in q as a result of an incremental change in p shown by Δp.

(1.4.3)
$$\frac{\Delta q}{\Delta p} = \frac{q_2 - q_1}{p_2 - p_1}$$

where $q_1 = q_1(p_1)$, $q_2 = q_2(p_2)$, $p_2 = (p_1 + \Delta p)$, $q_2 = q_2(p_1 + \Delta p)$ or

(1.4.4)
$$\frac{\Delta q}{\Delta p} = \frac{q_2(p_1 + \Delta p) - q_1(p_1)}{\Delta p} = \text{slope}.$$

In analytic geometry, it is proved that the graph of any quadratic equation $q(p) = ap^2 + bp + c$ is a *parabola*, which opens upward if $a > 0$ and opens downward if $a < 0$. A parabola is a curve which has a turning point and the curve unlike the curve of the linear equation has a changing slope over the curve. Generally, for plotting a quadratic equation we must find a series of points the locus of which will offer a parabola. It is interesting to note that if the graph of $q(p)$ crosses the p-axis in two distinct points, the roots of $q(p) = 0$ are real and unequal; if the graph of $q(p)$ touches the p-axis but does not cross it, the roots of $q(p) = 0$ are real and equal; and if the graph of $q(p)$ does not cross or touch the p-axis, the roots of $q(p) = 0$ are not real. These three cases are illustrated in Figure 1.6.

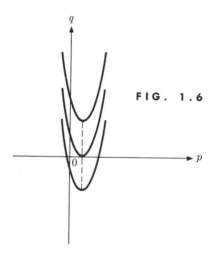

FIG. 1.6

$q_1(p) = p^2 - 4p - 1$							
p	-1	0	1	2	3	4	5
$q_1(p)$	4	-1	-4	-5	-4	-1	4

$q_2(p) = p^2 - 4p + 4$							
p	-1	0	1	2	3	4	5
$q_2(p)$	9	4	1	0	1	4	9

$q_3(p) = p^2 - 4p + 8$							
p	-1	0	1	2	3	4	5
$q_3(p)$	13	8	5	4	5	8	13

The above quadratic equations are the general explicit forms of quadratic equations. The general implicit form of a quadratic equation is

(1.4.5) $ax^2 + by^2 + cxy + dx + ey + f = 0 = f(x, y)$

where $a, b, c, d, e,$ and f are constants. If we assume that $b, c,$ and e are zero, the remaining terms form an explicit quadratic equation in one variable x. We are back at the quadratic equation of the preceding paragraph. If, however, $a, b, d,$ and e are set equal to zero, the remaining terms

(1.4.6) $cxy = -f$

will form an equation the curve of which has been referred to as the *rectangular hyperbola*. The curves of the rectangular hyperbola are symmetrical with respect to the origin of the axes. One curve is composed of two branches both single-valued; one branch on one side of the origin and the other branch on the opposite side of the origin, as illustrated in Figure 1.7. In economics, since we are interested in positive values, a branch or part of a branch which lies in the negative quadrant is neglected.

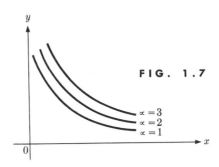

FIG. 1.7

$\alpha = 3$
$\alpha = 2$
$\alpha = 1$

Let us suppose that we are given $xy = 1$. The positive section of the graph is given in Figure 1.7. If 1 is replaced by 2, a new graph will be plotted as shown in Figure 1.7. Accordingly, one can draw an infinite number of curves by allotting different values to $(-f)$ of (1.4.6). When we compare the position of these curves $(-f)$ is called a parameter. A hyperbola is conventionally written in the general form $xy = \alpha$ where a is either a constant or a parameter depending on the position of the curve(s) belonging to the equation.

Deduced from Figure 1.7, it is recognizable that as x gets continually smaller (yet not actually taking the value zero), the values of y increase indefinitely. This means that the y-axis is a vertical *asymptote*. Conversely, as y becomes continually smaller (yet not actually taking the value zero), the values of x increase indefinitely and the x-axis will be the horizontal asymptote. Generally, the branches of a hyperbola are asymptotic to either the axes of the coordinates, lines parallel to them or to its own asymptotes such as the curves of Figure 1.8 for equation $4x^2 - 9y^2 = 13$.

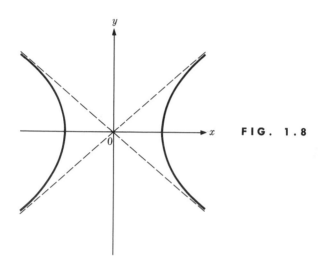

FIG. 1.8

In economic theory, especially in indifference analysis, the system of non-intersecting curves in the positive quadrant is of special importance and interest. We noticed that by changing the values of a parameter of a given equation, a family of curves could be obtained. This was instanced above and is true with the straight line, parabola, and hyperbola. The explicit form of all these curves can be written as

(1.4.7) $$f(x, y) = \alpha$$

and its implicit form would be

(1.4.8) $$f(x, y; \alpha) = 0.$$

The general form of the equations which give rise to a family of non-intersecting curves in the positive quadrant are:

$$\frac{x + a}{a - \sqrt{y + b}} = \alpha, \; (x + a)(y + b) = \alpha, \; x + y + \sqrt{2xy} = \alpha.$$

EXERCISES 1

1. Express each of the following statements symbolically in functional notations and then give its particular form.

   a. The area of a square as a function of a side.
   b. The area of a square as a function of a diagonal.
   c. The volume of a cube as a function of an edge.
   d. The cost of X hours of labor in cents at 100 cents per hour as a function of X.
   e. The simple interest I in dollars on \$100 at 3% as a function of time t in years.
   f. The area of a triangle as a function of its base and its altitude.
   g. The total revenue of X pounds of a commodity in dollars at \$2.00 per unit as a function of X.
   h. If $f(x) = 2x^2 + 3x + 4$, find $f(3)$, $f(5)$ and $f(6)$.
   i. If $g(x) = 3x^2 + 2x$, find $g(-1)$, $g(0)$, $g(4)$ and $g(8)$.
   j. If $h(x) = x^3 - x^2 - 2x + 3$, find $h(-3)$, $h(1)$, $h(2)$, $h(3)$ and $h(5)$.
   k. If $G(x) = x(x+1)(x-1)(x-2)$, show that

   $$\frac{G(x+1)}{x-1} = \frac{G(x+2)}{x+3}.$$

   l. If $F(x) = (1+x)/(1-x)$, find $F(x + \Delta x) - F(x)$.
   m. If $H(x) = (x+1)/(2x-1)$, find $H(x + \Delta x) - H(x)$.
   n. If $F(z) = z + \dfrac{1}{z^2 - 1}$, find $\dfrac{F(z + \Delta z) - F(z)}{\Delta z}$.
   o. If $f(x) = ax^2 + bx + c$ and $f(x) = f(-x)$, show that $b = 0$, if $x \neq 0$.
   p. If $f(x) = ax^2 + bx + c$ and $-f(x) = f(-x)$, show that $a = c = 0$.
   q. A chartered plane company agrees to take 80 passengers from the U.S. to Europe at \$150 per person. The air lines company agrees, however, to reduce the rate 10 per cent per person for each additional passenger. Find the cost C in dollars when there are X additional passengers.

2. Plot each of the following points and state the quadrant, if any, in which it lies.

   $(5, 3)$, $(-3, 2)$, $(2, -3)$, $(-5, 0)$, $(0, 0)$,
   $(1\frac{1}{2}, 2\frac{1}{4})$, $(\sqrt{3}, 2\sqrt{2})$, $(-2\sqrt{5}, -2)$.

3. Draw the triangles whose vertices are:

   a. $(2, 4)$, $(-4, -2)$, $(4, -4)$.
   b. $(3, -4)$, $(-2, 1)$, $(-7, -4)$.

4. Plot the points in each of the following tables and draw a smooth curve through them.

x	1	2	3	4	5	6
y	5	8	11	14	17	20

x	1	2	3	4	5	6
y	3	1	−1	−3	−5	−8

5. Plot the graph of each of the following functions:

$y = 3x.$

$y = 2 - 5x.$

$y = x^2 + 1.$

$y = x^2 + 4x + 3.$

$y = x^2 - x + 1.$

$y = x^3 - 3x^2 + 3.$

$y = 4x^2 - x^3.$

$y = 3 + 2x - 2x^2.$

$y = x^3 - 6x - 4.$

$y = x - x^3.$

6. Plot the graphs of the following functions and compare them.

$y = x^2 - 3x + 2.$

$y = x^2 - 3x - 2.$

$y = x^2 - 3x + 4.$

7. Plot the graph of each of the following functions and from the graphs read off, at least approximately, each value of x for which y is a maximum or a minimum.

$y = x^2 + 3x + 1.$

$y = -x^2 + 5x + 1.$

$y = x^3 - 3x.$

$y = x^2 + 3x - 1.$

8. According to the *Vital Statistics* of the Department of Health, Education and Welfare, life expectancy for different ages in 1957 is the following:

Age	Expec.	Age	Expec.	Age	Expec.
0	69.3	25	47.4	50	24.8
5	66.5	30	42.7	55	20.9
10	61.6	35	38.0	60	17.3
15	56.8	40	33.4	65	14.0
20	52.0	45	29.0	70	11.7

Draw the graph of this function and show the life expectancy at 53 and 67.

9. Classify the following equations as identities or equations:

$4(x - 1) + 1 = x - 3(1 - x).$

$(x - 1)(x^2 + x + 1) = x^3 + 1.$

$(3x + 4y)^2 = 24(xy + 6).$

$(2x + y)(2x - y) = 4x^2 - y^2.$

$x(x - 1) = x(x - 2) + 6.$

10. Solve the following systems of equations algebraically and graphically. Classify as consistent and independent, consistent and dependent, or inconsistent. (Graphically, if two lines have one and only one point of intersection, they are called consistent and independent. If the two lines are coincident, they are said to be consistent and dependent. Finally, if the two lines have no point in common, they are said to be inconsistent.)

$$\begin{cases} 3x + 2y = 4 \\ x - 4y = 5 \end{cases}$$

$$\begin{cases} 4x - 5y = 6 \\ 8x - 10y = 12 \end{cases}$$

$$\begin{cases} 5y - 3x = 15 \\ 9x - 15y = -10 \end{cases} \qquad \begin{cases} 3y + x = 5 \\ 6y - x = 6 \end{cases}$$

$$\begin{cases} x - 2y = 7 \\ 2x + 3y = -10 \end{cases}$$

11. Form quadratic equations whose roots are as follows:

$$(5, -2), \quad (-3, 6), \quad (1, 7), \quad (3, 2), \quad (3, 4), \quad (10, -1)$$
$$(-3, -1), \quad (-2, -2), \quad (8, 4), \quad (1, 3).$$

12. Solve the following quadratic equations:

$2x^2 - 11x + 12 = 0.$ $x - 2x^2 + 15 = 0.$

$3x^2 - 4x = 2.$ $3x(x - 1) + 1 = 0.$

$5y - 3y^2 - 3 = 0.$

2 FUNDAMENTAL FUNCTIONS AND SERIES

2.1 Power and Exponential Functions

A power function is a function composed of a variable base and a constant exponent. Hence, $y = x^a$ is a power function where $y = y(x)$; x, being continuous, is called the base and a the exponent, (sometimes called the index), of the function; a is a real number which takes on positive or negative values. Definitionally, $x^0 = 1$; *i.e.*, any base to zero power is equal to unity. Obviously, $x^1 = x$ and

$$x^a \cdot x^b = x^{a+b},$$

$$(x^a)^b = x^{a \cdot b},$$

$$(xy)^a = x^a y^a,$$

$$\left(\frac{x}{y}\right)^a = \frac{x^a}{y^a},$$

$$\frac{1}{x^a} = x^{-a},$$

$$\frac{x^a}{x^b} = x^{a-b} = \frac{1}{x^{b-a}},$$

$$x^{\left(\frac{a}{b}\right)} = \sqrt[b]{x^a}.$$

An exponential function is a function with a constant base and a variable exponent. $y = a^x$ where x, being a continuous variable and a a constant, exemplifies an exponential function. Usually the base of an exponential function is chosen to be the "natural" base $e = 2.7182. \ldots$[1]

There are certain advantages in using the "natural" base in place of any other constant base. This will be discussed later in relation to logarithmic

---

[1]For the mathematical and precise definition of e see pp. 85–86.

functions. A more general form of an exponential function is

$$y = ae^{bx}$$

where a and b are real numbers. All laws of power functions enumerated above are applicable to exponential functions.

Since in $y = e^x$ we have $y = y(x)$, then the function $y = e^x$ is *smooth* if and only if x is a continuous variable. Also, the exponential function $y = e^x$ is positive for all positive and negative values of x. Graphically, the function lies always above the x-axis. In addition, the continuous function

$$y = e^x$$

is single-valued and monotonically increasing and approaches plus infinity, that is, "increases without bound," as x increases and the function decreases and becomes asymptotic to x-axis as x approaches minus infinity. Graphically, the curve is concave from below and the x-axis is its asymptote in minus infinity and rises to the right while crossing the y-axis at $y = 1$ and $x = 0$. Theoretically, the value of an exponential function is zero when $x = -\infty$. Moreover, two or more exponential functions with the same exponent and different bases are non-intersecting; the function with the larger base lies above the one with the smaller base. Two exponential functions with the same base and different exponents are intersecting only at $x = 0$ where both functions have the same ordinates. Graphically, the position of the exponential functions depends on the values allotted to the base and the exponent of the functions as illustrated in the diagram. As we said before, an exponential function may take bases other than the "natural" base e, such as a which can take on arbitrarily any positive or negative values. If in the exponential function $y = a^x$ the range of the admissible values of a is given by $1 > a > 0$, the curve of the function will fall from left to right and it becomes asymptotic to the x-axis in the positive quadrant as shown in Figure 2.1.

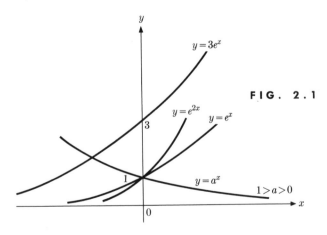

FIG. 2.1

In economics, by and large, we need only to consider the exponential functions with the natural base e which are supposed in most writings on economic theory. A very interesting example is a compound interest rate relative to present and capital values.

In bankers' parlance, *interest* is a contractual sum of money which is paid for the use of a certain sum of money. The amount of money which is borrowed is called the *principal* and the ratio of the interest over the principal is referred to as *the rate of interest* and is generally expressed in *per cent*. The interest which is computed on the original principal for the entire period during which the principal is borrowed is called "simple." If, however, at the end of each time period one *adds* the interest to its corresponding principal and computes the interest for the succeeding period on the basis of the compounded principal, the interest is called "compound" for that period. The *compound interest period* is usually a year, six months or three months being described by the terms *compounded annually, compounded semi-annually,* or *compounded quarterly*. The borrowers should remember that when a bank announces that it gives an interest of 4% compounded quarterly, it will only add, at the end of each three months, 1% of the principal of that period to form a new principal. Likewise, a 3% compounded semi-annually means the addition of $1\frac{1}{2}$% to the principal at the end of six months.

Let us suppose that a bank loans out $100 to a student at a *simple interest* rate of 6% per annum. The bank at the end of one year should receive

$$100 + 100(.06) = 100(1 + .06)$$
$$= \$106.$$

Similarly, if the loan is for only nine months out of one year, the bank is to receive

$$100 + 100(\tfrac{9}{12})(.06) = 100(1 + \tfrac{9}{12}.06)$$
$$= \$104.5.$$

These two examples can lead us to a general formula for the simple interest rate. Let A stand for the principal, i for the interest rate, x the period, and Y for the amount that must be received at the end of the given period, thus the formula for computation is

(2.1.1) $$Y = A(1 + xi).$$

If, however, the interest is compounded on an *annually* compounded basis, the formula is

(2.1.2) $$Y = A(1 + i)^x.$$

It is because, at the end of the first year, one receives

$$Y_1 = A(1 + i),$$

and at the end of the second year

$$Y_2 = Y_1 + Y_1(i) = Y_1(1 + i) = A(1 + i)^2,$$

and finally at the end of the x-th year

$$Y_x = Y = A(1 + i)^x.$$

If the interest is compounded less than a year such as semi-annually, quarterly, and so forth, let us say m times a year, the formula will be

$$Y = A\left(1 + \frac{i}{m}\right)^{mx}$$

(2.1.3)

$$= A\left\{\left(1 + \frac{i}{m}\right)^{\frac{m}{i}}\right\}^{ix} = A\left\{\left(1 + \frac{1}{n}\right)^{n}\right\}^{ix}$$

where $\dfrac{m}{i} = n$. As m approaches infinity so does n, and if n approaches to

infinity, the expression $\left(1 + \dfrac{1}{n}\right)^n$ will be equal to e, according to our defini-

tion given above. Thus, if interest payments within a year are extended infinitely, the formula for compound interest can be written as

(2.1.4) $$Y = Ae^{ix}$$

where $Y = Y(i)$ and is of the general type given in the previous para-graphs. Many economists have applied this formula to investment theory and concluded that investment is a function of the rate of interest.[2] Incidentally, (2.1.4) can be written as

$$\frac{Y}{e^{ix}} = A$$

and by using one of the rules of the power or exponential functions we have

(2.1.5) $$A = Ye^{-ix}.$$

If the compound interest rate is i annually, one can from (2.1.5) de-termine the amount of money which is to be invested in order to produce Y at the end of x years. In (2.1.5), the sum A is called the *present value* of Y available x years hence. The superiority of (2.1.4) and (2.1.5) over (2.1.2) or (2.1.3) is in the sense that one does not need to bother with the periods of interest payments during a specific year. (2.1.4) and (2.1.5) are both direct for computations. One of the uses to which (2.1.5) has been put is for the computation of an *annuity*, which is a sequence of equal periodic pay-ments, and the *present value of an annuity*, which is the sum of the present values of the various payments.

---

[2]For a more comprehensive treatment of investment theory see Chapter 8, Section 8.5.

Let us suppose that the bank around the corner announces that it pays 4% semi-annually for new savings deposited with the bank. Further, suppose one wants to know how much one must deposit today in order to get $100.00 three years hence. We have: $i = .04$, $x = 3$ and $y = 100$; thus the present value, A, or the amount which must be invested today is given by:

$$A = 100e^{-.04(3)} = 88.80,$$

which means that if one invests $88.80 today at 4% compounded semi-annually after 3 years, one will receive $100.00, or

$$100 = 88.80e^{+.04(3)}.$$

Now consider an annuity whereby $100.00 is paid at the end of each six-month period for six payments and the interest rate is compounded semi-annually at 4%. The results are given in the following table:

Payments Made at the End of	Present Value of the Payments	
6 months ($x = \frac{1}{2}$)	$100e^{-.04(\frac{1}{2})}$	$= 98.04$
1 year ($x = 1$)	$100e^{-.04(1)}$	$= 96.12$
$1\frac{1}{2}$ years ($x = 1\frac{1}{2}$)	$100e^{-.04(1\frac{1}{2})}$	$= 94.23$
2 years ($x = 2$)	$100e^{-.04(2)}$	$= 92.38$
$2\frac{1}{2}$ years ($x = 2\frac{1}{2}$)	$100e^{-.04(2\frac{1}{2})}$	$= 90.57$
3 years ($x = 3$)	$100e^{-.04(3)}$	$= 88.80$

(The calculations being done with logarithms which will be explained in the succeeding section.) Thus, the present value of the payments over three years is

$$98.04 + 96.12 + 94.23 + 92.38 + 90.57 + 88.80 = 560.14.$$

That is, 560.14 represents the sum of money that one must invest at 4% compounded semi-annually in order to receive $100.00 every six months for three years. We can utilize the concept of *present value* and apply it to investment and capital theory. If a firm desires to acquire the stream of incomes

$$Y_0, Y_1, Y_2, \ldots, Y_x$$

for periods $0, 1, 2, \ldots x$ respectively, it must now invest

$$Y_0 + Y_1e^{-i1} + Y_2e^{-2i} + Y_3e^{-3i} + \cdots + Y_xe^{-ix}$$

where the interest rate is reckoned at i% per annum.

2.2 Logarithmic Functions

The logarithm of a positive number Y to a positive base a, other than unity, is the exponent x of the power to which the base must be raised to equal the number. Thus, if $a > 0$, $a \neq 1$ and a, x and Y are so related that

(2.2.1)
$$Y = a^x,$$

x is called the logarithm of Y with respect to the base a. This relation is expressed in symbols by

(2.2.2)
$$x = \log_a Y$$

where $x = x(Y)$. The two functions (2.2.1) and (2.2.2) express the same relationship between a, x and Y in exponential and logarithmic forms. The two functions are, however, single-valued and *inverse*.

Let us suppose that we wish to find the unknown number Y if $\log_3 Y = -2$. Writing in exponential form, we can evaluate

$$Y = 3^{-2} = \frac{1}{3^2} = \frac{1}{9}.$$

Or suppose that we wish to find the unknown base a if

$$\log_a 16 = \tfrac{2}{3}.$$

Writing it in exponential form, we have

$$a^{(\frac{2}{3})} = 16$$
$$(a^{(\frac{2}{3})})^{\frac{3}{2}} = 16^{(\frac{3}{2})}$$
$$a = 64.$$

The base of a logarithm can be any positive number other than unity since negative numbers do not possess logarithms.

Generally, there are two bases which are extensively used in mathematics and mathematical economics. These are the common base which is 10, and the natural base which is $e = 2.7182\ldots$ (the base of the exponential functions) of which we spoke before. For these two often-used bases, there are tables written which appear in most books on college algebra and elementary statistics. In quantitative economics, the natural base is used mostly, and if a logarithm is mentioned without its base, one should know that the assumed logarithm is to the base e. If, however, there is a logarithm to the base other than 10, or e, the logarithm can be transformed to a logarithm with any base that we desire. For instance

$$x = \log_a Y = \frac{\log_e Y}{\log_e a} = \frac{\log_{10} Y}{\log_{10} a}$$

indicates that we can transform one logarithm with any base that we desire with the numerator being the logarithm of a given value and the denominator being the logarithm of the base of the original logarithm.

Logarithms possess certain properties that we list without proofs. It is obvious that the logarithm of unity to any base is zero; *i.e.*, $\log_a 1 = 0$ since $a^0 = 1$. Definitionally, any number to zero power is unity. Also, the logarithm of any number with respect to itself is unity; *i.e.*, $\log_a a = 1$ since obviously any number raised to unity power is equal to itself, $a^1 = a$. Furthermore

$$\log_e(XY) = \log_e X + \log_e Y,$$

$$\log_e \left(\frac{X}{Y}\right) = \log_e X - \log_e Y,$$

$$\log_e Y^n = n(\log_e Y).$$

It is obvious that function $Y = \log_e X$ is continuous if X is continuous. Graphically, the curve of the function is continuous. For all values of X more than one the function $Y = \log_e X$ is positive and approaches infinity as X approaches infinity; and for all values of X from zero to one the function is negative, and as X approaches zero the function becomes asymptotic to Y-axis in the fourth quadrant.

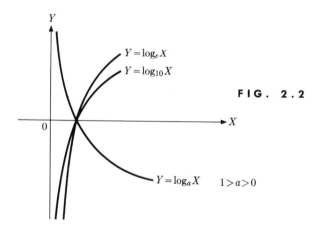

FIG. 2.2

Two logarithmic functions with the same logarithms and different bases more than unity are intersecting; the one with the smaller base is to the left and rises faster than the one with the larger base for $X > 1$, and for $1 > X > 0$, the logarithm with the smaller base lies to the right of the one with the larger base. Of the two logarithmic functions with the same base and different logarithms, the one with the larger logarithm rises faster than the one with the smaller logarithm. If in the function $Y = \log_a X$ the range of the admissible values for a is given by $1 > a > 0$, the function is monotonically decreasing from left to right and is asymptotic to the Y-axis in the positive quadrant and approaches minus infinity as X approaches infinity. All these cases are illustrated in Figure 2.2.

The logarithms are powerfully useful in solving certain problems, especially in econometrics. There is one cardinal rule which one must always remember. The rule is that the logarithm of both sides of an equation does not change the equation. Suppose that we have

$$A = Ye^{-ix}.$$

Further, suppose that Y, i, and x are known and that we wish to evaluate A. (This is a computational problem of the previous section which we postponed until we could explain the logarithms.) According to our rule, we write

$$\log A = \log(Ye^{-ix}).$$

Using one of the properties of the logarithms, we can expand it to

$$\log A = \log Y + \log e^{-ix}$$
$$= \log Y - ix(\log e).$$

Since everything is known and given on the right-hand side, the left-hand side can be evaluated. As an example, let us take

$$A = 100e^{-.04(2)}.$$

Applying the above rule, we have

$$\log_e A = \log_e 100 - .08(\log_e e),$$
$$\frac{\log_{10} A}{\log_{10} e} = \frac{\log_{10} 100}{\log_{10} e} - .08.$$

Since, according to the table of logarithms, $\log_{10} e = .4343$ and $\log_{10} 100 = 2$, we write

$$\log_{10} A = .4343(4.6051 - .08)$$
$$= 1.9653$$

or

$$A = 92.38.$$

We are assuming that the reader is already familiar with the logarithm tables and knows how to look for certain values therein. If the reader is not familiar with the way that a table of logarithm should be used, he should immediately consult a book on college algebra.

2.3 Trigonometric Functions

Trigonometry is that branch of mathematics which treats methods of subjecting angles, triangles, and oscillations to numerical computations. While the derivation of the word "trigonometry" would seem historically to confine the subject to triangles, the treatment of triangles is merely a part of the general subject which includes many other investigations involving angles and oscillations.

Trigonometric Functions.   Trigonometric functions relate to angles of different sizes. Figure 2.3 is composed of two *half-lines*, two straight lines terminating at 0 and extending indefinitely in the direction away from 0. The angle $\angle BOA$ is the amount of rotation about 0 that OB makes with OA. Therefore, an angle is constituted of an *initial line* OA, a *terminal line* OB and an amount of rotation θ. The vertex of an angle $\angle BOA$ is the intersection 0 of OA and OB. The rotation of an initial line around the vertex may be clockwise or counterclockwise. The counterclockwise rotation, θ, is positive and the clockwise one, ω, is negative.

Degree and Radian.   Degree and radian are two units of angular measure. A degree is defined as $\frac{1}{360}$ of a complete rotation, $\frac{1}{180}$ of a straight line, and $\frac{1}{90}$ of a right angle. Thus, an angle which makes a complete rotation is 360 degrees, (being written usually 360°). Let us suppose that a circle of radius r (Figure 2.4) with AB arc is equal to r. The positive angle $\angle AOB$ at the center of the circle, subtended by the arc of length r is one radian. Since a complete rotation requires 360° or 2π radian, then

$$2\pi \text{ rad.} = 360° \quad \text{or} \quad 1 \text{ rad.} = \frac{180}{\pi}.$$

All angles are measured with radian unless otherwise specified.

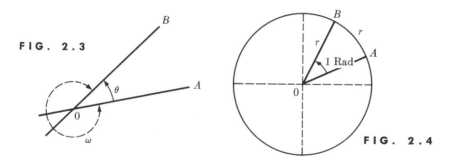

FIG. 2.3

FIG. 2.4

Common Forms of Trigonometric Functions.   In the coordinate system (Figure 2.5), the line OP drawn from the origin to point P is called the *radius vector* of the point whose length is named the *polar distance*. MP and OM are termed the polar coordinates of P. Let P, with polar coordinates x and y and polar distance r, be a point on the terminal line of θ when so placed. The trigonometric functions of θ are defined as follows.

$$\sin \theta = \frac{y}{r} = \frac{\text{ordinate of } P}{\text{polar distance of } P} = \frac{MP}{OP}$$

$$\cos \theta = \frac{x}{r} = \frac{\text{abscissa of } P}{\text{polar distance of } P} = \frac{OM}{OP}$$

$$\tan \theta = \frac{y}{x} = \frac{\text{ordinate of } P}{\text{abscissa of } P}$$

$$\cot \theta = \frac{x}{y} = \frac{\text{abscissa of } P}{\text{ordinate of } P}$$

$$\sec \theta = \frac{r}{x} = \frac{\text{polar distance of } P}{\text{abscissa of } P}$$

$$\csc \theta = \frac{r}{y} = \frac{\text{polar distance of } P}{\text{ordinate of } P}$$

The signs of the trigonometric functions are different in various quadrants. x and y are positive in the first quadrant; y is positive and x is negative in the second one; both x and y are negative in the third quadrant; and finally x is positive and y negative in the fourth quadrant. Accordingly, the functions of θ are positive or negative. There exist tables of trigonometric functions for all angles from which the reader can easily find any angle that he seeks.

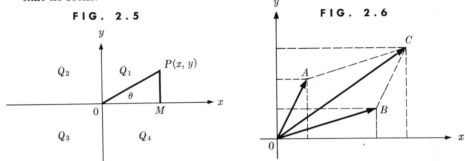

FIG. 2.5

FIG. 2.6

Vectors. The line which connects a point P in the plane to a fixed origin is called a *vector*. In trigonometry, any line which is making angle θ with the horizontal axis of coordinates system is called a *vector* which has a length and a direction. A vector which is the radius of a unit circle is called a *unit vector*.

The sum of two vectors $0A$ and $0B$ is the diagonal $0C$ of the parallelogram constructed with $0A$ and $0B$ as sides. Polar coordinates of $0C$ are the sum of respective polar coordinates of $0A$ and $0B$ as in Figure 2.6. Likewise, the sum of n vectors is the vector whose polar coordinates are the sum of the coordinates of n vectors.

Periodicity and Oscillations of the Trigonometric Functions. Impose a circle of radius 1 with its center at 0 on a coordinate system of Figures 2.7 and 2.8. Let P, on the terminal line of any angle θ, have $0M$ and MP as its coordinates. Then, from Figure 2.7, we can write

$$\sin \theta = \frac{MP}{0P} = \frac{MP}{1} = MP,$$

$$\cos \theta = \frac{0M}{0P} = \frac{0M}{1} = 0M.$$

From Figure 2.8, we write

$$\tan \theta = \frac{MP}{OM} = \frac{MP}{1} = MP,$$

$$\tan\left(\theta + \frac{\pi}{2}\right) = \frac{M'P'}{OM'} = \frac{M'P'}{-1} = -M'P'.$$

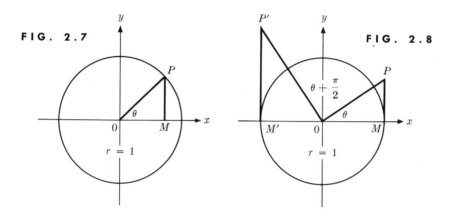

FIG. 2.7

FIG. 2.8

Hence, to examine the variations of $\sin \theta$, $\cos \theta$, $\tan \theta$, we need merely examine the length of MP and OM in both diagrams as θ rotates counterclockwise. Accordingly, we can define the following variations:

	0	θ in Q_1	$\frac{\pi}{2}$	θ in Q_2	π	θ in Q_3	$\frac{3\pi}{2}$	θ in Q_4	2π
$\sin \theta$	0	$0 \nearrow 1$	1	$1 \searrow 0$	0	$0 \searrow -1$	-1	$-1 \nearrow 0$	0
$\cos \theta$	1	$1 \searrow 0$	0	$0 \searrow -1$	-1	$-1 \nearrow 0$	0	$0 \nearrow 1$	1
$\tan \theta$	0	$0 \nearrow \infty$	∞	$-\infty \nearrow 0$	0	$0 \nearrow \infty$	∞	$-\infty \nearrow 0$	0
$\cot \theta$	∞	$\infty \searrow 0$	0	$0 \searrow -\infty$	∞	$\infty \searrow 0$	0	$0 \searrow -\infty$	∞
$\sec \theta$	1	$1 \nearrow \infty$	∞	$-\infty \nearrow -1$	-1	$-1 \searrow -\infty$	∞	$\infty \searrow 1$	1
$\csc \theta$	∞	$\infty \searrow 1$	1	$1 \nearrow \infty$	∞	$-\infty \nearrow -1$	-1	$-1 \searrow -\infty$	∞

As shown above, the trigonometric functions are periodic; *i.e.*, the same function possesses the same value after certain variations. In general, the value of any trigonometric function of $(\theta + 2n\pi)$ is equal to the same function of θ.

In addition to the periodicity of the trigonometric functions, the regularity of the oscillation between the maximum and minimum values of these functions is another important feature of them. One-half of the maximum minus minimum values of a regularly oscillating function is its *amplitude*. Accordingly, the amplitudes of $\sin x$ and $\cos x$ are both 1.

The Graphs of the Trigonometric Functions.   The combination of all points (x, y) whose coordinates satisfy an equation is the graph of the function of the equation.   Let us take

(2.3.1) $y = \cos x$

whose graph, accordingly, consists of all points which satisfy equation (2.3.1).   If x assumes values from 0 to 2π, the values of y would be, according to the following table, altering from -1 to 1 as x changes and takes on different values.

x	0	$\pi/6$	$\pi/4$	$\pi/3$	$\pi/2$	$2\pi/3$	$3\pi/4$	$5\pi/6$	π	$7\pi/6$	$5\pi/4$	$4\pi/3$	$3\pi/2$
$\cos x$	1	.87	.71	.50	0	$-.50$	$-.71$	$-.87$	-1	$-.87$	$-.71$	$-.50$	0

The graph of $y = \cos x$ is given below.

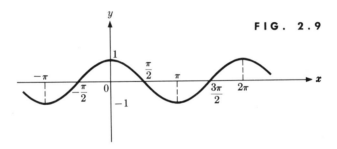

FIG. 2.9

Another important feature of trigonometric functions, aside from being periodic, is oscillation.   For this reason they are often called *sinusoidal* or *circular* functions.   The specific properties of these functions are dealt with under *Complex Numbers*.

The Inverse Trigonometric Functions.   Each trigonometric function has an inverse function.   The following are the trigonometric functions and their inverses:

$$x = \sin^{-1} y \text{ is the inverse of } y = \sin x$$
$$x = \cos^{-1} y \text{ is the inverse of } y = \cos x$$
$$x = \tan^{-1} y \text{ is the inverse of } y = \tan x$$
$$x = \cot^{-1} y \text{ is the inverse of } y = \cot x$$
$$x = \sec^{-1} y \text{ is the inverse of } y = \sec x$$
$$x = \csc^{-1} y \text{ is the inverse of } y = \csc x$$

The inverse triogonometric functions are infinitely many-valued.   The graph of inverse functions is the inverse of those trigonometric functions.

Logarithms of the Trigonometric Functions. A simple method of computing trigonometric functions is by logarithm. Suppose that we wish to compute $a = 143 \sin 29° \, 20'$. We put

$$\log a = \log 143 + \log \sin 29° \, 20'.$$

Since

$$\sin 29° \, 20' = .4899$$
$$\log .4899 = (9.6901 - 10) \quad \log 143 = 2.1553$$

then

$$\log a = 1.8454$$
$$a = 70.0.$$

Properties of the Trigonometric Functions. The following properties are given without proof. (The angles are imposed on the trigonometric system.)

$$\sin \theta = \frac{1}{\csc \theta},$$

$$\cos \theta = \frac{1}{\sec \theta},$$

$$\sin \theta \csc \theta = 1,$$

$$\cos \theta \sec \theta = 1,$$

$$\tan \theta \cot \theta = 1,$$

$$\sin^2 \theta + \cos^2 \theta = 1,$$

$$\sec^2 \theta = 1 + \tan^2 \theta,$$

$$\csc^2 \theta = 1 + \cot^2 \theta,$$

$$\sin \theta = \sin(\pi - \theta) = \sin(2\pi + \theta) = \sin[-(\pi + \theta)],$$

$$\sin(-\theta) = -\sin \theta,$$

$$\cos \theta = \cos(-\theta),$$

$$\cot(-\theta) = -\cot \theta,$$

$$\tan(-\theta) = -\tan \theta,$$

$$\sin(A \pm B) = \sin A \cos B \pm \cos A \sin B,$$

$$\cos(A \pm B) = \cos A \cos B \mp \sin A \sin B,$$

$$\tan(A \pm B) = \frac{\tan A \pm \tan B}{1 \mp \tan A \tan B},$$

$$\sin 2A = 2 \sin A \cos A,$$

$$\cos 2A = \cos^2 A - \sin^2 A = 1 - 2 \sin^2 A = 2 \cos^2 A - 1,$$

$$2 \sin^2 A = 1 - \cos 2A,$$

$$\tan 2A = \frac{2 \tan A}{1 - \tan^2 A},$$

$$\sin \frac{A}{2} = \pm \sqrt{\frac{1 - \cos A}{2}},$$

$$\cos \frac{A}{2} = \pm \sqrt{\frac{1 + \cos A}{2}},$$

$$\tan \frac{A}{2} = \pm \sqrt{\frac{1 - \cos A}{1 + \cos A}},$$

$$\sin A \cos B = \tfrac{1}{2}[\sin(A + B) + \sin(A - B)],$$
$$\cos A \cos B = \tfrac{1}{2}[\cos(A + B) + \cos(A - B)],$$
$$\sin A \sin B = \tfrac{1}{2}[\cos(A - B) - \cos(A + B)],$$
$$\sin A + \sin B = 2 \sin[\tfrac{1}{2}(A + B)] \cos[\tfrac{1}{2}(A - B)],$$
$$\sin A - \sin B = 2 \sin[\tfrac{1}{2}(A - B)] \cos[\tfrac{1}{2}(A + B)],$$
$$\cos A + \cos B = 2 \cos[\tfrac{1}{2}(A + B)] \cos[\tfrac{1}{2}(A - B)],$$
$$\cos A - \cos B = -2 \sin[\tfrac{1}{2}(A + B)] \sin[\tfrac{1}{2}(A - B)].$$

Trigonometric Equations. A trigonometric equation consists of trigo-nometric elements.

(2.3.2)
$$F(u) = \frac{u}{\tan u} + \log \frac{\sin u}{u}$$

is an example. The solution of a trigonometric equation is a value of the variable which satisfies the equation. As an example, let us solve $2 \cos^2 \theta + 3 \sin \theta = 0$. Since

$$\cos^2 \theta = 1 - \sin^2 \theta$$

then

$$2 \sin^2 \theta - 3 \sin \theta - 2 = 0,$$

which is a quadratic equation the solutions of which are

$$\sin \theta_1 = -\tfrac{1}{2}, \ \sin \theta_2 = 2,$$
$$\theta = 210° + n(360°), \ \theta = 330° + n(360°).$$

Thus, the general solution of the equation

$$y = a(\sin x) + b(\cos x)$$

can be written in either of the two forms

$$r \sin(x + \alpha) \quad \text{where} \quad r = \sqrt{a^2 + b^2}, \ \cos \alpha = \frac{a}{r}, \ \sin \alpha = \frac{b}{r}$$

$$r \cos(x + \alpha) \quad \text{where} \quad r = \sqrt{a^2 + b^2}, \ \cos \alpha = \frac{b}{r}, \ \sin \alpha = \frac{a}{r}.$$

This is a simple method for solving trigonometric equations of the form

$$a(\sin x) + b(\cos x) = c.$$

Systems of Trigonometric Equations. The methods, mentioned before, for solving systems of algebraic equations apply equally well to solving systems of trigonometric equations. As an example let us solve the follow-ing system for r and θ:

$$r(\cos \theta) = a$$
$$r(\sin \theta) = b.$$

Dividing the second equation by the first one, we have

$$\tan \theta = \frac{b}{a}$$

$$\theta = \tan^{-1} \frac{b}{a}.$$

Squaring the members of the first and second equations and adding yield

$$r = \pm\sqrt{a^2 + b^2}.$$

2.4 The $\sum$ Notation

The sigma $\sum$ sign is a simple and convenient shorthand notation for expressing sums. Thus, for example, we write

$$x_1 + x_2 + x_3 = \sum_{j=1}^{3} x_j,$$

where j is usually called the index of summation. Of course, j is a variable which ranges over the integers 1, 2, 3. The *summand*, x_j, which takes on the values x_1, x_2, and x_3 is a function of j which takes on the values 1, 2, and 3. The number 3 written over the sigma sign $\sum$ defines that the terminal value of j is 3; and the expression $j = 1$ written below the $\sum$ notation indicates that first value of j is one. One more point, the sigma sign $\sum$ defines and indicates that the values x_1, x_2, and x_3 which are taken on by x_j should be added.

Likewise, if we write

$$x_4 + x_5 + x_6 = \sum_{j=4}^{6} x_j$$

where x_j takes on the values x_4, x_5, x_6, 4 and 6 are the initial and the terminal values of j, respectively. Again, the *index of summation* ranges over the integers 4, 5, and 6; the number 6 written over the sigma sign denotes that the terminal value of j is 6 and 4 is the initial value taken on by j. Finally, the sigma sign indicates that the values x_4, x_5, x_6, which are taken on by x_j, are to be added.

Putting the two examples together, we have

$$x_1 + x_2 + x_3 + x_4 + x_5 + x_6 = \sum_{j=1}^{6} x_j$$

or

$$\sum_{j=1}^{3} x_j + \sum_{j=4}^{6} x_j = \sum_{j=1}^{6} x_j.$$

The following formula does generalize the two examples which we have used for illustration:

(2.4.1)
$$x_1 + x_2 + \cdots + x_i + \cdots + x_n = \sum_{j=1}^{n} x_j$$

or

(2.4.2)
$$(x_1 + x_2 + \cdots + x_k) + (x_{k+1} + x_{k+2} + \cdots + x_n)$$
$$= \sum_{j=1}^{n} x_j = \sum_{j=1}^{k} x_j + \sum_{k+1=j}^{n} x_j.$$

In the formulas, the values represented by $x_1, x_2, \ldots x_n$ have to be given before the sums can be evaluated. Here, (as in special cases), the entire expression $\sum_{j=1}^{n} x_j$ is to be read as follows: "the summation of x_j as j ranges from 1 to n." As special illustrations of the above rules, we can write

$$1^2 + 2^2 + 3^2 + 4^2 = \sum_{j=1}^{4} j^2.$$

Also, if y stands for income we can write

$$\frac{y}{(1+r)} + \frac{y}{(1+r)^2} + \frac{y}{(1+r)^3} + \cdots + \frac{y}{(1+r)^n} = \sum_{j=1}^{n} \frac{y}{(1+r)^j}$$

which is the present value of income stream $\$y$ starting next year and continuing for n years at the interest rate $100r$ per cent annually. In each case we can obtain the first three terms of the left-hand side of (2.4.2) by substituting $j = 1, 2, 3$, respectively, into the *general term* of the series, namely, the term containing the index j which appears on both the left and the right in the appropriate equation. As many more terms as may be desired can, of course, be found in the same manner.

In each example given, the letter used for the index of summation is an entirely arbitrary one; that is the reason why it is called *dummy index*. Further, the following example indicates another way of using the index of summation:

$$\sum_{j=1}^{n} x_j = \sum_{j=0}^{n-1} x_{j+1} = \sum_{j=2}^{n+1} x_{j-1}.$$

This is a very useful way of using the index of summation. In the above example, although we changed the initial and terminal values, the net sum remains constant since the alteration has been in a compensating way.

Some Rules Concerning Summation $\sum$. The first rule, already proved by induction, is given by

(2.4.3)
$$x_1 + x_2 + \cdots + x_n = \sum_{j=1}^{n} x_j.$$

Special cases of the above rule are the following examples:

(2.4.4) $$\left(\sum_{j=1}^{n} x_j \right) + x_{n+1} = \sum_{j=1}^{n+1} x_j,$$

(2.4.5) $$\sum_{j=k+1}^{n} x_j = \sum_{j=1}^{n} x_j - \sum_{j=1}^{k} x_j, \ (k+1 \leq n)$$

$$\sum_{j=1}^{k} x_j + \sum_{j=1}^{n-k} x_{k=j} = \sum_{j=1}^{n} x_j.$$

The second rule relates to the case when each element of the summand x_j is equal to a fixed and same quantity k. In this case

$$k + k + k + \cdots + k = \sum_{j=1}^{n} x_j$$

or

(2.4.6) $$\sum_{i=1}^{n} k = nk.$$

The third rule, derived from the first one, holds when we have $x_i = k y_i$ where k is a constant. Then

$$k y_1 + k y_2 + \cdots + k y_n = k(y_1 + y_2 + \cdots + y_n) = \sum_{i=1}^{n} x_i = k \left(\sum_{i=1}^{n} y_i \right).$$

Thus, our third rule will be

(2.4.7) $$\sum_{i=1}^{n} (k y_i) = k \sum_{i=1}^{n} y_i.$$

The fourth rule, again derived from the first rule, applies to the case when $x_i = y_i + z_i + w_i$, Then we have

$$\sum_{i=1}^{n} x_i = \sum_{i=1}^{n} (y_i + z_i + w_i) = (y_1 + z_1 + w_1) + \cdots + (y_n + z_n + w_n)$$

$$= (y_1 + y_2 + \cdots + y_n) + (z_1 + z_2 + \cdots + z_n) + (w_1 + \cdots + w_n)$$

$$= \sum_{i=1}^{n} y_i + \sum_{i=1}^{n} z_i + \sum_{i=1}^{n} w_i.$$

Thus, we can phrase our fourth rule:

(2.4.8) $$\sum_{i=1}^{n} (A_i + B_i + \cdots + W_i) = \sum_{i=1}^{n} A_i + \sum_{i=1}^{n} B_i + \cdots + \sum_{i=1}^{n} W_i.$$

One observation should be made in passing. Sometimes, the range of summation is clearly defined and specified by the context. In this case, some authors may omit the index of summation. Accordingly, we may write Σx in place of $\sum_{i=1}^{n} x_i$ when there is no room for possible misunderstanding. We wish to suggest that it is usually safe to use the index of summation.

Using the third and the fourth rules, the following cases will be solved:

$$\textbf{(2.4.9)} \qquad \sum_{i=1}^{n} (ax_i + by_i) = a \sum_{i=1}^{n} x_i + b \sum_{i=1}^{n} y_i,$$

$$\textbf{(2.4.10)} \qquad \sum_{i=1}^{n} x_i(x_i - 1) = \sum_{i=1}^{n} x_i^2 - \sum_{i=1}^{n} x_i,$$

$$\textbf{(2.4.11)} \qquad \sum_{i=1}^{n} (x_i - 1)(x_i + 1) = \left(\sum_{i=1}^{n} x_i^2 \right) - n.$$

At this juncture, we should point out a fact which causes a great deal of trouble for many students and those who have to employ the summation signs. The students of statistics seldom write

$$\sum_{i=1}^{n} (x_i + a)(y_i + b) = \left[\sum_{i=1}^{n} (x_i + a) \right] \left[\sum_{i=1}^{n} (y_i + b) \right].$$

This is wrong. The reader notices that we have to complete the multiplication first, then if there is any possibility for factorization, such as (2.4.11) above, we can factor proper terms and write them separately.

Finite Double Sums. Let us suppose that there is a set of mn quantities of A_{ij}, where, of course, $i = 1, 2, \ldots m$ and $j = 1, 2, \ldots n$. Let us arrange these quantities in the rectangular order

$$\begin{array}{cccc} A_{11} & A_{12} & \cdots & A_{1n} \\ A_{21} & A_{22} & \cdots & A_{2n} \\ \cdots & \cdots & \cdots & \cdots \\ A_{m1} & A_{m2} & \cdots & A_{mn}, \end{array}$$

where there are m rows and n columns. If we are to add all the quantities, we may proceed in two ways: we may add, first, the various columns and then add the column totals to obtain the desired result; or we may add, first, all the various rows and then add the row totals to have the result. We take, for exposition, the first alternative

$$\sum_{i=1}^{m} A_{i1} + \sum_{i=1}^{m} A_{i2} + \cdots + \sum_{i=1}^{m} A_{in}$$

or written more compactly

$$\textbf{(2.4.12)} \qquad \sum_{j=1}^{n} \left(\sum_{i=1}^{m} A_{ij} \right).$$

Since the sum will be the same in either alternative, we write

$$\sum_{j=1}^{n}\left(\sum_{i=1}^{m} A_{ij}\right) = \sum_{i=1}^{m}\left(\sum_{j=1}^{n} A_{ij}\right).$$

Since the order of summation, in finite double sums, is immaterial, the double sums can be written without parentheses:

(2.4.13)
$$\sum_{j=1}^{n}\sum_{i=1}^{m} A_{ij} = \sum_{i=1}^{m}\sum_{j=1}^{n} A_{ij}$$

viz., if we want to add all the A's, it does not make any difference if we first add all the elements in the various rows and then add the row totals to get the results, or we first add all the elements in the various columns and then add the column totals to have the desired results.

The finite double sums can be applied to the bilinear form

$$A_{ij} = a_{ij}x_iy_j \qquad \begin{matrix}(i = 1, 2, \ldots m) \\ (j = 1, 2, \ldots n)\end{matrix}$$

and get

(2.4.14)
$$\sum_{i=1}^{m}\sum_{j=1}^{n} a_{ij}x_iy_j.$$

The expanded form of this sum is

(2.4.15)
$$\sum_{i=1}^{m}\sum_{j=1}^{n} a_{ij}x_iy_j = \begin{cases} a_{11}x_1y_1 + a_{12}x_1y_2 + \cdots + a_{1n}x_1y_n \\ \quad + \qquad\qquad + \qquad\qquad\qquad + \\ a_{21}x_2y_1 + a_{22}x_2y_2 + \cdots + a_{2n}x_2y_n \\ \quad + \qquad\qquad + \qquad\qquad\qquad + \\ \cdots\cdots\cdots\cdots\cdots\cdots\cdots\cdots \\ \quad + \qquad\qquad + \qquad\qquad\qquad + \\ a_{m1}x_my_1 + a_{m2}x_my_2 + \cdots + a_{mn}x_my_n \end{cases}$$

which is a polynomial in the $n + m$ variables $x_1, \ldots x_m, y_1, y_2, \ldots y_n$. A special case of great importance is obtained when $A_{ij} = a_{ij}x_j = b_i$ where $i = 1, 2, \ldots m$ and $j = 1, 2, \ldots n$. We have then

$$\sum_{i=1}^{m}\sum_{j=1}^{n} a_{ij}x_j = \sum_{i}^{m} b_i = \begin{cases} a_{11}x_1 + a_{12}x_2 + \cdots + a_{1n}x_n = b_1 \\ \quad + \qquad + \qquad\qquad + \qquad\quad + \\ a_{21}x_1 + a_{22}x_2 + \cdots + a_{2n}x_n = b_2 \\ \quad + \qquad + \qquad\qquad + \qquad\quad + \\ \cdots\cdots\cdots\cdots\cdots\cdots\cdots\cdots \\ \quad + \qquad + \qquad\qquad + \qquad\quad + \\ a_{m1}x_1 + a_{m2}x_2 + \cdots + a_{mn}x_n = b_m \end{cases}$$

which is a polynomial in n unknowns. If in $A_{ij} = a_{ij}x_j = b_i$, we only want to add the rows, we should not use two summation signs. One is all we need. In this case, we have $i = 1, \ldots m$ and

$$\sum_{j=1}^{n} a_{ij}x_j = b_i = \begin{cases} a_{11}x_1 + a_{12}x_2 + \cdots + a_{1n}x_n = b_1 \\ a_{21}x_1 + a_{22}x_2 + \cdots + a_{2n}x_n = b_2 \\ \cdots\cdots\cdots\cdots\cdots\cdots\cdots\cdots\cdots \\ a_{m1}x_1 + a_{m2}x_2 + \cdots + a_{mn}x_n = b_m \end{cases}$$

(2.4.16)

which is called the system of non-homogeneous linear equations in n unknowns. Remember that we should not use double summation sign for a system of equations.

2.5 The $\prod$ Notation

The notation for multiplication is Π. If there are n variables x_i which are to be multiplied, the convention is to write them in the following way

(2.5.1)
$$\prod_{i=1}^{n} x_i = x_1 x_2 \ldots x_n.$$

The multiplication notation is, in essence, analogous to the summation sign. That is to say, there is the index of multiplication which is below the multiplication notation and denotes the initial value of the range, and the letter above the notation indicates the terminal value of the range. Thus, the range of the multiplication is defined by the index of multiplication and the letter which is over the notation X_i is a function of i and takes on different values as i takes on values over its range. Unless the x's are all distinct, (2.5.1) is zero.

The following rules are deduced, and can be proved easily, from the rules given for the summation.

If there are n fixed constants which are equal, we can write

(2.5.2)
$$\prod_{i=1}^{n} k = k^n.$$

If the variables x_i are all multiplied by the same given fixed constant k, we can write the product

(2.5.3)
$$\prod_{i=1}^{n} (kx_i) = k^n \left(\prod_{i=1}^{n} x_i \right).$$

The product of two sets of variables x_1 and y_1 will be written as

(2.5.4)
$$\prod_{i=1}^{n} x_i y_i = \left(\prod_{i=1}^{n} x_i \right) \left(\prod_{i=1}^{n} y_i \right).$$

Finally, we write

(2.5.5)
$$\prod_{i=1}^{m} \left(\prod_{j=1}^{n} A_{ij} \right) = \prod_{j=1}^{n} \left(\prod_{i=1}^{m} A_{ij} \right)$$

where A_{ij} is a set of mn quantities arranged in a rectangular pattern

$$
\begin{array}{cccc}
A_{11} & A_{12} & \cdots & A_{1n} \\
A_{21} & A_{22} & \cdots & A_{2n} \\
\cdot\cdot\cdot & & & \cdot\cdot \\
A_{m1} & A_{m2} & \cdots & A_{mn}.
\end{array}
$$

2.6 Sequence and Series

A *sequence* of numbers is a set of numbers so arranged that there is a first, a second, a third, . . . , number in the set. For example

$$a_1, a_2, \ldots a_n,$$

is a sequence in n terms. The successive numbers are called the *terms* of a sequence. If a sequence has a definite terminal value as in

(2.6.1)
$$a_1, a_2, \ldots a_n$$

it is called a *finite sequence* and the symbols $a_1, a_2, \ldots, a_n$ are its terms. If, however, a sequence does not terminate as in

(2.6.2)
$$a_1, a_2, \ldots \text{ ad infinitum}$$

it is called an *infinite sequence*. An arbitrary term of a sequence is spoken of as the i-th term of the sequence, such as a_i where $i = 1, 2, \ldots, n$. The letters j, k, m, n, p, r and s are also used.

The indicated sum of the numbers of a sequence is called a *series*. For instance, the series of (2.6.1) is

(2.6.3)
$$S_n = a_1 + a_2 + \cdots + a_n.$$

(2.6.3) is a *finite series* which is the indicated sum of a finite sequence. On the other hand, the sum of an infinite sequence will produce an infinite series. We explained before (Section 2.4) that the sum of a sequence can be shown by the sigma Σ sign. Thus for finite and infinite series we can write respectively:

(2.6.4)
$$\sum_{i=1}^{n} a_i,$$

and

(2.6.5)
$$\sum_{i=1}^{\infty} a_i.$$

Progressions. The Arithmetic Progression (abbreviated as A.P. hereafter) and the Geometric Progression (abbreviated as G.P.) are used often in mathematics and mathematical economics. Malthus was the first economic theorist to announce that population has a tendency to grow geometrically while the means of subsistence tends to grow arithmetically. An A.P. is a sequence of numbers in which each term, after the first, is obtained from the preceding one by adding to it a fixed number called the *common difference.* For example, the sequence 1, 3, 5, 7 is an A.P. with the common difference 2; and the sequence 1, -1, -3, -5 is another A.P. with the common difference -2. If we denote the first term of an A.P. by a, the common difference by d, the number of terms by n and the n-th term by L, then, according to the definition of an A.P., we can write mathematically:

$$\text{the first term} = a$$
$$\text{the second term} = a + d$$
$$\text{the third term} = a + 2d$$
$$\text{the fourth term} = a + 3d$$
$$\cdots\cdots\cdots\cdots\cdots\cdots\cdots$$
$$\text{the } i\text{-th term} = a + (i - 1)d$$
$$\cdots\cdots\cdots\cdots\cdots\cdots\cdots$$
$$\text{the } n\text{-th term} = a + (n - 1)d = L.$$

Hence the n-th term of an assumed A.P. is given by

(2.6.6) $$L = a + (n - 1)d.$$

Let us suppose that one desires to find the seventh term of the A.P. 1, 3, 5, 7 where $a = 1$, $d = 2$ and $n = 7$. Hence the seventh term will be:

$$L = 1 + (7 - 1)2 = 13,$$

or the eighth term of 1, -1, -3, -5 is

$$L = 1 + (8 - 1)(-2) = -13.$$

Also, the *sum* of an indicated A.P. is given by

(2.6.7) $$S = \tfrac{1}{2}n(a + L).$$

Hence the sum of the first eight terms of 1, 3, 5, 7 is

$$S = \tfrac{1}{2}8(1 + L)$$

where $L = 1 + (8 - 1)2 = 15$ which in substituting in the sum will entail

$$S = \tfrac{1}{2}(8)(1 + 15) = 64.$$

We indicated that we have also a Geometric Progression. A G.P. is a sequence of numbers in which each term, after the first, is obtained from the preceding one by multiplying it by a fixed number called the *common ratio*. If we denote the first term of a G.P. by a, the common ratio by r, the number of terms by n and the n-th term by L, then, according to the definition of a G.P., we can write mathematically:

$$\begin{aligned}
\text{the first term} &= a \\
\text{the second term} &= ar \\
\text{the third term} &= ar^2 \\
&\cdots\cdots\cdots \\
\text{the } i\text{-th term} &= ar^{i-1} \\
&\cdots\cdots\cdots \\
\text{the } n\text{-th term} &= ar^{n-1}.
\end{aligned}$$

Hence, the n-th term of an assumed G.P. is given by

(2.6.8) $$L = ar^{n-1}.$$

Let us suppose that we wish to find the ninth term of the G.P. 1, 2, 4, 8, where $a = 1$, and $r = 2$. The ninth term is

$$L = 1(2)^{9-1} = 256.$$

Also, the sum of an indicated G.P. is given by

$$S = a\,\frac{1 - r^n}{1 - r} = \frac{a - rL}{1 - r}$$

if and only if $r \neq 1$. In case $r = 1$, since the i-th power of unity is itself, the i-th term of a G.P. is the same as its first term and the sum of its first n terms is the product of n and a. If, however, $|r| < 1$, (*i.e.*, the *absolute value* of the common ratio is less than one), and the number of terms is unlimited, the sum of the unlimited progression is given by

$$S = \frac{a}{1 - r}.$$

This result is useful for converting repeating decimals. Suppose that we should convert the repeating decimal $1.3757575\ldots$ into an equivalent common fraction. The given decimal may be written in the form

$$1.3757575\ldots = 1.3 + .075 + .00075 + \cdots$$

It is noticed that the terms of the right number, after the first term, form an unlimited geometric progression where $r = .01$ and $a = .075$ thus,

$$S = \frac{.075}{1 - .01} = \frac{5}{66}.$$

Hence

$$1.3757575\ldots = \tfrac{13}{10} + \tfrac{5}{66} = \tfrac{83}{66}.$$

A summary of the relationship of certain equations with their graphs is given.

Equation	Condition	Graph
$y = a + bx$ or $y = ax + b$	linear	straight line, constant slope
$y = ax^2 + bx + c$	parabola	one turning value
$y = ax^3 + bx^2 + cx + d$	cubic	two turning values
. . . .	. . . .	. . . .
$y = a_0x^n + a_1x^{n-1} + \cdots + a_n$	polynomial	n-1 turning values
$xy = a$	hyperbola	asymptotic to either or both axes
$y = ae^{bx}$	exponential	asymptotic to x-axis only
$y = \log x$	logarithmic	asymptotic to y-axis only
$x^2 + y^2 = a$	circle	symmetrical about any diameter
$y = \sin x$ or $y = \cos x$	sin-curve cos-curve	many turning values

EXERCISES 2

1. Express in logarithmic form:

$$4^3 = 64, \quad 6^2 = 36, \quad 3^2 = 9, \quad 2^4 = 16, \quad 5^3 = 125.$$

2. Express in exponential form:

$$\log_7 49 = 2, \quad \log_3 27 = 3, \quad \log_{10} .001 = -3,$$
$$\log_{16} \tfrac{1}{64} = -\tfrac{3}{2}, \quad \log_{\frac{1}{8}} 16 = -\tfrac{4}{3}.$$

3. Find the value of each of the following:

$$\log_{27} 3 \qquad \log_8 64 \qquad \log_8 4 \qquad \log_{25} 125 \qquad \log_{\sqrt{2}} 124$$

4. Find the unknowns b, x, or N in each of the following:

$$\log_3 64 = x, \quad \log_{\sqrt{3}} 9 = x, \quad \log_2 16 = x, \quad \log_3 27 = x,$$
$$\log_b 81 = 2, \quad \log_b 49 = 2, \quad \log_b 125 = 3, \quad \log_b 16 = -\tfrac{4}{3},$$

$$\log_9 N = 2, \qquad \log_4 N = \tfrac{1}{2}, \qquad \log_3 N = 3, \qquad \log_4 N = \tfrac{1}{2}.$$

5. In each of the following solve for x in terms of y:

$$\log_e x = 2y, \qquad \log_a x = -y^3, \qquad \log_e x = \log_a y,$$

$$\log_a x = \log_a y + \log_a 4, \qquad \log_a(x + y) = 2\log_a(x - y),$$

$$y = ae^{bx}, \qquad y = ae^{-bx}, \qquad y = ae^{-x+1},$$

$$y = a\,\frac{1 - d^x}{1 - d}, \qquad y = A(1 + i)^x.$$

6. A corporation has borrowed \$5,000 which is to be paid off by payments of \$100 at the end of each month at which times interest on the principal outstanding during the month is also to be paid at 6% per annum. Find the total amount paid in discharging the debt.

7. If in the previous example the interest rate is dropped to 3% after payments have been made for 18 months, how much less will be paid in discharging the debt?

8. An automobile may be an item included in a consumer's purchase plan. Let there be a consumer wishing to purchase a car through a bank, paying off his indebtedness of \$2400 by payments at the end of each month of \$60 to the principal and \$6.00 on the interest. What is the total amount of money paid to discharge the debt and what interest rate is paid?

9. If a man deposits \$1,000 at the end of each year for 8 years in a savings and loan association that pays $4\tfrac{1}{2}$% compounded annually, what amount shall his account be credited immediately after the eighth payment? What would be his credit if the association pays $4\tfrac{1}{2}$% compounded semi-annually?

10. What sum has a person to his credit if he deposits his \$1,000 annual savings in a bank which pays 3% compounded annually and leaves the whole amount for 10 years after the final deposit has been made?

11. An entrepreneur makes equal annual deposits at the end of the years for 10 years in order to meet the cost of replacing a piece of capital earning asset at the end of the tenth year. If the entrepreneur receives 4% compounded semi-annually, find his annual deposit, if the replacement cost is \$12,020.00.

12. Use the values of the trigonometric functions of the indicated angles to verify the following statements:

$$\sin^2 180° + \cos^2 180° = 1.$$

$$\sin 120° = 2\sin 60° \cos 60°.$$

$$\sin \frac{\pi}{6} \cos \frac{\pi}{3} - \cos \frac{\pi}{6} \sin \frac{\pi}{3} = -\frac{1}{2}.$$

$$\tan^2 225° + 1 = \sec^2 225°.$$

$$2 \sin \frac{3\pi}{4} \cos \frac{3\pi}{4} = -1.$$

$$\sin \left(\pi - \frac{\pi}{3} \right) = \sin \frac{\pi}{3}.$$

$$\cos(90° - 30°) = \sin 30°.$$

13. Solve for the trigonometric functions

$$\frac{9 - 14 \sin x}{2 - 3 \sin x} = 5.$$

$$\frac{5 \cos x}{\cos x + 1} + 2 = \frac{\cos x}{1 + \cos x}.$$

$$\frac{\cos x}{\cos x + 1} + 2 = \frac{3 \cos x}{\cos x + 2}.$$

$$\frac{\tan x - 1}{\tan x + 1} = \frac{2 \tan x + 3}{\tan x + 1} - \frac{11}{12}.$$

14. Solve each of the following systems of equations for r and θ, or for x and y, whichever appear.

$$\begin{cases} r \sin \theta = a \\ r \cos \theta = b \end{cases}$$

$$\begin{cases} \sin^2 x + \sin^2 y = a \\ \cos^2 x - \cos^2 y = b \end{cases}$$

$$\begin{cases} \sin x + \sin y = \sin A \\ \cos x + \cos y = 1 + \cos A \end{cases}$$

$$\begin{cases} r + \sin^2 \theta = a \\ r + \cos^2 \theta = b \end{cases}$$

$$\begin{cases} \sin x + \sin y = 2a \sin A \\ \cos x + \cos y = 2b \cos A \end{cases}$$

15. Let $x_1 = 1$, $x_2 = 3$, $x_3 = 5$, $x_4 = 8$ and $x_5 = 6$. Find:

$$\sum_{i=1}^{4} x_i, \quad \sum_{i=1}^{5} x_i, \quad \sum_{i=2}^{5} x_i, \quad \sum_{i=1}^{5} (3x_i + 5), \quad \sum_{i=1}^{5} (x_i - 2)(2x_i + 3).$$

16. Rewrite in $\sum$ notation

$$3x + 9x^2 + 27x^3 + 81x^4 + 243x^5. \quad \frac{2}{3} + \frac{4}{5} + \frac{6}{7} + \cdots + \frac{2n}{2n + 1}.$$

$$\frac{3}{2} + \frac{4}{6} + \frac{5}{12} + \cdots + \frac{n + 2}{n(n + 1)} \quad 1 + \frac{1}{2} + \frac{1}{4} + \cdots + \frac{1}{2^{n-1}}.$$

17. Expand the following:

$$\sum_{i=1}^{8} x_i(2x_i - 1).$$

$$\sum_{n=0}^{\infty} \frac{R}{(1 + i)^n}$$

$$\sum_{i=5}^{10} x_i(3x_i + 2).$$

$$\sum_{n=1}^{\infty} \frac{1}{n^p}$$

$$\sum_{n=1}^{n} \frac{nx^n}{1 + 2^n}.$$

18. If $\bar{z} = \dfrac{\sum z}{n}$:

   (a) Show that $\sum (z - \bar{z}) = 0$.

   (b) And if $z = ax + b$, show that

$$\bar{z} = a\bar{x} + b.$$

(c) If, however, $z = ax$, show that
$$\bar{z} = a\bar{x}.$$

(d) If $z_i = x_i + y_i$, show that
$$\bar{z} = \bar{x} + \bar{y}.$$

(e) If
$$s_z = \sqrt{\frac{1}{n}\sum(z_i - \bar{z})^2}$$

and $z_i = ax_i + b$, show that
$$s_z = as_x.$$

19. Show that
$$\sum_{i=1}^{n}(ax_i + by_i) = a\sum_{i=1}^{n}x_i + b\sum_{i=1}^{n}y_i.$$

$$\sum_{i=1}^{n}(x_i - \bar{x})^2 = \sum_{i=1}^{n}x_i^2 - n\bar{x}^2$$

where $\bar{x} = \dfrac{\sum x}{n}$.

$$\sum_{i=1}^{n}(x_i - 1)(x_i + 1) = \sum_{i=1}^{n}x_i^2 - n.$$

$$\sum_{i=1}^{n}[i^2 - (i - 1)^2] = n^2.$$

$$\sum_{i=1}^{n}i = \frac{n + n^2}{2}$$ if i takes on only positive integers from 1 to n.

20. Write out in full
$$\sum_{i=1}^{n}\sum_{j=1}^{n}a_{ij}x_ix_j.$$

21. Show that
$$(x - x_1)(x - x_2)\cdots(x - x_n) = \prod_{i=1}^{n}(x - x_i).$$

$$\prod_{\substack{i,j=1,2,\ldots,n \\ i \neq j}}(x_i - x_j) = (-1)^{\frac{n(n-1)}{2}}\left[\prod_{\substack{i,j=1,2,\ldots,n \\ i<j}}(x_i - x_j)\right]^2.$$

22. Find the first five terms and the $(n + 1)$st term of each of the series whose nth terms are given below:

$$\frac{2n - 1}{2n}.$$

$$(-1)^{n-1}\frac{1}{(n + 2)n}.$$

$$(-1)^n\frac{x^{3n}}{3n(2n + 1)}.$$

$$\frac{(2n + 1)x^{n-1}}{(3n)}.$$

$$(-1)^{n+1}\frac{x^{3n-2}}{n(n + 1)(n + 2)}.$$

23. Find an nth term of each of the following series and verify it for $n = 1, 2, 3$ and 4.

$$1 - \frac{x^2}{2!} + \frac{x^4}{4!} - \frac{x^6}{6!} + \cdots$$

$$\frac{3}{1.2} + \frac{4}{3.4} + \frac{5}{5.6} + \cdots$$

$$x - \frac{x(x-1)}{2!} + \frac{x(x-1)(x-2)}{3!} - \cdots$$

$$x^2 + 3^3 x^4 + 5^5 x^6 + \cdots$$

$$x - \frac{x^3}{1.2} + \frac{x^5}{1.2.3} - \frac{x^7}{1.2.3.4} + \cdots$$

24. Find the limit of each of the following sequences as n increases without bound; in each case the nth term is given.

$$\frac{4n}{3n - 1} \qquad\qquad \frac{(n-1)^2(n-1)!}{(n-2)2 \cdot n!}$$

$$\frac{3n + 5}{4 + n} \qquad\qquad \frac{n^2 \cdot 6^{n+2}}{(n+1)23^{n+2}}$$

$$\frac{n - 3}{2 + n^2}$$

25. Find an nth term of each of the following sequences, then find the limit of each sequence as the number of terms increases without bound.

$$\frac{1}{2}, \frac{1}{4}, \frac{1}{6}, \frac{1}{8}, \cdots$$

$$\frac{1}{3}, \frac{2}{5}, \frac{3}{7}, \frac{4}{9}, \cdots$$

$$-\frac{1}{2}, -\frac{1}{4}, -\frac{1}{6}, -\frac{1}{8}, \cdots$$

$$1, \frac{1.2}{2^2}, \frac{1.2.3}{3^2}, \frac{1.2.3.4}{4^2}, \cdots$$

3 SOME BASIC FUNCTIONAL EQUATIONS IN ECONOMICS

Throughout this chapter, we will apply the important mathematical tools which were conceived of in the preceding chapters. In what ensues, we will distinguish an identity from an equation, examine the solution of an equation and the application of the summation sign and the concept of an incremental change. We have endeavored to use the examples which would be cohesive.

3.1 Demand

There are at least two ways to demonstrate the downward-sloping demand curve in the positive quadrant of a two-dimensional diagram. The first method is contained in the statement that the curvature of a demand curve can be established by examining the corollaries of the law of the marginal diminishing utilities. But there is a second opinion in general currency which purports to explain the negative slope and single-valued conditions of the demand curve via the indifference-curve analysis. Today, there is a tendency to maintain, perhaps correctly, that although the utility theorists started from otiose or unacceptable foundations, they were not misled into false inquiries; that their conclusion, the downward slope of the demand curve and its welfare ramifications coincide with those of the indifference-curve analysis. In this section, our task is to express the demand for a consumer good in terms of an equation and its diagrammatic representation.

It was propounded in the first chapter that mathematical conclusions, and those of mathematical economics, are based on their corresponding assumptions and postulates. In order to deduce the shape of the demand for a consumer good, the first assumption that one should make is the prevalence of pure competition (among buyers) where no individual buyer has any appreciable influence on the market price; namely, the price is fixed by either the market or the seller. Let us suppose that in a specified time period there are n commodities which the household includes in its purchase plan: q_1 of the first commodity, q_2 of the second commodity, ... q_n of the nth commodity. Further, assume that the prices of these goods are respectively $p_1, p_2, \ldots p_n$. Hence, the budget equation or total expenditures of the household will be

$$\textbf{(3.1.1)} \qquad y = p_1 q_1 + p_2 q_2 + \cdots + p_n q_n = \sum_{i=1}^{n} p_i q_i.$$

We observed that p_i cannot be altered by a consumer's efforts while the total income, y, allocable to different commodities in his plan can be controlled by him yet fixed in amount. Moreover, it is assumed that the consumer is out to maximize his satisfaction.

Of course, the decision to purchase a certain quantity of one or many commodities depends on y, the fixed allocable income of a consumer. It is fixed because the households generally do not anticipate any change in their incomes within very short periods. It can, by all means, be supplemented by the accumulated past income called savings or future expected income called credit. Naturally for all consumers the present income is the most important determinant of their demand for certain commodity or commodities. Accordingly, equation (3.1.1) is commonly referred to as the budget constraint.

Having decided on the amount that a consumer wants to spend on certain commodities, he must next decide what quantity of each commodity to buy. The decision to acquire a certain quantity of a good, q, called the demand for that good, or the decision to allocate a sum of money to a good, *inter alia*, depends on consumer's taste for that good (T), the price of this good p_q and the prices of all other goods p_i which are either competitive or complementary to this good. If these variables, y, T, p_q, p_i, are the only elements which determine explicitly the purchase plan of a household, we can write the demand for q mathematically

$$\textbf{(3.1.2)} \qquad q = q(y, T, p_q, p_i).$$

Needless to say, a consumer's demand for a certain good may be changed and his plan may be revised if his income changes, if the price of this good or the prices of all other complementary or competitive goods in relation to this good change; and/or if his taste alters so that he changes his decision concerning the ratio of the combination of goods that he includes in his purchase plan. Although the explicit form of (3.1.2) will remain the same, the particular forms which emanate from (3.1.2) will vary under changing conditions.

It is convenient to begin by assuming that the prices of other goods, and the taste and income of the consumer are all fixed. On this simplifying assumption, one can reduce (3.1.2) to

(3.1.3) $$q = q(p_q, y).$$

Furthermore, many econometricians have approximated a particular type of the demand equation for many agricultural commodities. The general type is

(3.1.4) $$q = ap_q + by.$$

Since the consumer income in a given period is assumed to remain fixed, by is to be constant. Let us suppose that $by = c$ and rewrite (3.1.4)

(3.1.5) $$q = ap_q + c.$$

Mention was made in Chapter 1, when discussing linear equations and their graphs, that the term c is called a *constant* if its composition, in this instance by, remains unmodified. It will, however, represent a *parameter* if the elements which constitute it vary so that a change in the parameter will shift the demand curve to the left or right depending on income variations. An incomplete form of a demand for sugar for the United States approximated by Henry Schultz is[1]

(3.1.6) $$q = -2.26p_q + 70.62.$$

The rows in Table 1 describe the content of the purchase plan that is illustrated in Figures 3.1 and 3.2.

It is convenient to assume that p_q and q are continuous. It is not imperative that we should make this assumption.

TABLE 1

p_q	0	1	2	3	4	5	6
q	70.62	68.36	66.10	63.84	61.58	59.32	57.06

To keep the table manageable in size, we have only included a few values of the admissible range of values that p_q and q may take on. Figure 3.1 depicts a continuous curve of Table 1 where both variables are taken to be continuous, while Figure 3.2 exhibits the case where price is taken to be discrete but quantity may be either continuous or discrete.

The difference is that the second curve illustrates a "step function" in which the curve is not "smooth" and connected, while the first curve is smooth and continuous. We have also reversed the conventional economics rule by allotting the price to the x-axis and quantity to the y-axis. It was pointed out before that, according to the rules of geometry, the vertical axis is used for the dependent variable and the horizontal axis for the independent variable.

---

[1] The original equation by Schultz has a time variable which is omitted here.

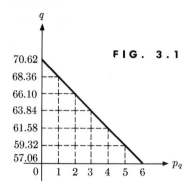

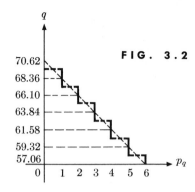

It should be pointed out that if it is tempting to approximate the zigzag appearance of the curve in Figure 3.1 by means of a smooth curve, thus eliminating the gaps and spreading the steps over a continuous curve, we should make the distance between two price units as short as possible so that the limit of the corresponding values for the quantities would no longer appear as steps.   This procedure is advisable since the variables such as price could be quoted theoretically at small units of measurement. Economists always find it convenient to assume that the variables with which they operate are continuous.

A monotonic single-valued and decreasing demand curve depicted in Figure 3.2 (or in Figure 3.1) has a slope, measured by the steepness of the curve, which is constant and is equal to

(3.1.7)
$$\frac{\Delta q}{\Delta p} = -2.26 < 0.$$

Fortunately, it is very easy to measure and show the slope of a straight line, the *rate of change of the corresponding* equation, by the left-hand side term of (3.1.7).   Nevertheless, if our demand, for instance, is contained in $pq = a$, it is obvious that the above method becomes inaccurate in determining the slope of the curve since the incremental change of one point and of the adjacent points differ slightly.   Therefore, it is desirable, first, to determine the slope for any point of the curve; secondly, to assume that a demand curve, in its very special form, is linear for which the slope is constant over the whole curve.   In the next chapter we shall develop a method to determine the slope of any nonlinear as well as any linear functions.   In the meantime we should assume that all demand functional equations are represented by

$$q = ap_q + c.$$

The second property of a linear demand equation is its elasticity.   The elasticity of a demand is defined as the proportional change of the quantity demanded with respect to the proportional change in the price of that commodity. Or

$$\text{Elasticity} = \frac{\text{Proportional change of } q}{\text{Proportional change of } p_q}$$

(3.1.8)
$$= \frac{\dfrac{\Delta q}{q}}{\dfrac{\Delta p_q}{p_q}} = \frac{\Delta q}{\Delta p_q} \frac{p_q}{q}.$$

It is clear that the elasticity of demand, shown by the right-hand side combined term of (3.1.8), is composed of the slope of the curve and the price-quantity ratio. Hence, if a demand is graphed against the *natural scales*, as we have done in the preceding pages, nobody can detect its elasticity by just observing the curve. The only thing that one can judge is the slope of a given demand curve, and that is all. The statement that one often finds in some elementary textbooks that a given demand is elastic or inelastic because the curve is positioned in such a way is *incorrect*. If, of course, price and quantity are plotted against *logarithmic scales*, the elasticity of a given demand can be readily detected by the slope of the curve. This point is of crucial importance.

On the Shape of a Demand Curve. The negativity of the slope of a demand curve, that the planned quantity of a good purchased by a consumer moves in the opposite direction relative to its price movement, a conclusion reached in the preceding paragraph, shown by (3.1.5) and (3.1.6) and illustrated by Figures 3.1 and 3.2, is an empirical one. The same conclusion, indicated in the opening paragraph of this chapter, can be reached theoretically via the utility analysis and the indifference approach.

On the basis of the "revealed preference" Samuelson[2] has, with very simple mathematics, shown the downward slope of a demand curve. We follow him in what ensues. Let us assume that the consumer possesses a utility function for $q_1, q_2, \ldots q_n$

(3.1.9)
$$U = U(q_1, q_2, \ldots q_n),$$

and that the measure of utility is ordinal so that the consumer can only compare the utility derived from different combinations of these commodities. If we assume that the prices of these commodities are p_1, $p_2, \ldots p_n$, the budget or income constraint of the consumer is given by

(3.1.10)
$$y = p_1 q_1 + p_2 q_2 + \cdots + p_n q_n = \sum_{i=1}^{n} p_i q_i.$$

---

[2] *Foundations of Economic Analysis*, 1961, pp. 108–9. Hereafter, it is called *Foundations*.

Let us, further, assume that the consumer wants to attain one level of utility in the cheapest possible way. Related to a set of prices $p_1^0, p_2^0, \ldots p_n^0$, there is a batch of optimal commodities $q_1^0, q_2^0, \ldots q_n^0$ such that the consumer minimizes the cost as much as possible; *i.e.*,

$$\textbf{(3.1.11)} \qquad \sum_{i=1}^{n} p_i^0 q_i \geqq \sum_{i=1}^{n} p_i^0 q_i^0.$$

Consider an alternative batch of commodities $q_1^1, q_2^1, \ldots q_n^1$ with their respective prices $p_1^1, p_2^1, \ldots p_n^1$ locating on the same indifference locus as the prices and quantities of (3.1.11). We have

$$\textbf{(3.1.12)} \qquad \sum_{i=1}^{n} p_i^1 q_i \geqq \sum_{i=1}^{n} p_i^1 q_i^1.$$

(3.1.11) and (3.1.12) hold if we replace q_i with any other quantity such as q_i^1 and q_i^0 in particular. Then, (3.1.11) and (3.1.12) can be rewritten as

$$\textbf{(3.1.13)} \qquad \sum_{i=1}^{n} p_i^0 q_i^1 \geqq \sum_{i=1}^{n} p_i^0 q_i^0,$$

and

$$\textbf{(3.1.14)} \qquad \sum_{i=1}^{n} p_i^1 q_i^0 \geqq \sum_{i=1}^{n} p_i^1 q_i^1.$$

By transposing the left-hand side terms of (3.1.13) and (3.1.14) to the right and factoring we have

$$\textbf{(3.1.15)} \qquad \sum_{i=1}^{n} p_i^0 (q_i^0 - q_i^1) = \sum_{i=1}^{n} (-p_i^0)(q_i^1 - q_i^0) \leqq 0,$$

and

$$\textbf{(3.1.16)} \qquad \sum_{i=1}^{n} p_i^1 (q_i^1 - q_i^0) \leqq 0.$$

According to the rules of algebra, if we add the left-hand side term of (3.1.16) to that of (3.1.15), the sign of the inequality will not change, or

$$\textbf{(3.1.17)} \qquad \sum_{i=1}^{n} (-p_i^0)(q_i^1 - q_i^0) + \sum_{i=1}^{n} p_i^1 (q_i^1 - q_i^0) \leqq 0.$$

On taking the common factor $(q_i^1 - q_i^0)$ on the left-hand side, we have

$$\textbf{(3.1.18)} \qquad \sum_{i=1}^{n} (p_i^1 - p_i^0)(q_i^1 - q_i^0) \leqq 0,$$

or

$$\textbf{(3.1.19)} \qquad \sum_{i=1}^{n} (\Delta p_i)(\Delta q_i) \leqq 0.$$

This last inequality states that if the consumer moves along the same indifference locus to maintain the same utility level, the sum of the products of all incremental price changes and incremental quantity changes is nonpositive. And if the two equilibrium points (p_i^0, q_i^0) and (p_i^1, q_i^1) are taken to be distinct; *i.e.*, to each value of price there corresponds one and only one value of quantity so that quantity-price function is a single-valued one, the inequality (3.1.19) can be reduced to absolute inequality

(3.1.20)
$$\sum_{i=1}^{n} (\Delta p_i)(\Delta q_i) < 0.$$

Let us suppose that only the price of the k-th commodity changes while the prices of all other commodities are kept constant; then all but the k-th term of (3.1.20) vanishes and we have

(3.1.21)
$$\Delta p_i \, \Delta q_i < 0.$$

If we divide both sides of (3.1.21) through by $(\Delta p_i)^2$, which is positive, we can have

(3.1.22)
$$\frac{\Delta q_i}{\Delta p_i} < 0$$

which, being the same as (3.1.7), indicates that the price of the k-th commodity and the quantity of that commodity demanded move in the opposite directions; viz., *the law of demand*.

3.2 Supply

All firms, irrespective of their goals, organization, and size, must purchase the required inputs and sell their outputs. The supply curve depicts the sales plan of the firm. If the firm sells only one commodity the price of which is p_1, the total revenue that the firm wishes to get from implementing its sales plan would be $R = pq$ where q represents the quantity that the firm hopes to sell. If the firm is engaged in multi-product operations where $q_1, q_2, \ldots q_n$ are the quantities that the firm hopes to sell with their corresponding prices $p_1, p_2, \ldots p_n$, the gross revenue from carrying out the plan would be

$$R = p_1 q_1 + p_2 q_2 + \cdots + p_n q_n,$$

(3.2.1)
$$= \sum_{i=1}^{n} p_i q_i.$$

If the sales plan is to be accomplished and the gross revenue is to be obtained, the firm must incur certain cost. Let the cost for undertaking a productive project be C and the inputs, or productive services, be x_1, $x_2, \ldots x_m$ with their respective prices $p_{x_1}, p_{x_2}, \ldots p_{x_m}$, then the general form of the firm's cost is

$$C = p_{x_1} x_1 + p_{x_2} x_2 + \cdots + p_{x_m} x_m,$$

(3.2.2) $$= \sum_{i=1}^{m} p_{x_i} x_i.$$

In order to realize (3.2.1), the firm must incur (3.2.2). Thus, the decision to sell certain quantities of given commodities which a firm wishes to implement and often should revise depends on a number of data; the means and method of production, referred to as the production possibilities open to the firm, the expected price that the firm can charge its customers, and also the expected prices of the inputs. In analyzing the sales plan of the firm, its supply function, we confine ourselves only to the short-run during which some of the inputs are fixed and others can vary.

If a typical firm hopes to sell more at the higher prices and vice versa, the supply curve should slope upward from left to right. We assume in this section that the supply curve is linear and can be approximated by

(3.2.3) $$q = ap_q + b,$$

the curve of which is a straight line, where a is the slope of the curve and is positive and b is the q-intercept. We should have no problem in plotting this equation on a two-dimensional diagram. In order to distinguish between the demand and supply, henceforward we designate q_s for the expected offer of the firm and q_d for the household's expected purchase so that the negativity of $\dfrac{\Delta q_d}{\Delta p_q}$ is the essence of the law of demand and the positivity of $\dfrac{\Delta q_s}{\Delta p_q}$ would be the gist of the law of supply.

Analogous to the mathematical procedure for the derivation of the demand, we are set to deduce the supply curve mathematically. Let us assume that a firm's production function for an output is given by

(3.2.4) $$q_i = q_i(x_1, x_2, \ldots, x_m),$$

and its total revenue by

(3.2.5) $$R = R(q_1, q_2, \ldots, q_n),$$

where, as before, R stands for total revenue, q_i for outputs, and x_i for inputs. Further, it is assumed that the relevant segments of the isoquants are convex to the origin and that as we increase all inputs together, output cannot decrease; *i.e.*,

(3.2.6) $$\Delta q_s \geqq 0 \quad \text{for} \quad \Delta x_i \geqq 0.$$

In addition, we suppose that the firm wishes to maximize its total revenue; *i.e.*,

(3.2.7)
$$\frac{\Delta R}{\Delta q} = \frac{\Delta C}{\Delta q}$$

which gives the equality of marginal cost and marginal revenue, where the total revenue is shown by (3.2.1) and the total cost by (3.2.2). Moreover, we assume that the firm wishes to remain on the same isoquant in the cheapest possible way while maximizing its revenue. Related to a set of prices $p_1^0, p_2^0, \ldots, p_n^0$, there is a batch of optimal commodities $q_1^0, q_2^0, \ldots, q_n^0$ in the sense that it maximizes its total revenue compared with another batch of commodities $q_1, q_2, \ldots, q_n$ on the same isoquant; *i.e.*,

(3.2.8)
$$\sum_{i=1}^{n} p_i^0 q_i^0 \geqq \sum_{i=1}^{n} p_i^0 q_i.$$

Reckon another alternative batch of commodities $q_1^1, q_2^1, \ldots, q_n^1$, with their respective prices $p_1^1, p_2^1, \ldots, p_n^1$, locating on the same isoquant as the quantities and prices of (3.2.8). We, therefore, have

(3.2.9)
$$\sum_{i=1}^{n} p_i^1 q_i^1 \geqq \sum_{i=1}^{n} p_i^1 q_i.$$

(3.2.8) and (3.2.9) hold, of course, if we replace q_i with any other quantity such as q_i^1 and q_i^0 in particular. Then, (3.2.8) and (3.2.9) can be rewritten

(3.2.10)
$$\sum_{i=1}^{n} p_i^0 q_i^0 \geqq \sum_{i=1}^{n} p_i^0 q_i^1,$$

and

(3.2.11)
$$\sum_{i=1}^{n} p_i^1 q_i^1 \geqq \sum_{i=1}^{n} p_i^1 q_i^0.$$

By transposing the right-hand side terms of (3.2.10) and (3.2.11) to the left and factoring the common factor, we have

(3.2.12)
$$\sum_{i=1}^{n} p_i^0 (q_i^0 - q_i^1) = \sum_{i=1}^{n} (-p_i^0)(q_i^1 - q_i^0) \geqq 0,$$

and

(3.2.13)
$$\sum_{i=1}^{n} p_i^1 (q_i^1 - q_i^0) \geqq 0.$$

According to a theorem of algebra mentioned before, if we add the left-hand side term of (3.2.13) to that of (3.2.12), the sign of the inequality will not alter, or

(3.2.14)
$$\sum_{i=1}^{n} (-p_i^0)(q_i^1 - q_i^0) + \sum_{i=1}^{n} p_i^1 (q_i^1 - q_i^0) \geqq 0.$$

On taking the common factor $(q_i^1 - q_i^0)$ on the left-hand side, we have

(3.2.15)
$$\sum_{i=1}^{n} (p_i^1 - p_i^0)(q_i^1 - q_i^0) \geqq 0,$$

or

(3.2.16)
$$\sum_{i=1}^{n} (\Delta p_i)(\Delta q_i) \geqq 0.$$

Remember, q_i stands for the quantities supplied by the firm at their given prices.

This last inequality asserts that the sum of the products of all incremental price changes and the incremental quantity supplied changes is non-negative, if the firm moves along the same isoquant locus in order to maintain the same maximum total revenue. And if the two equilibrium points (p_i^0, q_i^0) and (p_i^1, q_i^1) are taken to be distinct; *i.e.*, to each value of the price there corresponds one and only one value of the quantity demanded so that quantity-supplied and price function is a single-valued one, the inequality (3.2.16) will be reduced to the absolute inequality

(3.2.17)
$$\sum_{i=1}^{n} (\Delta p_i)(\Delta q_i) > 0.$$

Let us suppose that the prices of all other commodities are unchanged but the kth one; then all but the kth term of (3.2.17) vanishes and we have

(3.2.18)
$$(\Delta p_i)(\Delta q_i) > 0.$$

If one divides both sides of (3.2.18) through by $(\Delta p_i)^2$ which is positive, one can have

(3.2.19)
$$\frac{\Delta q_i}{\Delta p_i} > 0$$

which indicates that the price of the kth commodity and the expected quantity of that commodity supplied move in the same directions; viz., *the law of supply.*

3.3 Market Equilibrium

In Section 3.1 of this chapter, we described how to deduce mathematically a consumer's demand function for a commodity. It was demonstrated that the demand for a commodity is a schedule that relates the quantity demanded in a given time period to each price at which the commodity might be sold, *ceteris paribus.* It was also pointed out that the consumer's tastes, his income and the prices of all other competitive and substitutable commodities are the *cetera* which must be kept *paria.* Further, the firm's planned supply of a commodity, at each price at which the commodity might be purchased, was derived intuitively and mathematically in Section 3.2. Again, the supply function, *ceteris paribus*, is a schedule which connects the firm's sales plan and its possible revision with the expected price of the commodity. The cetera which must remain unchanged are the convexity of the relevant segments of the isoquants, the constancy of the prices of other commodities, the constancy of the factor prices, and the firm's income which is allocable to these inputs.

The whole discussion in Sections 3.1 and 3.2 revolved around a typical household and a firm for which we attempted to adduce general behavior. If, however, we proceed to picture the market, which is the conglomeration of finite or infinite households and firms, and market behavior on the simultaneous price-quantity determination, we should use the market supply and demand which are the sum of the individual supply and demand curves respectively. In Chapter 1, allusion was made to the fact, and Alfred Marshall was cited as our authority, that in order to have a set of unique values for two variables, there must exist two curves based on two consistent equations the simultaneous solution of which would provide the unique values. For this reason, the demand and supply curves are needed to give one unique solution for the market price and one for the quantity.

There should exist a market for each commodity, and for each commodity there is a demand and a supply. The sum of all firms producing the same commodity is called conventionally an *industry*. Thus, the industry's supply curve for one commodity is the sum of the supply curves of the firms which produce that commodity. Also, the demand curve facing the industry is the sum of the demand curves of all households belonging to this market. It is true that the expected price of a commodity is given to a firm, but the combination of all firms into an industry can exercise a certain influence on price formation. The following is an attempt to explain the simultaneous determination of price and quantity if a commodity is planned to be produced by many firms and is expected to be purchased by its demanders. In what follows we continue to assume that the market demand and supply are simply straight lines.

Short-run Price Determination. In Figure 3.3, the quantity, either of the expected sales by firms or of the planned purchases by consumers, is measured along the horizontal axis while the expected price per unit of the commodity is measured along the vertical line. According to Figure 3.3, $0A$ and $0B$ are the *equilibrium price* and the *equilibrium supply* for which the plans of the firms coincide with the plans of the consumers. If the price, for instance, were $0C$, the firms would plan to sell $0D$ and the households would plan to purchase $0E$, and if $0C$ is actually offered by the firms, the consumers must abstain from having DE units of the commodity which would force, then, the price to rise to $0A$ and increase the quantity to $0B$. If, however, the price were $0F$, the consumer would plan to buy no more than $0G$ and the firms would plan to sell $0H$. Again, if the price is actually $0F$, the producers will be left with GH units of the commodity unsold. The existence of this surplus would naturally force the price down and also quantity down to $0A$ and $0B$.

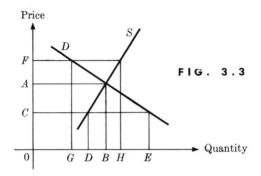

FIG. 3.3

We pointed out before that the demand for a commodity can *shift* to the right or left if there is a change in one of the parameters of the demand: if the income of a consumer rises, his corresponding demand will shift to the right. This is true as long as there is a change in the components of c in $q_d = ap_q + c$. Let us suppose that there is a shift in demand to the right. If there is no change on the supply side, the equilibrium price will tend to rise from its original position to a new location. The rise in equilibrium price depends on the slope of the supply. For any increase in demand, the rise in price will be the greater the larger is the slope of the supply and it will be the less the smaller is the slope of the supply curve.

Likewise, the supply curve can shift to the right or left if there is any change in the parameters of the supply equation. If there is no change in the demand curve, the equilibrium price will tend to rise or fall depending on how the supply curve shifts. Let us suppose that there is a shift in supply to the left while demand rests in its original position. For any fall in supply, the rise in price will be the greater the larger is the slope of the demand curve, and it will be less the smaller is the slope of the demand. The effects of simultaneous shifts in demand and supply in the same directions or in the opposite can be explained by the combined effects of the two cases mentioned before.

Static Stability and Market Equilibrium. The preceding analysis demonstrates changes in the *price-ratios* of some commodities with the one the demand for and/or supply of which shift from their original position to a new one. Further, it was pointed out that the short-run equilibrium price is that price which equates firms' planned sales and households' planned purchases; and if there is a change in either demand for or supply of a commodity, certain market forces will generally, though not always, restore the equilibrium conditions. The process of restoration and the path by which the price and quantity after a disturbance move from an initial to a new position of equilibrium is referred to as the *stability of the competitive equilibrium*. A competitive equilibrium is said to be *stable* if after an initial disturbance a new or the original equilibrium can be reached. Otherwise, the equilibrium is not stable. This is actually a mathematical concept of cardinal importance and is employed especially in mathematical physics. At this stage, we endeavor to expose the reader to this concept, but in later chapters we shall discuss it more fully.

Here, we should assume that the demand and supply curves are straight lines and that there is a permanent increase in demand in one period. In this situation, there are three cases which one must study, and we have shown them in Figures 3.4a, 3.4b and 3.4c. We take, first, the condition which is exemplified by Figure 3.4a.

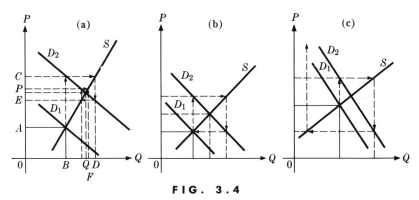

FIG. 3.4

According to Figure 3.4a, $0A$ and $0B$ are the market price and quantity in equilibrium. In the first period, there is a positive *excess demand* for the commodity, and since supply is constant, there will be a tendency for the price to rise to $0C$ in the next period. If, however, the price is raised to $0C$, the firms wish to sell $0D$, and in the second period they will produce that quantity of the commodity. But the price will fall to $0E$, which is less than $0C$, if the firms actually offer $0D$. The excess demand, at this price, is less than what it was when the price was to be $0A$; that is to say, as the price increased per unit of output the excess demand shrunk so that there is a converging behavior for the price and quantity toward the new equilibrium position. Finally, if the price is to be $0E$, which is less than $0P$, the quantity that the firms will produce and offer the market will be $0F$ which is less than $0D$ of the previous period. The price and quantity will eventually converge to the new equilibrium price and quantity. By examining the curves of Figure 3.4a, one can keenly observe that the numerical slope of the demand curve is less than the slope of the supply curve. We can state this last statement mathematically by

(3.3.1)
$$\left| \frac{\Delta p_q}{\Delta q_d} \right| < \frac{\Delta p_q}{\Delta q_s}.$$

This is very crucial. On the other hand, when we examine the curves of (3.4b) and (3.4c), we notice that either the slopes of the two curves are the same or the slope of the demand is larger than the one for the supply curve. Concretely, these two figures illustrate two cases for which, after an initial disturbance, there will develop a diverging attitude for the price and quantity equilibrium where the attainment of a new equilibrium position is impossible. Thus, we learn that the slopes of the curves are essentially important for the existence of a competitive equilibrium.

The foregoing analysis has been called the *Cobweb Theorem* for *dynamic* stability. A special case of the dynamic stability is the static stability which we wish to emphasize in what follows.[3] We gathered from the preceding examination that a system of two curves can be rendered dynamically stable if and only if the numerical slope of the demand curve is less than that of the supply curve. The static stability has, however, been confounded by unnecessary oversimplifications. Often do we hear that if either the price or quantity falls short of the equilibrium values, the initial equilibrium will be revived statically. In particular, if the price is forced down below the equilibrium price, the quantity adjustments will establish the equilibrium. This conclusion cannot be realized unless the system is statically stable.

The designers of the architecture of static analysis are Marshall and Walras. They both assumed initially that there exists an equilibrium condition as the result of the intersection of the demand and supply curves. Marshall analyzed the consequences of a fall or rise in the quantity demanded, *not a shift in the supply curve*. While, Walras examined the effects of a price increase or decrease, *not a shift in the demand curve*. We shall survey Walras' case first.

For the positively or negatively sloped supply curve, the Walrasian stability condition rests on the assumption that if price is set too low which could produce a positive excess demand, the buyers will tend to raise price to equilibrium; and if price is set too high which could generate a negative excess demand, the producers will lower price to equilibrium. The Walrasian stability condition is shown in the following table.

There are two assumptions which are necessary for Marshall's analysis: (1) that the demand curve is negatively sloped, (2) the quantity on offer

---

[3] The time variable is not necessarily the line of demarcation between static and dynamic systems as some economists have propounded it. As Professor Samuelson has keenly observed, "It is possible, however, that certain *subsets* of the solutions of the dynamical equations are defined by equations which are structurally identical with those which define a statical system. (Thus, the stationary solutions of a time-sequence analysis, say, of the multiplier-block-diagram variety, may be determined by a formula exactly like that of a timeless, instantaneous system.)" *Foundations* p. 285. He correctly suggests that "*statical* refers to the form and the structure of the postulated laws determining the behavior of the system. . . . Ordinarily, it is 'timeless' in that nothing is specified concerning the duration of the process, but it may very well be defined as a general term including statical as a special rather degenerate case. Or, on the other hand, it may be defined as the totality of all systems which are *not* statical." *Foundations*, p. 313.

TABLE   2

Equilibrium Condition	When	If
Stable	$\left\|\dfrac{\Delta p_q}{\Delta q_d}\right\| < \dfrac{\Delta p_q}{\Delta q_s}$	$\dfrac{\Delta p_q}{\Delta q_s} > 0$
Stable	$\left\|\dfrac{\Delta p_q}{\Delta q_d}\right\| < \left\|\dfrac{\Delta p_q}{\Delta q_s}\right\|$	$\dfrac{\Delta p_q}{\Delta q_s} < 0$

FIG.   3.5

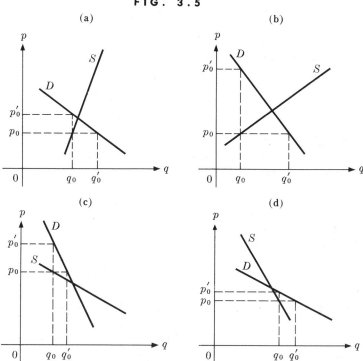

differs from the equilibrium quantity in such a way as to generate a positive excess demand. If the supply curve is sloped positively, the equilibrium is rendered stable if and only if the numerical slope of the demand curve is less than the slope of the supply curve when quantity is measured along the x-axis and price along the y-axis. Otherwise, in case of an initial disturbance, the price and quantity will not converge to their equilibrium values. Moreover, when the supply curve is negatively sloped, the equilibrium is stable in the Marshallian sense if the demand curve is steeper than the supply curve. However, the equilibrium will not be stable if the supply is steeper than the demand curve. These results, reached at intuitively, are illustrated in Figures 3.5a, 3.5b, 3.5c, and 3.5d. It is clear from Figures 3.5a (or 3.5c) that when the quantity falls short of (or exceeds) equilibrium, there is a convergence toward equilibrium on the part of price and quantity. We can summarize the Marshallian conditions in the following table.

TABLE   3

Equilibrium Condition	When	If
Stable equilibrium	$\left\|\dfrac{\Delta p_q}{\Delta q_d}\right\| < \dfrac{\Delta p_q}{\Delta q_s}$	$\dfrac{\Delta p_q}{\Delta q_s} > 0$
Unstable equilibrium	$\left\|\dfrac{\Delta p_q}{\Delta q_d}\right\| > \dfrac{\Delta p_q}{\Delta q_s}$	$\dfrac{\Delta p_q}{\Delta q_s} > 0$
Stable equilibrium	$\left\|\dfrac{\Delta p_q}{\Delta q_d}\right\| > \left\|\dfrac{\Delta p_q}{\Delta q_s}\right\|$	$\dfrac{\Delta p_q}{\Delta q_s} < 0$
Unstable equilibrium	$\left\|\dfrac{\Delta p_q}{\Delta q_d}\right\| < \left\|\dfrac{\Delta p_q}{\Delta q_s}\right\|$	$\dfrac{\Delta p_q}{\Delta q_s} < 0$

In comparing Table 3 with Table 2 where the supply curve is negatively sloped, the condition which provides for the Walrasian stability renders the Marshallian system unstable.

3.4 Lange's Model

Lange's model is an attempt to investigate the implications of Say's Law with respect to the theory of money and to the general theory of prices and employment.[4]

Let us assume that there are n commodities to be exchanged in a closed economy. Further, assume that the nth commodity functions as a medium of exchange; *i.e.*, numeraire, $p_n \equiv 1$ where p_i stands for the price of the ith commodity. Let $D_i = D_i(p_1, p_2, \ldots p_{n-1})$ and $S_i = S_i(p_1, p_2, \ldots p_{n-1})$ stand for the demand for and the supply of the ith commodity. Deduced from the analysis of market equilibrium, the $n - 1$ equations

(3.4.1) $S_i(p_1, p_2, \ldots p_{n-1}) = D_i(p_i, p_2, \ldots p_{n-1})$

determine simultaneously $n - 1$ equilibrium prices, and each market is stable in the sense articulated in 3.3, if

(3.4.2) $\left|\dfrac{\Delta D_i}{\Delta p_i}\right| < \dfrac{\Delta S_i}{\Delta p_i}$

when the demand and supply curves are straight lines.[5]

---

[4] "Say's Law: A Restatement and Criticism," in *Studies in Mathematical Economics and Econometrics*, O. Lange, Ed., University of Chicago, 1942, pp. 49–68.

[5] This condition is incomplete for the stability of the multimarket equilibrium but sufficient for market equilibrium. For additional conditions for the stability of multi-market equilibrium see J. R. Hicks, *Value and Capital*, London: 1961, pp. 66–67.

If one assumes that money is solely a medium of exchange, then the supply of all commodities which form $n - 1$ independent supply functions is identical with the demand for money; also the demand for all commodities which give $n - 1$ independent demand functions is identical with the supply of money, or

(3.4.3)
$$\sum_{i=1}^{n-1} p_i D_i \equiv S_n,$$

and

(3.4.4)
$$\sum_{i=1}^{n-1} p_i S_i \equiv D_n.$$

The total demand for and the supply of all commodities inclusive of money can be given by:

(3.4.5)
$$\sum_{i=1}^{n} p_i D_i \equiv \sum_{i=1}^{n-1} p_i D_i + D_n \equiv S_n + D_n$$

and

(3.4.6)
$$\sum_{i=1}^{n} p_i S_i \equiv \sum_{i=1}^{n-1} p_i S_i + S_n \equiv D_n + S_n.$$

Therefore,

(3.4.7)
$$\sum_{i=1}^{n} p_i D_i \equiv \sum_{i=1}^{n} p_i S_i.$$

It is recognizable that the existence of (3.4.7) depends on the establishment of (3.4.1) or any other conditions. (3.4.7), which proposes that the total demand for all commodities inclusive of money is identical with the total supply of all commodities inclusive of money, has been referred to as Walras' Law. We can also arrive at (3.4.7) by assuming

(3.4.8)
$$\sum_{i=1}^{n-1} p_i D_i \equiv \sum_{i=1}^{n-1} p_i S_i$$

which implies that

(3.4.9)
$$D_n \equiv S_n$$

or

(3.4.10)
$$D_n - S_n \equiv \Delta M \equiv 0.$$

By adding (3.4.9) to (3.4.8) and summing over i, identity (3.4.7) can be obtained. Identity (3.4.8) is called Say's Law which states that the aggregate supply exclusive of money is identical with the aggregate demand exclusive of money. Say's Law assumes explicitly that the demand for money is identical with the supply of money so that there is no positive or negative excess demand for cash balances over their supply, according to (3.4.10). Thus, Say's Law makes a very much more heroic assumption than Walras' Law.

The very heroic assumption underlying Say's Law is that the people have no desire to increase or decrease their cash balances for purposes other than those of facilitating the exchange between commodities. This view clearly rules out the possibility of hoarding and speculation in money markets.

As related to the theory of employment and production, Say's Law suggests that although a "partial glut" may occur, a general "glut" is impossible. Any partial over-production in one place is to be accompanied with underproduction somewhere else, or a deficiency of receipts in one place is to be accompanied with surplus receipts somewhere else.[6] According to Say's Law

$$(3.4.11) \qquad \sum_{i=1}^{n-1} A_i \equiv \sum_{i=1}^{n-1} C_i + \sum_{i=1}^{n-1} E_i$$

where A denotes the total receipts of all entrepreneurs, C the aggregate cost of production incurred by all entrepreneurs, and E the aggregate profits planned to be earned by all entrepreneurs.

In order to show the relation of "gluts" to the nature and realization of profit, we shall assume that in a purely capitalistic economy there are only four kinds of commodities: (1) those commodities which entrepreneurs purchase from and sell to other entrepreneurs. Let those commodities be called "intermediate products" and be designated by I. The intermediate products are usually composed of two sections: those which are bought for net investment such as the addition to the existing stock of capital and those which are used only for replacement. Let the former be shown symbolically by (IN) and the latter by (IR). (2) There are also those commodities which the producers purchase from the households. Let these commodities be called "labor power" and be denoted by L. (3) The final products, called "products" and shown by P, are those commodities which the firms sell to households; and finally (4) the demand for and the supply of money as a "neutral" commodity. Deriving (3.4.7) from (3.4.8) by assuming (3.4.9), or (3.4.10), we have

$$(3.4.12) \qquad \sum_{i=1}^{n} p_i D_i \equiv D_L + D_{IN} + D_{IR} + D_P + D_n$$

$$(3.4.13) \qquad \sum_{i=1}^{n} p_i S_i \equiv S_L + S_I + S_P + S_n.$$

---

[6] *On the Principles of Political Economy and Taxation*, (Cambridge University Press, 1951), pp. 289–300.

If it is assumed that $\Delta M \equiv D_n - S_n$, we can write

(3.4.14) $(D_L + D_{IR}) + D_{IN} + D_P + \Delta M \equiv S_L + (S_I + S_P).$

Since $(D_L + D_{IR})$ is the total cost that the firms are ready to take and $(S_I + S_P)$ is the total planned revenues, the difference between the two is the entrepreneurial planned profits and shown by

(3.4.15) $\pi = (S_I + S_P) - (D_L + D_{IR}).$

We also recognized that under Say's Law (3.4.10) must hold. Substituting (3.4.10) and (3.4.15) into (3.4.14) and transposing yields

(3.4.16) $(D_P - S_L) \equiv (\pi - D_{IN})$

which means that the net stream of money demanded by entrepreneurs is identical with the net stream of money offered to them. Since $(\pi - D_{IN}) = E$, $S_L = C$ and $D_P = A$ all of (3.4.11), one can deduce (3.4.11) from (3.4.16). Hence, irrespective of the level and condition of economic activity, the firms can, in the aggregate, realize their planned profits. It is possible that in one section of the economy there might be an under-realization of the planned profits but this would be cancelled by the over-realization of profits in another section of the economy so that there would be no general "overproduction," though there might be partial underproduction and overproduction in different parts of the system.

It was the merit of Malthus' criticism to demonstrate that, under certain circumstances — a deficiency of demand — the planned profits may not be realized by producers. If the aggregate demand falls short of the aggregate supply, and if this is the general case,[7] then the rate of growth of production would lag behind the "warranted rate of growth," and that in general the possibility of profit realization would vanish *in toto*. The fallacy of Say's Law becomes obvious when the real process of production is observed. In actuality, production reaches a standstill at the point of realizing planned profits. In a real sense, limits to investment and production, at a certain rate of profit, must be taken into consideration, not the factors which limit the exchange.

Let us rearrange (3.4.14) and have

(3.4.17) $(S_I + S_P) - (D_{IR} + D_{IN} + D_P) \equiv D_L - S_L + \Delta M.$

Under Say's Law, where $\Delta M \equiv 0$, we obtain

(3.4.18) $(S_I + S_P) - (D_{IR} + D_{IN} + D_P) \equiv D_L - S_L.$

The right-hand side of (3.4.18) is the excess of labor supply over its demand. The difference between the two parentheses on the left-hand side of

---

[7] J. M. Keynes, *The General Theory of Employment, Interest and Money*, New York: 1936, p. 26.

(3.4.18) gives the excess demand for commodities in general over the supply. Assuming the validity of (3.4.18), it is, of course, correct to argue, as Ricardo did: "It is quite true that commodities may exist in such abundance, compared with labor, as they make their value so to fall, estimated in labor, as not to afford any inducement to their further production. In that case labor will demand a great quantity of commodities."[8]

This implies that the excess of commodities supplied over those demanded must give rise to an excess demand for labor over its supply, which will in turn increase the price of labor relatively to the price of other commodities so that the households can command more commodities in general. Hence, there will be the impossibility of an everlasting overproduction, and the system can automatically correct its own mistakes. Malthus, on the other hand, held that when there is a positive excess supply of commodities, the price of labor will be depressed which is an articulation of the deficiency of effective demand and, consequently, general overproduction will ensue.[9] This means that there may be a general redundancy of commodities the prices of which will decrease as compared with the price of labor which may cause profits to fall. This occurs when monetary equilibrium is no longer maintained.

Now, let us examine the relation of Say's Law to the theory of prices. When Say's Law holds, the equilibrium prices are indeterminate since there are only $n - 2$ independent equations while there are $n - 1$ equilibrium prices which are to be determined. According to a rule enunciated in Chapter 1, the number of equations should be exactly equal to the number of variables for the determination of unique values. Also, since Say's Law states that the commodities are only exchanged for commodities, it precludes the possibility of substitution between commodities and money. Therefore, a change in the prices of all commodities will not affect the demand and supply functions of all commodities with respect to the demand for and the supply of money; it cannot create the substitutability effect among the commodities, either.

Thus, mathematically, it is said that under Say's Law the demand and supply functions are homogeneous of degree zero; *i.e.*, a rise or fall in all prices at the same time will not affect the demand for and supply of all commodities; only through the *relative prices* the quantities demanded and offered can alter. From the $n - 1$ prices let us suppose that p_{n-1} is taken as the arbitrary one and write

(3.4.19) $$\frac{p_1}{p_{n-1}} , \frac{p_2}{p_{n-1}} , \ldots \frac{p_{n-2}}{p_{n-1}}$$

as the relative prices with respect to p_{n-1}. Let $e_i = \dfrac{p_i}{p_{n-1}}$ for the relative price of the ith commodity. Then, the demand and supply equilibrium

---

[8] *Notes on Malthus' Principles of Political Economy*, Baltimore: 1928, p. 163. Also see *Works and Correspondence of D. Ricardo*, Volume II, p. 308.

[9] *Principles of Political Economy*, London: 1836, p. 316.

conditions in terms of the relative prices can be expressed by

(3.4.20) $$D_i(e_1, e_2, \ldots e_{n-2}) = S_i(e_1, e_2, \ldots e_{n-2}).$$

It is recognizable that there are $n - 2$ independent equations for the demand and supply functions which can uniquely determine the $n - 2$ variables, price ratios. Again, under Say's Law, though the *price relatives* are determined, the $n - 1$ prices are indeterminate. If we determine the value of, say, p_{n-1}, by outside forces, then all prices will be resolved. We can either determine p_{n-1} by rejecting the assumption that money is only a medium of exchange, which is the rejection of Say's Law or by solving its value through the "equation of exchange," which again rejects the assumption that money is only a medium of exchange if it is not used as an identity. But if the equation of exchange is used as an identity, it cannot solve p_{n-1} for an identity cannot express functionality, nor can it solve any value.

At any rate, if Say's Law is assumed, the equilibrium prices of all commodities are rendered indeterminate. But if we wish to have prices determined which requires a theory of money, then Say's Law must vanish. Therefore, Keynes (Malthus and Marx before him, as well) was correct and justified in rejecting Say's Law and its implications *in toto* before he could erect his own edifice.

3.5 Kaldor's Model

Having been mindful of the effects of the returns to scale, Mr. Kaldor has remarked that in the case of increasing returns to scale "the principle of multiplier (which in some way was anticipated in Keynes' *Treatise*) could be alternatively applied to a determination of the relation between prices and wages, if the level of output and employment is taken as given, or the determination of the level of employment if distribution (*i.e.*, the relation between prices and wages) is taken as given."[10] Utilizing the mathematical tools described in Chapter 1, we wish to explain how, according to Kaldor, profit becomes a time function of investment and the propensities to investment and save.

Let us assume that society is composed of two classes: (1) profit-takers, and (2) wage-earners. In addition, let the following notations be given:

0_i = Net sales, an approximation of output, of the ith firm,
P_i = Net income to surplus, profit, of the ith firm,
W_i = Wage-bill,
I = Investment,
S = Savings,
s_p = Profit-earners' propensity to save,
s_w = Wage-receivers' propensity to save.

---

[10] "Alternative Theories of Distribution," *Review of Economic Studies.* XXIII (1955–56), pp. 94 and 95.

If it is assumed that the economy consists of n firms, m profit-earners and q wage-receivers, for the whole economy we can write

(3.5.1)
$$O = \sum_{i=1}^{n} 0_i = 0_1 + 0_2 + \cdots + 0_n,$$

(3.5.2)
$$P = \sum_{j=1}^{m} P_j = P_1 + P_2 + \cdots + P_m,$$

(3.5.3)
$$W = \sum_{k=1}^{q} W_k = W_1 + W_2 + \cdots + W_q.$$

By definition and from macroeconomics we have

(3.5.4)
$$0 \equiv P + W.$$

On substituting from (3.5.1), (3.5.2) and (3.5.3) into (3.5.4), we can write

(3.5.5)
$$\sum_{i=1}^{n} 0_i \equiv \sum_{j=1}^{m} P_j + \sum_{k=1}^{q} W_k,$$

or

(3.5.6)
$$\sum_{k=1}^{q} W_k \equiv \sum_{i=1}^{n} 0_i - \sum_{j=1}^{m} P_j.$$

On multiplying both sides of (3.5.6) by s_w, we have

(3.5.7)
$$s_w \left(\sum_{k=1}^{q} W_k \right) \equiv s_w \left(\sum_{i=1}^{n} 0_i \right) - s_w \left(\sum_{j=1}^{m} P_j \right).$$

According to macroeconomic definitions

(3.5.8)
$$I \equiv S,$$

and

(3.5.9)
$$S \equiv S_p + S_w$$

where

$$S_p = s_p P \quad \text{and} \quad S_w = s_w W$$

or

(3.5.10)
$$S \equiv I \equiv s_p P + s_w W.$$

On putting (3.5.2) and (3.5.3) into (3.5.10), we obtain

(3.5.11)
$$\sum_{i=1}^{n} I_i \equiv s_p \left(\sum_{j=1}^{m} P_j \right) + s_w \left(\sum_{k=1}^{q} W_k \right).$$

Let us substitute (3.5.7) into the above identity to obtain

$$\sum_{i=1}^{n} I_i \equiv s_p \left(\sum_{j=1}^{m} P_j \right) + s_w \left(\sum_{i=1}^{n} 0_i \right) - s_w \left(\sum_{j=1}^{m} P_j \right),$$

(3.5.12) $$\equiv (s_p - s_w) \left(\sum_{j=1}^{m} P_j \right) + s_w \left(\sum_{i=1}^{n} 0_i \right).$$

On writing (3.5.12) in macroterms, we have

(3.5.13) $$I \equiv (s_p - s_w)P + s_w 0.$$

or

$$(s_p - s_w)P \equiv I - s_w 0.$$

Let us divide both sides of the last identity by 0 and $(s_p - s_w)$ to have

(3.5.14) $$\frac{P}{0} \equiv \frac{1}{(s_p - s_w)} \frac{I}{0} - \frac{s_w}{(s_p - s_w)}.$$

This is Kaldor's fundamental identity.[11] It was emphasized in Chapter 1 that an identity does not render functionality. The only expression, it was added, that can express functionality is an equation. However, (3.5.14) can be considered as an equation if the contained variables of the expression are related somehow. If (3.5.14) is taken to be an equation, it will be

---

[11] One can deduce the same identity in macroterms directly. By definition we had

$$I \equiv S,$$
$$0 \equiv P + W,$$
$$W \equiv 0 - P,$$
$$S \equiv S_p + S_w,$$
$$I \equiv S_p + S_w,$$
$$S_w \equiv I - S_p,$$
$$S_w W \equiv W(I - S_p),$$
$$S_w(0 - P) \equiv W(I - S_p),$$
$$S_w 0 - S_w P \equiv WI - WS_p,$$
$$WS_p - S_w P \equiv WI - S_w 0,$$
$$P \equiv \frac{PW}{WS_p - S_w P} I - \frac{PS_w}{WS_p - S_w P} 0.$$

Since

$$WS_p = s_p PW, \quad \text{and} \quad PS_w = s_w PW \quad \text{and}$$
$$WS_p - PS_w = PW(s_p - s_w),$$

then

$$\frac{P}{0} \equiv \frac{1}{(s_p - s_w)} \frac{I}{0} - \frac{s_w}{(s_p - s_w)}. \qquad \text{Q.E.D.}$$

indeterminate for there are three unknown variables, P, 0, and I, and only one equation

(3.5.15)
$$\frac{P}{0} = \frac{1}{(s_p - s_w)} \frac{I}{0} - \frac{s_w}{(s_p - s_w)}.$$

If, however, one wishes to render (3.5.15) determinate, one must reduce the number of unknown variables to only one. Economically speaking, since the second term on the right-hand side of (3.5.15) is negligibly small, it may be omitted. If it is assumed that $s_p > s_w$ so that the denominator of the first right-hand side fraction is made positive and that there exists full employment for which the level of output is given and investment is treated as an exogenous variable as in the Keynesian multiplier model, the given equation will be determinate and functionally stable; *i.e.*, the ratio of profit to total output depends on the ratio of investment to total output, given the appropriate propensities to save for different groups.

On the balance of these considerations, equation (3.5.15) tells us that: (1) the profit ratio is a single function of the investment ratio, that is, the greater is the investment the greater will be output and consequently the greater profit; (2) profit is a "functional share" while wages are "residual payments," the incidence of taxation ought to fall on wages rather than on profits — that is exactly the reverse of Ricardo's model; (3) the stability condition is that the profit-recipients' propensity to save must exceed that of the wage-receivers, otherwise the system is unstable; (4) the factor which influences the businessmen's decision to invest is profit expectation and profit anticipation or if they wish to increase their profits they should increase their volume of investment, given the demand for their products; and finally (5) profit does not depend on wages, as Ricardo argued, nor can it be sought in surplus-value as Marx argued, but it originates in investment if one adopts the Keynesian multiplier analysis.

EXERCISES 3

1. The market price p per pound of a commodity and the demand in x hundred pounds of it are given in the following table:

p	1	2	3	4	5
x	97	94	91	88	85

Show that the demand curve approximates $x = 100 - 3p$. Draw the demand curve and discuss the elasticities at different points of quantity.

2. Let the demand curve for a commodity be shown by

$$x = \frac{20}{p + 6}$$

Plot a graph of the demand curve and discuss the elasticities at different quantity.

3. What is the shape of the demand curve for the following:

$$x = 10(a^p)$$
$$x = 8(a^{3p})$$
$$x = 9(a^{2p-1})$$

where $1 > a > 0$. Plot a graph of the demand curve for each function.

4. Determine the shape of the supply curve for each of the following:

$$x = 3e^{2p-1}. \qquad\qquad x = 2e^{3p+1}.$$
$$x = 2e^{2p}. \qquad\qquad x = \log_e p.$$

Plot a graph of the supply curve for each function.

5. What is the mathematical as well as economic difference between the following demand equations:

$$x = 70 - 2p.$$
$$p = 35 - \tfrac{1}{2}x.$$

6. A simple linear model of a commodity is given by

$$D = 15 - 2p$$
$$S = 3 + p$$
$$D \equiv S.$$

Solve the system for the equilibrium output and price, and discuss the Marshallian and Walrasian stability conditions.

7. Consider the simple linear model of a commodity

$$D = 20 - 2.5p$$
$$S = 15 + 3p$$
$$D \equiv S.$$

Solve the system and discuss the Marshallian and Walrasian stability conditions.

8. Let us denote the price of commodity A by p_a and its demand by D_a and the supply by S_a. Likewise, the price of commodity B by p_b, its demand by D_b and its supply by S_b. Let us take the following linear model

$$D_a = 20 - 3p_a - 2p_b$$
$$D_b = 4 - p_a - 3p_b$$
$$S_a = 12 + 2p_a + 5p_b$$
$$S_b = -1 + 2p_a + 4p_b$$
$$D_a \equiv S_a$$
$$D_b \equiv S_b.$$

Solve the system and find the equilibrium prices and quantities, then keep one price constant and discuss the stability conditions in each market.

9. Consider the simple linear log model of a commodity

$$\log D = 7 - 2 \log p$$
$$\log S = 13 + 3 \log p$$
$$D \equiv S.$$

Solve the system and determine the equilibrium price and quantity.

10. Henry Schultz estimated the demand functions for beef, pork, and mutton in the U.S. in 1922–33. They are respectively:

$$D_b = 63.3 - 1.9p_b + 0.2_{pk} + 0.5p_m,$$
$$D_k = 71.0 + 0.4p_b - 1.2p_k - 0.1p_m,$$
$$D_m = 10.3 + 0.1p_b + 0.1p_k - 0.3p_m,$$

where B stands for beef, K for pork, and M represents mutton. Solve the system and determine the equilibrium prices if $S_b = 60$, $S_k = 50$, and $S_m = 35$.

11. Henry Schultz estimated the demand functions for barley, corn, hay, and oats in the United States in 1896–1914 as follows:

$$D_b = 2.24 - 0.01p_b - 0.01p_c + 0.01p_o,$$
$$D_c = 49.07 - 0.02p_b - 0.36p_c - 0.03p_h + 0.03p_o,$$
$$D_h = 1.30 - 0.05p_h + 0.01p_o,$$
$$D_o = 24.16 + 0.03p_b + 0.07p_c - 0.61p_h - 0.30p_o$$

where B, C, H, and O stand respectively for barley, corn, hay, and oats. If $S_b = 5.6$, $S_c = 50$, $S_h = 3$, and $S_o = 24$, determine the equilibrium prices.

12. Econometricians usually divide the variables of a model into *dependent* and *predetermined* ones. Dependent variables are often called *endogenous* since they are determined by the system, while the predetermined variables which include exogenous and lagged or prior values of endogenous variables are determined by outside forces. Furthermore, it is often necessary econometrically to cut down a model to a *reduced form* which expresses all endogenous variables in terms of the predetermined variables of a system. Let us consider a simple macro model

$$C = a + bY$$
$$Y = C + I$$

the reduced form of which is

$$Y = \frac{a}{1 - b} + \frac{1}{1 - b} I$$

$$C = \frac{a}{1 - b} + \frac{b}{1 - b} I.$$

Is the reduced form solvable? If not, how could we make it determinate?

PART III

Differential and
Integral Calculus

4 SETS, LIMITS, AND CONTINUITY

4.1 Sets

The notion of a *set* is so fundamental that no attempt should be made to define it. However, according to G. Cantor, a set is "a collection into a whole of definite well-distinguished objects called the *elements* of our perception or of our thought."[1] For instance, the collection of mathematics instructors in a given mathematics department constitutes a set of elements. The mathematics instructors are the elements of the set. Similarly, all economics instructors in an economics department of an assumed university comprise a set whose elements are the economics instructors. Let M denote the set of all economics instructors and m stand for one instructor. The fact that m "belongs to" M; or m is "a member of" M; or m is "an element of" M is shown by $m \in M$. Hence, set membership is demonstrated by $\in$. For example, if s is an element of S, this fact is shown by $s \in S$, whereas $s \notin M$ indicates that s is *not* a member of M.

A set may be identified either in terms of its elements or the exclusive property that the members of the set possess. In fact, M was characterized by the property of teaching economics in a given department. Generally, any property identifies a set so that the set circumscribes all elements having that property. Conversely, any set defines a property, namely, the property of belonging to a set. Braces are usually used to specify sets. If, for example, the members of an economics department are Professors Bright, Odd, and Brown, the set M is shown by

$$M = \{\text{Prof. Bright, Prof. Odd, Prof. Brown}\}.$$

---

[1] Quoted by E. Kemke in his *Theory of Sets,* (Eng. Translation) New York: Dover Publications, 1950, p. 1.

In this case, we do not mention explicitly the unique property of the elements of the set which collects them in a set. If the property of all members is teaching economics, shown by E, our set will be described by

$$M = \{x \in N \colon x \text{ has } E\},$$

or

$$M = \{x \in N \mid x \text{ has } E\}$$

where N is the set of all instructors of the university to which M belongs. The colon or the vertical line in the notation is read: "such that." Either a colon or the vertical line can be used to express the "such that" phrase. The entire expression reads: "the set of all elements belonging to N such that those elements have property E is M." As another example, let J^+ stand for all positive integers and J for all integers, then

$$J^+ = \{x \in J \colon x \text{ is positive}\},$$

read J^+ equals the set of all x in J such that x is positive.

Two sets M and N are said to be equal, in symbols $M = N$, if and only if they consist of the same elements, *i.e.*, if every element of M is also an element of N and, conversely, every element of N is also an element of M. Therefore, the equality of two sets M and N means that $x \in M$ if and only if $x \in N$ assuming that x is an element of M. When every element of M is also an element of N, it is said that M is a subset of N and is denoted by $M \subset N$. If N is the set of all instructors in a given university and M is the set of economics instructors, then $M \subset N$, *i.e.*, M "is contained in" N. From the subsets and the equality of sets, it is intuitively recognizable that if L, P, and Q are three sets such that:

(1) if $P = Q$, then $P \subset Q$ and also $Q \subset P$,
(2) conversely, if $P \subset Q$ and $Q \subset P$, then $P = Q$,
(3) if $P \subset Q$ and $Q \subset L$, then $P \subset L$,
(4) $P \subset P$ means that every set is a subset of itself, a fact which is always true.

If $M \subset N$ but $M \neq N$, then M is said to be a *proper* subset of N. Therefore, the set of economics instructors is a proper subset of the set of all instructors in an assumed university, and the set of positive integers is always a proper subset of the set of integers.

If P stands for mathematics instructors of a given university and M for the instructors in the economics department, then

$$V = M \cup P,$$

called the *union* of M and P, is the set of all instructors who teach either economics or mathematics. On the other hand, if W is the set of all mathematics instructors who teach mathematical economics, which is a proper subset of P, then W is the *intersection* of M and P and written as

$$W = M \cap P,$$

which refers to instructors who teach mathematics and economics. The subset, union, and intersection can best be represented by means of Venn diagrams:

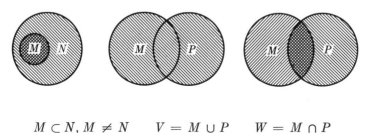

$$M \subset N, M \neq N \qquad V = M \cup P \qquad W = M \cap P$$

By means of Venn diagram, we can also display an odd set called the *empty* set. As one may imagine, an empty set contains no elements. The Danish letter $\emptyset$ is used to denote this set. If A and B are two sets which have nothing in common in any respect, their intersection constitutes an empty set shown by

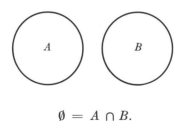

$$\emptyset = A \cap B.$$

It is obvious that the empty set is a subset of every set, namely, if W is a set we have $\emptyset \subset W$.

Let there be two sets G and H so that to every element g of G there corresponds one and only one element h of H in a one-to-one manner, and, conversely, to every element h of H there corresponds one and only one element g of G in a one-to-one manner, the two sets G and H are said to be equivalent, in symbol: $G \sim H$. It is clear that the empty set is equivalent only to itself and:

(1) $G \sim H$ implies $H \sim G$,

(2) if $G \sim H$ and $H \sim F$, then $G \sim F$,

(3) $G \sim G$, *i.e.*, every set is equivalent to itself.

It is very easy to prove that if a, b, and c are three real numbers and if

$a > b$, then $a + c > b + c$. Or, if $a > b$ and $c > 0$, then $ac > bc$. Or, if $a > b$ and $c < 0$, then $ac < bc$. In addition, if $a > b$ and $b > c$, then $a > c$. We can also show that

$$\{x \in M : 4x + 5 < 3\} = \{x \in M : x < -\tfrac{1}{2}\}.$$

Similarly, it is noticed that

$$\{x \in M : |x| < a\} = \{x \in M : -a < x < a\}.$$

To extend this last result, we can write

$$\{x \in M : |x - b| < a\} = \{x \in M : b - a < x < b + a\},$$

if a and b are real numbers.

A set $M \subset N$ is *bounded above* if there is a real number μ such that if $m \in M$ then $m \leq \mu$. Or,

$$M \subset \{x \in N : x \leq \mu\}.$$

In this case, μ is an upper bound of M. Likewise, $M \subset N$ is *bounded below* if there is a real number λ such that if $m \in M$ then $m \geq \lambda$. Or

$$M \subset \{x \in N : x \geq \lambda\}.$$

Here λ is a *lower bound* of M. It is clear that there are infinitely many upper bounds for a bounded above set and many lower bounds for a bounded below set. Let us suppose that $x \in N$ takes on $1 < x < 8$, thus

$$M = \{x \in N : 1 < x < 8\}.$$

From the definition, M is bounded above for all values of $m \in M$, for example $m \leq 12$. Therefore, 12, among all other values more than 8, is an upper bound of M. Or,

$$M \subset \{x \in N : x \leq 12\}.$$

A similar example can be advanced for a lower bound. In the last example, 8 is called the least upper bound and 1 the greatest lower bound; and it goes without saying that $8 \notin M$ and $1 \notin M$. There are times that the least upper bound and the greatest lower bound, one or both, are members of the nonempty set M. Thus, let us assume that M is a nonempty set of real numbers, L is the *least upper bound* of M if $m \in M$ implies $m \leq L$ and if $L' < L$, then $m > L'$. Also, G is the *greatest lower bound* of M if $m \in M$ implies $m \geq G$ and if $G' > G$, then $m < G'$.

Let a, b, and c be three elements of $M \subset N$. M is an *interval* if $a \in M$, $b \in M$ and $a \leq c \leq b$ implies that $c \in M$. Let a and b be two elements of N, then

$$[a, b] = \{x \in N : a \le x \le b\}$$ ("The *closed interval* from a to b"),

$$]a, b[= \{x \in N : a < x < b\}$$ ("The *open interval* from a to b"),

$$]a, b] = \{x \in N : a < x \le b\}$$ ("The *lower half-open interval* from a to b"),

$$[a, b[= \{x \in N : a \le x < b\}$$ ("The *upper half-open interval* from a to b").

4.2 Functions

In Chapter 1, it was said that a *function* establishes a correspondence or dependence between two or more variables. Naturally, a function being a correspondence or dependence can be thought of as a *graph*. So to each function there relates a graph which exhibits the behavior of a function. The graph of a function, being the locus of many points in the coordinate plane, forms a subset of the coordinate plane. More generally, when a graph is intersected with a vertical line in not more than one point, that graph displays a function. Thus, the graph in Figure 4.1 does not represent a function since the line $L'L$ crosses the graph at four points. It is important to note that the vertical line should parallel that axis to which the dependent variable is assigned. It is obvious that the graphs of Figures 4.2–4.3 depict functions.

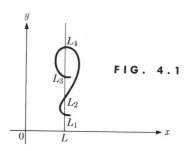

FIG. 4.1

With respect to the coordinate plane, commonly the projection of a function on the x-axis is called the domain of the function whereas the projection of the function on the y-axis is referred to as the range of the function. Definitionally, let there be a function $f(x)$, the set

$$\{x \in N : \text{ there is a } y \in N \text{ such that } (x, y) \in f(x)\}$$

is the domain of $f(x)$ and shown by $Do(f)$. Also

$\{y \in N:$ there is an $x \in N$ such that $(x, y) \in f(x)\}$ is the range of $f(x)$.

As x approaches ∞, $y = f(x) = e^x$ will diverge to ∞. Or

$$\text{as } x \to \infty, y \to +\infty.$$

As x approaches ∞,

$$y = f(x) = e^{\alpha x} \sin x, (\alpha > 0),$$

will oscillate infinitely. Or

$$\text{as } x \to \infty, y \to \pm\infty.$$

As x approaches ∞, $y = f(x) = -e^x$ will approach $\to\infty$. Or,

$$\text{as } x \to \infty, y \to -\infty.$$

As x approaches ∞,

$$y = f(x) = e^{\alpha x} \sin x, (\alpha = 0),$$

will oscillate finitely. Or

$$\text{as } x \to \infty, y \to \pm\infty.$$

FIG. 4.2

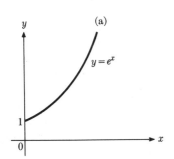

(a) $y = e^x$

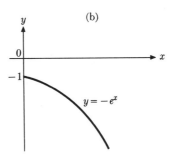

(b) $y = -e^x$

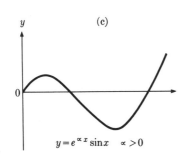

(c) $y = e^{\alpha x} \sin x$ $\alpha > 0$

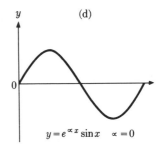

(d) $y = e^{\alpha x} \sin x$ $\alpha = 0$

As x approaches ∞,

$$y = f(x) = \frac{2^x - 3}{2^x}$$

will converge to 1. Or

$$\text{as } x \to \infty, y \to 1, \text{ i.e.,}$$

$$\lim_{x \to \infty} \frac{2^x - 3}{2^x} = 1.$$

As x approaches ∞,

$$y = f(x) = 4 + \frac{1}{3^x}$$

will converge to 4. Or

$$\text{as } x \to \infty, y \to 4, \text{ i.e.,}$$

$$\lim_{x \to \infty} \left(4 + \frac{1}{3^x} \right) = 4.$$

As x approaches ∞, $y = f(x) = 1$ will be constant. Or

$$\text{as } x \to \infty, y = 1.$$

As x approaches ∞,

$$y = f(x) = e^{\alpha x} \sin x, (\alpha < 0),$$

will converge to zero. Or

$$\text{as } x \to \infty, y \to 0, \text{ i.e.,}$$

$$\lim_{x \to \infty} (e^{\alpha x} \sin x) = 0.$$

FIG. 4.3

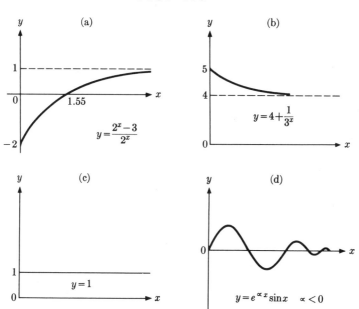

4.3 Limits and Limit Theorems

The limiting value of a function is a concept of fundamental importance in the Calculus. In Algebra one seeks the limit of a sequence of numbers when the number of the terms of the sequence *increases without bound*. The phrase "increases without bound" means "approaches infinity." For example

$$\lim_{x \to \infty} 2 - (\tfrac{1}{3})^x = 2$$

since $\left(\dfrac{1}{3}\right)^x$ would be zero when x approaches infinity. Or, take

$$\lim_{x \to \infty} \frac{2^x - 3}{2^x} = 1$$

the graph of which is 4.3.a. Also consider $\lim\limits_{x \to \infty} \left(1 + \dfrac{1}{x} \right)^x = e = 2.7182\ldots$ where x is a positive number. This symbolic expression is read: "the limit of $\left(1 + \dfrac{1}{x}\right)^x$ as x increases without bound is e." The two preceding examples are read in the same manner.

It should be remembered that not all functions have limits when x increases without bound. In fact, the graphs of Figure 4.2 do not possess limits. A necessary and sufficient condition for the existence of a limiting value of a sequence of numbers $f(1), f(2), f(3), \ldots$, is that corresponding to any preassigned positive number d, however small, there exists a value of n, say $n = k$, such that

$$|f(n + p) - f(n)| < d$$

for all values of $n \geq k$ and all positive integral values of p. That is, only convergent functions possess limits in contrast to divergent functions which suffer from not having limits. A close look at the graphs of Figures 4.3 and 4.2 will certainly reveal this fact.

Thus far, the discussion has revolved around the idea of a limit in so long as it was related to the phrase: "as x increases without bound." However, in Calculus one is concerned with limit idea when x approaches a definite value, say a. Let us take $y = 3 + \sqrt[3]{(x - 2)^2}$ whose graph is illustrated in Figure 4.4. By inspection, it is noticed that

$$\lim_{x \to \pm\infty} \{3 + \sqrt[3]{(x - 2)^2}\} = +\infty.$$

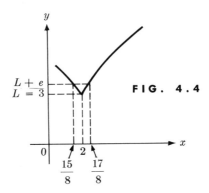

FIG. 4.4

It is also clear that

$$\lim_{x \to 2} \{3 + \sqrt[3]{(x - 2)^2}\} = 3.$$

That is to say, as x approaches 2 from both sides, $f(x)$ will approach 3, or as $x \to 2$, $y = f(x) \to 3$ which is the limit of the function.

The statement

$$\lim_{x \to a} f(x) = L$$

(read "the limit of $f(x)$ as x approaches a is L") states that for all x *close to but different from a*, $f(x)$ is close to L. The point $(2, 3)$ is a member of $y = 3 + \sqrt[3]{(x - 2)^2}$. Generally, the point (a, L) need not be a member of $f(x)$. The phrase "for all x close to" requires clarification. The statement "$f(x)$ is close to L for all x close to but different from a," simply means that if $f(x)$ is assigned a positive number e, no matter how small, a positive number d can be found for x such that

(i) $$x \in Do(f): 0 < |x - a| < d$$

is nonempty and

(ii) $$|f(x) - L| < e$$

for all x in the set. The (i) part of the statement encompasses the set of all numbers in the domain of $f(x)$ which are within d units of a yet different from a. The (ii) part states that $f(x)$ is within e units of L. Therefore, in order to be able to state

$$\lim_{x \to a} f(x) = L$$

one should be prepared to offer d for every positive number e, no matter how small. It is very easy to produce d for every e in $y = 3 + \sqrt[3]{(x - 2)^2}$.

Let $e = \frac{1}{4}$, then $f(x) = L + e$ which is related to two distinct points of the curve slightly higher than the sharp point in Figure 4.4. By substitution, we have $3 + \sqrt[3]{(x - 2)^2} = 3 + \frac{1}{4}$ which can be reduced to $(x - 2) = \pm\frac{1}{8}$ or

$$\tfrac{17}{8} > x > \tfrac{15}{8},$$

the two points on the x-axis. Also, since $|x - a| < d$ which means that $a + d > x > a - d$ or $2 + d > x > 2 - d$, then by comparing with the above inequality we have

$$2 + d = \tfrac{17}{8} \quad \text{and} \quad 2 - d = \tfrac{15}{8}$$

from which we deduce that $d = \frac{1}{8} > 0$ and within the domain of x. Thus, we may write the general definition: Let there be a function $f(x)$ and a and L real numbers, then

$$\lim_{x \to a} f(x) = L$$

means that for every positive number e there is a positive number d such that

$$\{x \in Do(f): 0 < |x - a| < d\}$$

is nonempty and related to

$$\{y \in N: |f(x) - L| < e\}.$$

From our example, it is noticeable that we had to search for L by allotting different values to x and find their range. Experience reveals that this practice is often long and laborious. There are some theorems on limits, (stated without proof), which will render the task of finding limits easy. Let $f(x)$ and $g(x)$ be two functions such that $\lim_{x \to a} f(x)$ and $\lim_{x \to a} g(x)$ exist. And let a be a real number:

Theorem 4.1. The limit of an algebraic sum of any finite number of variables is equal to the algebraic sum of their respective limits. Or

$$\lim_{x \to a} (f \pm g)(x) = \lim_{x \to a} f(x) \pm \lim_{x \to a} g(x).$$

Theorem 4.2. The limit of the product of any finite number of variables is equal to the product of their respective limits. Or,

$$\lim_{x \to a} fg(x) = \lim_{x \to a} f(x) \cdot \lim_{x \to a} g(x).$$

Theorem 4.3. The limit of the quotient of two variables is equal to the quotient of their respective limits, provided that the limit of the denominator is nonzero. Or,

$$\lim_{x \to a} \frac{f}{g}(x) = \frac{\lim_{x \to a} f(x)}{\lim_{x \to a} g(x)}, \text{ provided } \lim_{x \to a} g(x) \neq 0.$$

Theorem 4.4. Two equal functions have the same limits. Or, if $f(x) = g(x)$ for all $x \neq a$, and if $\lim_{x \to a} f(x) = L$, then, $\lim_{x \to a} g(x) = L$.

Theorem 4.5. If $y = x^n$ and $n > 0$, then

$$\lim_{x \to a} x^n = a^n.$$

Theorem 4.6. The limit of a constant is constant. Or, if $y = f(x) = c$, then

$$\lim_{x \to a} c = c.$$

With these theorems in mind, let us find the limit of

$$y = 3x^4 - 2x^2 + 4x + 5$$

as $x \to 3$. By virtue of theorems 4.1–4.6, we write

$$\lim_{x \to 3} (3x^4 - 2x^2 + 4x + 5) = \lim_{x \to 3} (3x^4) - \lim_{x \to 3} (2x^2) + \lim_{x \to 3} 4x + \lim_{x \to 3} 5$$
$$= 243 - 18 + 12 + 5$$
$$= 242.$$

Let us suppose also that we wish to evaluate the limit of

$$y = \frac{x^2 - 25}{x - 5}$$

as $x \to 5$. By virtue of theorem 4.3, since $\lim\limits_{x \to 5} (x - 5) = 0$, then the limit of y does not exist at $x = 5$. However, we can write

$$y = \frac{(x - 5)(x + 5)}{(x-5)}$$

and

$$\lim\limits_{x \to 5} \frac{(x - 5)(x + 5)}{(x - 5)} = \lim\limits_{x \to 5} (x + 5) = 10.$$

It is quite clear that for $y = \dfrac{x^2 - 25}{x - 5}$ to have a limit is that $x \neq 5$, *i.e.*, 5 should not belong to the domain of f, or

$$(5, 10) \notin \left(\frac{x^2 - 25}{x - 5} \right).$$

4.4 Continuity

Deducing from our analysis, we state that if $f(x)$ at a point such as a has a limit L, the point (a, L) may or may not belong to $f(x)$. For the first function that was solved in the previous paragraph

$$(3,242) \in (3x^4 - 2x^2 + 4x + 5)$$

whereas for the second function of the same paragraph

$$(5, 10) \notin \left(\frac{x^2 - 25}{x - 5} \right).$$

If there is a function $f(x)$ for which $\lim\limits_{x \to a} f(x) = L$ and $(a, L) \in f(x)$ then the function $f(x)$ is continuous at (a, L). It is known that $y = 3 + \sqrt[3]{(x - 2)^2}$ is continuous at $x = 2$, while $y = \dfrac{x^2 - 25}{x - 5}$ is not continuous at $x = 5$. Stated definitionally,[2] the function $y = f(x)$ is said to be continuous at $x = a$ if $\lim\limits_{x \to a} f(x) = L$ from either side of the point and each of these limits is equal to $f(a)$. For the continuity of $f(x)$ at a, the function calls for three requirements to be satisfied:

    (i) $f(a)$ must exist, *i.e.*, a must be in the domain of $f(x)$,

    (ii) $\lim\limits_{x \to a} f(x)$ must exist,

    (iii) $\lim\limits_{x \to a} f(x) = f(a)$.

---

[2] G. H. Hardy, *A Course of Pure Mathematics*, Cambridge University Press, 1960, p. 186.

In a word, a continuous function at a has no "jumps" or "holes." A function is said to be continuous if it is continuous at every point and number in its domain. On the other hand, a function is discontinuous if it is not continuous over one or more points in its domain. Therefore, point continuity is more important than general continuity. It is evident that:

$$f(x) = \begin{cases} 3x, \text{ if } x \in [0, 2[\\ 12 - 3x, \text{ if } x \in]2, 4] \end{cases}$$

is discontinuous at $x = 2$ since 2 does not belong to the domain of $f(x)$ although $\lim_{x \to 2} f(x) = 6$ exists. Thus, $f(x)$ has a "hole" at $x = 2$. Also

$$f(x) = \begin{cases} 2 \text{ if } x \in [0, 1[\\ 1 \text{ if } x \in [1, 2] \end{cases}$$

has a "jump" at $x = 1$, (which forms a "step function" of the type discussed in Chapter 1), thus it is discontinuous at $x = 1$ since $\lim_{x \to 1} f(x)$ does not exist.

4.5 Definition and Meaning of Derivatives

Let us suppose that we have a function whose graph is a straight line shown in Figure 4.5.

If we take two points, *e.g.*, A and B, having different coordinates, and if we divide the vertical differences by the horizontal difference belonging to these two points, the result is called *the average rate of change* of the function between those two points. Intuitively, since the slope of the function is the same for all the points of the function, the average rate of change of the function for any two points is the same all over the function. Hence, for any unknown pair of points we can write:

$$\text{The average rate of change} = \frac{f(x + h) - f(x)}{h}$$

where h is the horizontal difference between any two points and $f(x + h)$ is a change in the dependent variable due to h-increment in the independent variable. Since the average rate of change is the same for any two points of the function, it follows intuitively that the average rate of change is the same for any point all over the line. The phrase "average rate of change for a point" is usually called *the instantaneous rate of change* of the function for that point. Later on this phrase, awkward in appearance, will be called *derivative*, rather compact and charming!

Now, let us take a *continuous* function whose graph is curvilinear in contrast to the linear function of the preceding example. Figure 4.6 depicts a typical quadratic function on a two-dimensional system. With the method of the preceding example, that is, $\dfrac{f(x + h) - f(x)}{h}$, we can measure the average rate of change of the function for any two points. Unlike the previous example, we cannot measure the instantaneous rate of change of *any* point of the function with the method of our preceding example.

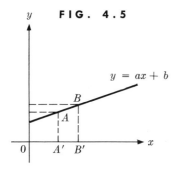

FIG. 4.5

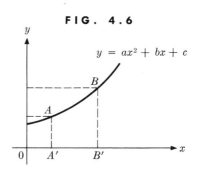

FIG. 4.6

If we allow one of the points, either A or B, to move so that it becomes closer and closer to the other one, in this way we can measure the average rate of change of the function for smaller and smaller variations of the function. The process can continue up to the point and location where two points are almost coincident and locate over one another. At this very point, changes in the dependent variable, via the changes of independent variable, measure the *instantaneous rate of change* or *derivative* of the function at that point. Intuitively, it can be noticed that the derivative of a linear function, $ax + b$, is constant for the domain of the function, whereas the derivative of a nonlinear function, (in this specific case, quadratic), is *not* equal for all values of x in its set. On the balance of what has been described, the following definition is to be deduced: The derivative of a continuous function, a derived function, at a point is the instantaneous rate of change of the function at that point. Formally, "the derivative of y with respect to x" written as

$$\frac{dy}{dx} = \frac{d}{dx} f(x) = y' = f'(x) = \lim_{h \to 0} \frac{f(x + h) - f(x)}{h}$$

exists provided this finite limit exists.

If $y = f(x)$ is defined by $y = (x + 1)^2$, then

$$\frac{dy}{dx} = \lim_{h \to 0} \frac{(x + h + 1)^2 - (x + 1)^2}{h}$$

$$= \lim_{h \to 0} \frac{x^2 + h^2 + 1 + 2xh + 2x + 2h - x^2 - 2x - 1}{h}$$

$$= \lim_{h \to 0} h + \lim_{h \to 0} 2x + \lim_{h \to 0} 2 = 2x + 2.$$

If the set of all values that x in $y = f(x)$ can take on is shown by D and if $\dfrac{dy}{dx}$ exists for all $x \in D$, then $f(x)$ is said to be differentiable over the set D. Thus, $y = f(x) = \sqrt{x}$ for $x \geq 0$ is not differentiable at $x = 0$ since

$$\frac{dy}{dx} = \lim_{h \to 0} \frac{\sqrt{x + h} - \sqrt{x}}{h}$$

$$= \lim_{h \to 0} \frac{x + h - x}{h(\sqrt{x + h} + \sqrt{x})}$$

$$= \lim_{h \to 0} \frac{1}{\sqrt{x + h} + \sqrt{x}}$$

$$= \frac{1}{2\sqrt{x}} \quad \text{provided } x \neq 0.$$

As another example, let us take

$$y = 3 + \sqrt[3]{(x - 2)^2}$$

which is illustrated in Figure 4.4 and for which we have

$$\frac{dy}{dx} = \frac{2}{3(\sqrt[3]{x - 2})}$$

which, of course, does not exist at $x = 2$.

4.6 Tangent Lines, Continuity, and Differentiation

The numerical value of a tangent to a curve at a point defines the instantaneous rate of change of the function at that point. Or, if $f(x)$ is a function and a is a number in its domain, if $f'(x)$ exists, then the tangent line to $f(x)$ at the point P whose coordinates are $(a, f(a))$ is the line on P with the slope equal to $f'(a)$. Let $f(x)$ be displayed in Figure 4.7 which is crossed by the secant line PQ. Of course, the slope of PQ is the average rate of change of $f(x)$ from P to Q. Let Q approach P so that in its limit, PQ will be the tangent to $f(x)$ at P, the slope of which is $f'(a)$. On the other hand, let the $f(x) = 3 + \sqrt[3]{(x - 2)^2}$ be represented by Figure 4.8. The graph of the function is crossed by the secant line PQ. If Q approaches P in its limit, PQ would be vertical. It is true that $f'(2)$ does not exist as we have shown above, yet the tangent does exist. Hence: Let $f(x)$ be a function and let a be a number in its domain, if $f'(a)$ does not exist but $\lim\limits_{h \to 0} \dfrac{h}{f(a + h) - f(a)} = 0$, then the tangent line to $f(x)$ at P is the vertical line at P. If, however, $f'(a)$ does not exist and $\lim\limits_{h \to 0} \dfrac{h}{f(a + h) - f(a)} \neq 0$, then $f(x)$ has no tangent line at P. It is intuitively obvious that as Q ap-

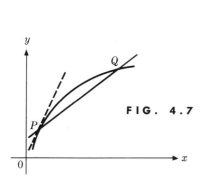

FIG. 4.7

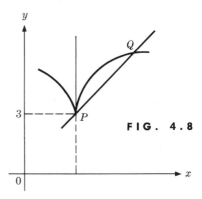

FIG. 4.8

proaches P, the slope of PQ becomes larger and increases without bound, and when it becomes vertical, its slope will be infinity which is the same as saying that its reciprocal would be zero. $\text{Lim}_{h \to 0} \dfrac{f(a + h) - f(a)}{h} = \infty$ is the same as saying that $\lim_{h \to 0} \dfrac{h}{f(a + h) - f(a)} = 0$.

It is not accurate to state, as some may do carelessly, that if $f(x)$ is continuous, say at $x = a$, and/or has a tangent at $x = a$, *then* $f(x)$ would necessarily have a derivative at that point. Tangency and point continuity do not, together, guarantee the existence of a derivative. However, the converse is true. That is, let $f(x)$ be a function and a a number in its domain, if $f'(a)$ exists, *then* $f(x)$ is continuous at $x = a$.

EXERCISES 4

1. Give five examples of sets, other than those in the book.

2. Let A be the set of all cars in the U.S. Find sets A' and A'' such that $A'' \subset A' \subset A$.

3. The set $\{a, b, c\}$ has eight subsets. List them.

4. Let A consist of the numbers $1, 2, \ldots, 15$ and the 26 letters of the alphabet, $a, b, c, \ldots, z$. If

$$B = \{1, 4, 5, 6, h, j, k, m, z\}$$
$$C = \{1, 2, 3, 4, 5, a, b, h, j, m, y\}$$

find $B \cup C$, $A \cup B$, $A \cup C$, $A \cap B$, $B \cap C$, $(A \cup B) \cup C$, $(B \cup A) \cap C$, $(A \cap B) \cup C$ and $(A \cap B) \cap C$.

5. Let U be the set of all points in the (x, y)-plane:

$$U = \{(x, y): x \text{ and } y \text{ are real numbers}\}.$$

Given that

$$A = \{(x, y): y = |x|\},$$
$$B = \{(x, y): y > |x|\},$$
$$C = \{(x, y): x + y = 2\},$$
$$D = \{(x, y): x + y < 2\},$$

indicate, by graphs, the following sets: (a) A, (b) B, (c) $A \cup B$, (d) the complement of B shown by $\bar{B}$, (e) C, (f) $A \cap C$, (g) $B \cap D$, (h) $\bar{D}$ and $\bar{C}$, (i) make a Venn diagram illustrating each of the above.

6. In a certain place 100 people like at least one of the three candidates A, B, C. In particular, 53 people like A, 30 people like B, 12 people like A and B more than C, 13 people like B and C more than A, 11 people like A and C more than B, and 2 people would be indifferent to all.

   a. How many people like only candidate A?

   b. How many people like only candidate B?

   c. How many people like only candidate C?

   d. How many people like candidate C?

7. Insert the appropriate inequality symbol between each of the following pairs of numbers.

$$4, -3 \qquad -7, 2 \qquad \sqrt{2}, 3\sqrt{4} \qquad -\tfrac{1}{3}, \tfrac{5}{6}.$$

8. Evaluate each of the following:

$$|7 - 3|, \qquad |3 - 7|, \qquad |2| + |-3|, \qquad |-5| + |-2|.$$

9. Sketch each of the following on a coordinate line:

$$\{x \in M: |x| < 5\},$$
$$\{x \in M: 3 < x < 7\},$$
$$\{x \in M: |x - 5| \leq 3\}.$$

10. If a, b, c, and d are any real numbers, would it be correct to write

$$|a + b + c + d| \leq |a| + |b| + |c| + |d|?$$

11. Prove each of the following:

$$\{x \in M: 5x - 3 < 2\} = \{x \in M: x < 1\},$$
$$\{x \in M: x^2 \leq 9\} = \{x \in M: |x| \leq 3\},$$
$$\{x \in M: |x - 3| < 2\} = \{x \in M: 1 < x < 5\},$$
$$\{x \in M: |x + 2| < 3\} = \{x \in M: -5 < x < 1\}.$$

12. Graph each of the following expressions. And for those which can be called functions give their domain, and range.

$$y = 3^x.$$
$$y = -x^2 + 2x - 6.$$

$$y = \log(2x + 3)$$
$$4(y^2 - 1) = x^2.$$

13. Use the definition in 4.3 and prove each of the following:

$$\lim_{x \to 3} x^2 = 9. \qquad \lim_{x \to 3} (x^2 + 1) = 10.$$

$$\lim_{x \to 0} \left(\frac{2x}{3} + x^2 \right) = 0. \qquad \lim_{x \to 2} \frac{1}{x^3} = \frac{1}{8}.$$

14. Let $\lim_{x \to a} f(x) = \alpha$, $\lim_{x \to b} g(x) = \beta$, and $\lim_{x \to c} h(x) = \gamma$, find:

$$\lim_{x \to a} [(f + h)(x)]$$

$$\lim_{x \to c} [(f + h)(x)]$$

$$\lim_{x \to b} g^2(x)$$

$$\lim_{x \to a} [(f - g)(x)]$$

$$\lim_{x \to a} [(f + gh)(x)].$$

15. Use the limit theorems and evaluate each of the following:

$$\lim_{x \to 0} (x^3 + 3x^2 + 2x - 6)$$

$$\lim_{x \to 2} (x^2 + 2x + 7)$$

$$\lim_{x \to 3} \left(\frac{1}{x^2} \right)$$

$$\lim_{x \to 1} \left(\frac{2x^2 + 3x - 1}{x^2 - 1} \right)$$

$$\lim_{x \to 1} \left(\frac{2x^3 - 2x}{x^2 - 1} \right).$$

16. Prove that if $\lim_{x \to a} g(x) = D$, then $\lim_{a \to x} [g(x) - D] = 0$.

17. Prove that if $k \in M$ and $\lim_{x \to a} g(x) = D$, then

$$\lim_{x \to a} kg(x) = kD.$$

and

$$\lim_{x \to a} [g(x) + k] = D + k.$$

18. Are the following functions continuous at the indicated numbers?

$$f(x) = x^2 - 2x + 1 \text{ at } x = 1.$$

$$f(x) = 2x^2 + 5x - 3 \text{ at } x = 2.$$

$$f(x) = \frac{x^2 - 9}{x + 3} \text{ at } x = -3.$$

$$f(x) = \frac{3}{5x} \text{ at } x = 0.$$

$$f(x) = \frac{1}{x(x^2 - 3)} \text{ at } x = 3.$$

19. If in the above examples a function is continuous at the specified value of x, find the value of x for which $f(x)$ is discontinuous. And for the discontinuous functions, determine the values for which $f(x)$ is continuous.

20. Find $\dfrac{d}{dx} f(x)$ for each of the following functions:

$$f(x) = 4x^2 - 3.$$
$$f(x) = 2x - 3x^2 + 4x^3.$$
$$f(x) = 2x^3 - 3.$$
$$f(x) = x - \frac{2}{3x}.$$
$$f(x) = \frac{1}{x^2}.$$
$$f(x) = \sqrt{2x + 3}.$$
$$f(x) = \frac{2x - 1}{x + 3}.$$
$$f(x) = \frac{1}{2(x^2 + 5)}.$$

21. Evaluate the derivative of all preceding functions at (a) $x = 1$, (b) $x = -3$, (c) $x = 3$, (d) $x = 7$. At what values do the derivative of all preceding functions not exist?

22. Find the derivative of $f(x)$ at $x = a$ for each of the following:

$$f(x) = \tfrac{2}{3}x^6 + 3x \quad \text{at} \quad x = 3.$$

$$f(x) = \frac{3x}{x^2 - 2} \quad \text{at} \quad x = 3.$$

$$f(x) = \frac{1}{3x - 5} \quad \text{at} \quad x = -3.$$

23. For $f(x) = ax^2 + bx + c$ where a, b, and c are real numbers show that

$$\frac{d}{dx} f(x) = 2ax + b$$

for all $x \in M$ where M is the set of all real numbers. In particular, when m and d are real numbers in $f(x) = mx + d$ show that

$$\frac{d}{dx} f(x) = m$$

for all $x \in M$.

24. Consider $f(x) = x^{\frac{2}{3}}$

   a. Graph the function.
   b. What is the slope of the line joining $(0, f(0))$ and $(3, f(3))$?
   c. What is the slope of the line joining $(1, f(1))$ and $(8, f(8))$?
   d. What is the slope of the line joining $(0, f(0))$ and $(\frac{1}{10}, f(\frac{1}{10}))$?
   e. Find the slope of the tangent line to $f(x)$ at each of the points $(0, f(0))$, $(8, f(8))$ and $(.10, f(.10))$.
   f. If there is a tangent line to $f(x)$ at $(0, f(0))$, find the equation of the tangent.

5 DERIVATIVES AND ECONOMIC APPLICATIONS

5.1 The Rules of Derivatives

(1) There are many ways to show a derivative. In this book, for the sake of consistency, we use only the following notations:

$$\frac{dy}{dx} = f'(x) = \lim_{\Delta x \to 0} \frac{\Delta y}{\Delta x} = Dy.$$

(2) Derivative notation is a combined expression. It is not to be viewed as d times y over d times x; or dy over dx.

(3) Since the derivative is a derived function of a continuous function at a point, it is continuous necessarily.

(4) A function need not have derivatives at all points. A function can have derivatives only at the points which are continuous in the sense defined in the previous chapter.

(5) The derivative of a function is an approximate value of the average rate of change of that function at a continuous point. That is to say,

$$f'(x) = \frac{\Delta y}{\Delta x} \quad \text{or} \quad \Delta y = f'(x)(\Delta x)$$

approximately when x is very small. It is clear that $\dfrac{\Delta y}{\Delta x}$ measures the slope of the tangent to the curve $y = f(x)$.

The Techniques of Derivation. The immediate function of the differential calculus is to obtain the derivative of different functions. The derivative of $y = ax + b$ where $y = f(x)$ is

$$\frac{dy}{dx} = \frac{d}{dx}(ax + b) = \lim_{h \to 0} \frac{[a(x + h) + b] - (ax + b)}{h}$$

$$= \lim_{h \to 0} \frac{ax + b + ah - ax - b}{h}$$

$$= a.$$

Also the derivative of $y = x^2$ where $y = f(x)$ is

$$\frac{dy}{dx} = \frac{d}{dx}(x^2) = \lim_{h \to 0} \frac{(x+h)^2 - x^2}{h}$$

$$= \lim_{h \to 0} \frac{x^2 + h^2 + 2xh - x^2}{h}$$

$$= 2x.$$

In this way we can find the derivative of any function and equation representing a functional relationship. But the method by which we solved and obtained the derivatives of the two examples is very laborious and cumbersome. There are tables of "standard forms" which are given in any book on calculus. The reader is usually asked to commit these rules to memory. Here we give some of these rules without proof.

5.2 The Rules of Differentiation

(1) The derivative of a constant with respect to a variable is zero. Thus, if k is a constant in

$$y = k$$

we have

$$\frac{dy}{dx} = \frac{dk}{dx} = 0.$$

For example

$$y = 5$$

$$\frac{dy}{dx} = \frac{d}{dx}(5) = 0.$$

(2) The derivative of any variable with respect to itself is unity. Thus, if

$$y = x \text{ where } y = f(x)$$

$$\frac{dy}{dx} = \frac{dx}{dx} = 1.$$

(3) The derivative of a constant multiplied by a variable is the constant multiplied by the derivative of the variable. Thus, if k is a constant in $y = kv$ where $v = f(x)$, we will have

$$\frac{dy}{dx} = k \frac{dv}{dx}.$$

Or, if

$$y = 4x$$

then

$$\frac{dy}{dx} = 4\frac{dx}{dx} = 4,$$

since from rule (2) $\dfrac{dx}{dx} = 1.$

(4) The derivative of the sum (or difference) of two (or more) variables is the sum (or difference) of the separate variables. Thus, if $y = u \pm v$ where $u = f(x)$ and also $v = g(x)$, then

$$\frac{dy}{dx} = \frac{d}{dx}(u \pm v) = \frac{du}{dx} \pm \frac{dv}{dx}.$$

Or, if

$$y = 5x + 9,$$

then

$$\frac{dy}{dx} = \frac{d}{dx}(5x + 9) = \frac{d}{dx}(5x) + \frac{d}{dx}(9) = 5.$$

(5) The derivative of the product of two variables is the sum of two terms: the first term of the sum is the first variable multiplied by the derivative of the second variable, and the second term of the sum is the product of the second variable and the derivative of the first variable. Thus, if $y = uv$ where $u = f(x)$ and $v = g(x)$, then,

$$\frac{dy}{dx} = u\frac{dv}{dx} + v\frac{du}{dx}.$$

For example, if

$$y = 5x,$$

then

$$\frac{dy}{dx} = 5\frac{dx}{dx} + x\frac{d}{dx}(5).$$

Since the derivative of a constant is zero, according to our first rule, and the derivative of a variable with respect to itself is unity, according to the second rule, we will have

$$\frac{dy}{dx} = 5.$$

(6) The derivative of a quotient is the derivative of the numerator multiplied by the denominator minus the derivative of the denominator multiplied by the numerator all divided by the square of the denominator. Thus if $y = \dfrac{u}{v}$ where $u = f(x)$ and $v = g(x)$, then

$$\frac{dy}{dx} = \frac{d}{dx}\left(\frac{u}{v}\right) = \frac{v\dfrac{du}{dx} - u\dfrac{dv}{dx}}{v^2}.$$

Or, if

$$y = \frac{3x - 3}{4x + 2},$$

$$\frac{dy}{dx} = \frac{d}{dx}\left(\frac{3x - 3}{4x + 2}\right)$$

$$= \frac{(4x + 2)3 - (3x - 3)4}{(4x + 2)^2}$$

$$= \frac{18}{(4x + 2)^2}.$$

(7) The derivative of a power function is the exponent times the power function with the exponent of the original function minus unity. Thus, if $y = x^a$ where $y = f(x)$, the derivative of the function is

$$\frac{dy}{dx} = \frac{d}{dx}(x^a) = ax^{a-1}.$$

If, for example, we have $y = x^4$, then

$$\frac{dy}{dx} = \frac{d}{dx}(x^4) = 4x^3.$$

(8) The derivative of a logarithm with a natural base such as

$$y = \log_e x$$

where $y = f(x)$, is given by

$$\frac{dy}{dx} = \frac{d}{dx}(\log_e x) = \frac{1}{x}.$$

If the logarithm has a base different from the natural base such as $y = \log_a x$ its derivative is

$$\frac{d}{dx}(\log_a x) = \frac{1}{x}(\log_a e).$$

The general rule of the previous case is that when we have $y = \log_a u$ where $u = f(x)$, we write

$$\frac{dy}{dx} = \frac{d}{dx}(\log_a u) = \frac{1}{u}(\log_a e)\frac{du}{dx}.$$

For example, if we have

$$y = \log_{10}(2x^3 + 4x),$$

we can write

$$\frac{dy}{dx} = \frac{1}{2x^3 + 4x}(\log_{10} e)\frac{d}{dx}(2x^3 + 4x).$$

Since

$$\log_{10} e = .4343, \quad \frac{d}{dx} (2x^3 + 4x) = 6x^2 + 4,$$

we obtain

$$\frac{dy}{dx} = \frac{(.4343)(6x^2 + 4)}{2x^3 + 4x}.$$

(8) The derivative of an exponential function is the exponential itself, if the base of the function is e, the natural base of an exponential. Thus, if

$$y = e^x$$

where $y = f(x)$, we will have

$$\frac{dy}{dx} = \frac{d}{dx} e^x = e^x.$$

The general case of the above rule is that when we have

$$y = e^u$$

where $u = f(x)$, we obtain

$$\frac{dy}{dx} = \frac{d}{dx} e^u = e^u \frac{du}{dx}.$$

For example, if the following function is given

$$y = e^{2x+4} = e^u$$

where $u = 2x + 4$ is a single-valued function, we can have

$$\frac{dy}{dx} = e^{2x+4}(2)$$

because

$$\frac{d}{dx} (2x + 4) = 2.$$

If the base of the exponential function is anything other than e, such as

$$y = a^x,$$

then the derivative of the function is given by

$$\frac{dy}{dx} = \frac{d}{dx} (a^x) = a^x \log_e a.$$

(9) The successive derivatives of a function of a variable: If we take the derivative of a derivative, we will obtain what has been called the *second derivative*. Since the derivative of a function of a variable x, a derived function, is the rate of change of the function, the second derivative measures the rate of change of the first derivative. Likewise, the third measures the rate of change of the previous derivative, and so on. The

notations for the successive derivatives of a function $y = f(x)$ can be written:

$$\text{1st derivative} = \frac{dy}{dx} = \frac{d}{dx} f(x) = y',$$

$$\text{2nd derivative} = \frac{d^2y}{d^2x} = \frac{d^2}{dx^2} f(x) = y'',$$

$$\text{3rd derivative} = \frac{d^3y}{dx^3} = \frac{d^3}{dx^3} f(x) = y''',$$

$$\cdots \cdots \cdots \cdots \cdots \cdots \cdots \cdots,$$

$$n\text{th derivative} = \frac{d^ny}{dx^n} = \frac{d^n}{dx^n} f(x) = y^{(n)}.$$

(10) The derivative of a function of function: If y is a function of u, where u is a function of x, then the derivative of y with respect to x is the product of the derivative of y with respect to u and the derivative of u with respect to x:

$$y = f(u),$$

where $u = g(x)$, we obtain

$$\frac{dy}{dx} = \frac{dy}{du} \cdot \frac{du}{dx}.$$

(11) It was suggested in Chapter 1 that for a conditional equation as well as an identity, the logarithms of both sides always hold. With respect to derivatives, we must emphasize that only the derivatives of each side of an identity hold. The derivatives of each side of a conditional equation which hold only for certain values of the variables cannot be assumed to be equal generally. For example, if we have

$$(2 + 3x)^2 \equiv 4 + 9x^2 + 12x,$$

hence

$$\frac{d}{dx} (2 + 3x)^2 = \frac{d}{dx} (4 + 9x^2 + 12x)$$

or

$$6(2 + 3x) = 6(2 + 3x).$$

But for

$$x^2 + 4 = 4x$$

which holds when $x = 2$, hence

$$\frac{d}{dx} (x^2 + 4) \neq \frac{d}{dx} (4x)$$

will hold only for $x = 2$.

(12) The derivative of trigonometric functions: Let $y = \sin x$ which indicates that $y = f(x)$, then $\dfrac{d}{dx} \sin x = \cos x$. Likewise, if

$$y = \cos x \qquad \text{then,} \qquad \frac{d}{dx} \cos x = -\sin x,$$

$$y = \tan x \qquad \text{then,} \qquad \frac{d}{dx} \tan x = \frac{1}{\cos^2 x},$$

$$y = \cot x \qquad \text{then,} \qquad \frac{d}{dx} \cot x = -\frac{1}{\sin^2 x},$$

$$y = \sec x \qquad \text{then,} \qquad \frac{d}{dx} \sec x = \sec x \cdot \tan x,$$

$$y = \csc x \qquad \text{then,} \qquad \frac{d}{dx} \csc x = -\csc x \cdot \cot x,$$

It is clear that the inverse of $x = \sin y$ is $y = \sin^{-1} x$ which represents $y = g(x)$. Thus, we can write:

$$\text{If} \quad y = \sin^{-1} x \qquad \text{then,} \qquad \frac{d}{dx} \sin^{-1} x = \frac{1}{\sqrt{1 - x^2}},$$

$$\text{if} \quad y = \cos^{-1} x \qquad \text{then,} \qquad \frac{d}{dx} \cos^{-1} x = \frac{-1}{\sqrt{1 - x^2}},$$

$$\text{if} \quad y = \tan^{-1} x \qquad \text{then,} \qquad \frac{d}{dx} \tan^{-1} x = \frac{1}{1 + x^2},$$

$$\text{if} \quad y = \cot^{-1} x \qquad \text{then,} \qquad \frac{d}{dx} \cot^{-1} x = -\frac{1}{1 + x^2},$$

$$\text{if} \quad y = \sec^{-1} x \qquad \text{then,} \qquad \frac{d}{dx} \sec^{-1} x = \frac{1}{x\sqrt{x^2 - 1}},$$

$$\text{if} \quad y = \csc^{-1} x \qquad \text{then,} \qquad \frac{d}{dx} \csc^{-1} x = -\frac{1}{x\sqrt{x^2 - 1}}.$$

The following examples illustrate the practical method of evaluating derivatives. Let $\frac{d}{dx} = D$ in all examples.

Example 1

$y = 3x^2 + 5x.$
$Dy = D(3x^2 + 5x) = D(3x^2) + D(5x)$ by Rule 4,
$\quad = (3)D(x^2) + (x^2)D(3) + (5)Dx + (x)D(5)$ by Rule 5,
$\quad = 6x + 5.$ by Rules 1, 2, 3, 7.

Example 2

$y = x^3 + 2x^{-2}.$
$Dy = D(x^3 + 2x^{-2}) = D(x^3) + D(2x^{-2}),$
$\quad = 3x^2 - 4x^{-3}.$

Example 3

$y = 3(2x^3 + 1).$

Set $2x^3 + 1 = v$ where $v = v(x)$ and $y = y(v)$, then, by Rule 10 we have

$$Dv = D(2x^3 + 1) = 6x^2,$$

$$\frac{dy}{dv} = 3\frac{dv}{dv} = 3,$$

$$Dy = \frac{dy}{dv}\,Dv = 3(6x^2) = 18x^2.$$

Alternatively, we might have proceeded as follows:

$$Dy = D[3(2x^3 + 1)] = (2x^3 + 1)D(3) + 3D(2x^3 + 1),$$
$$= 18x^2.$$

Example 4

$$y = (x^2 + 3x)(2x^3 + 4).$$
$$Dy = (x^2 + 3x)D(2x^3 + 4) + (2x^3 + 4)D(x^2 + 3x),$$
$$= (x^2 + 3x)(6x^2) + (2x^3 + 4)(2x + 3),$$
$$= 6x^4 + 18x^3 + 4x^4 + 6x^3 + 8x + 12,$$
$$= 10x^4 + 24x^3 + 8x + 12.$$

Example 5

$$y = x^3 + \frac{3x^2 + 3}{2x}.$$

$$Dy = D(x^3) + D\left(\frac{3x^2 + 3}{2x}\right),$$

$$= 3x^2 + \frac{(2x)D(3x^2 + 3) - (3x^2 + 3)D(2x)}{4x^2},$$

$$= 3x^2 + \frac{(2x)(6x) - (3x^2 + 3)2}{4x^2},$$

$$= \frac{6x^4 + 3x^2 - 3}{2x^2}.$$

Example 6

$$y = (x^4 + 4x^2 - 3x + 5)\left(\frac{1}{x^3} - \frac{1}{x^2}\right).$$

$$Dy = (x^4 + 4x^2 - 3x + 5)D\left(\frac{1}{x^3} - \frac{1}{x^2}\right) + \left(\frac{1}{x^3} - \frac{1}{x^2}\right)$$
$$D(x^4 + 4x^2 - 3x + 5),$$

$$= (x^4 + 4x^2 - 3x + 5)(-3x^{-4} + 2x^{-3})$$
$$+ (x^{-3} - x^{-2})(4x^3 + 8x - 3),$$

$$= 1 - 2x - 7x^{-2} + 16x^{-3} - 15x^{-4}.$$

Example 7

$$y = (3x^2 - 7x)^{12}.$$

Let $3x^2 - 7x = v$ where $v = v(x)$ and $y = y(v)$, then

$$Dv = 6x - 7 \quad \text{and} \quad \frac{dy}{dv} = 12v^{11}.$$

$$Dy = \frac{dy}{dv} \cdot Dv,$$

$$= (12v^{11})(6x - 7),$$

$$= (72x - 84)(3x^2 - 7x)^{11}.$$

Example 8

$$y = \sin 3x.$$

Set $3x = v$ and $Dv = 3$ and $y = \sin v$, then

$$Dy = \frac{dy}{dv} \cdot Dv,$$

$$= 3 \cos 3x.$$

Example 9

$$y = \cos^2 5x^3.$$
$$Dy = D(\cos^2 5x^3) = D(\cos 5x^3)(\cos 5x^3),$$
$$= (\cos 5x^3)D(\cos 5x^3) + (\cos 5x^3)D(\cos 5x^3),$$
$$= 2 \cos 5x^3(-\sin 5x^3)D(5x^3),$$
$$= -30x^2 \cos 5x^3 \sin 5x^3.$$

Example 10

$$y = \sin(3x - 2) \cos(4x - 3).$$
$$Dy = [\sin(3x - 2)]D[\cos(4x - 3)] + [\cos(4x - 3)]D[\sin(3x - 2)],$$
$$= [\sin(3x - 2)][-\sin(4x - 3)]D(4x - 3) + [\cos(4x - 3)]$$
$$[\cos(3x - 2)]D(3x - 2),$$
$$= -4 \sin(3x - 2) \sin(4x - 3) + 3 \cos(4x - 3) \cos(3x - 2).$$

Example 11

$$y = \tan 3x \cdot \cot 2x^2.$$
$$Dy = (\tan 3x)[D(\cot 2x^2)] + (\cot 2x^2)[D(\tan 3x)],$$
$$= \tan 3x(-\csc^2 2x^2)D(2x^2) + (\cot 2x^2)(\sec^2 3x)D(3x),$$
$$= -4x \tan 3x \csc^2 2x^2 + 3 \cot 2x^2 \sec^2 3x.$$

Example 12

$$y = \tfrac{1}{4} \sin 8x - \cos 3x^2.$$
$$Dy = \tfrac{1}{4} D(\sin 8x) - D(\cos 3x^2),$$
$$= (\tfrac{1}{4} \cos 8x) D(8x) + (\sin 3x^2) D(3x^2),$$
$$= 2 \cos 8x + 6x \sin 3x^2.$$

Example 13

$$y = \tfrac{1}{2} \cos 3x^2 + \tan^2 4x^3.$$
$$Dy = \tfrac{1}{2} D(\cos 3x^2) + D(\tan^2 4x^3),$$
$$= \tfrac{1}{2}(-\sin 3x^2)(6x) + (2 \tan 4x^3)(\sec^2 4x^3)(12x),$$
$$= \tfrac{1}{2}(-\sin 3x^2)(6x) + 24x \tan 4x^3 \sec^2 4x^3.$$

Example 14

$$y = \cot^{-1}\left(\frac{1}{x^3}\right).$$

$$Dy = D \cot^{-1}\left(\frac{1}{x^3}\right) D\left(\frac{1}{x^3}\right),$$

$$= -\frac{1}{1 + \dfrac{1}{x^6}}\left(-3\,\frac{1}{x^4}\right),$$

$$= \frac{3x^2}{x^6 + 1}.$$

Example 15

$$y = \log(x^3 + 8).$$
$$Dy = D \log(x^3 + 8),$$
$$= \frac{1}{x^3 + 8} D(x^3 + 8) = \frac{3x^2}{x^3 + 8}.$$

Example 16

$$y = \log \sqrt{(1 - x^2)(1 + x^2)}$$
$$Dy = D \log \sqrt{(1 - x^4)}.$$

Set $(1 - x^4)^{\frac{1}{2}} = v$ and $(1 - x^4) = u$ so that $y = y(v)$, $v = v(u)$ and $u = u(x)$, then

$$Du = -4x^3,$$

$$\frac{dv}{du} = \tfrac{1}{2} u^{-\frac{1}{2}} = \tfrac{1}{2}(1 - x^4)^{-\frac{1}{2}} = \frac{1}{2\sqrt{1 - x^4}},$$

$$Dv = \frac{dv}{du} \cdot Du = \frac{-2x^3}{\sqrt{1 - x^4}},$$

$$\frac{dy}{dv} = \frac{1}{v} = \frac{1}{\sqrt{1 - x^4}},$$

$$Dy = \frac{dy}{dv} \cdot Dv = \frac{-2x^3}{1 - x^4} \cdot$$

Example 17

$$y = x^2 \log(x^2 - 3).$$
$$Dy = (x^2)D[\log(x^2 - 3)] + [\log(x^2 - 3)]D(x^2),$$
$$= x^2 \left(2x \, \frac{1}{x^2 - 3} \right) + 2x \log(x^2 - 3),$$
$$= 2x \left[\left(\frac{x^2}{x^2 - 3} \right) + \log(x^2 - 3) \right].$$

Example 18

$$y = e^x \log x.$$
$$Dy = (e^x)D(\log x) + (\log x)D(e^x),$$
$$= e^x \frac{1}{x} + e^x \log x.$$

Example 19

$$y = e^{ax+b} \cdot \log(ax^2 + bx + c).$$
$$Dy = (e^{ax+b})D[\log(ax^2 + bx + c)] + [\log(ax^2 + bx + c)]D(e^{ax+b}),$$
$$= \frac{e^{ax+b}}{ax^2 + bx + c} (2ax + b) + (ae^{ax+b}) \log(ax^2 + bx + c).$$

Example 20

$$y = \log \sqrt{(e^x - e^{-x})(e^x + e^{-x})}.$$
$$Dy = D(\log \sqrt{e^{2x} - e^{-2x}}).$$
Set $v = (e^{2x} - e^{-2x})^{\frac{1}{2}}$ and $u = (e^{2x} - e^{-2x})$, then

$$\frac{dv}{du} = \tfrac{1}{2}u^{-\frac{1}{2}} = \frac{1}{2\sqrt{e^{2x} - e^{-2x}}},$$
$$Du = 2e^{2x} + 2e^{-2x},$$
$$Dv = \frac{dv}{du} \cdot Du = \frac{e^{2x} + e^{-2x}}{\sqrt{e^{2x} - e^{-2x}}},$$
$$Dy = \frac{dy}{dv} \cdot Dv = \frac{1}{\sqrt{e^{2x} - e^{-2x}}} \frac{e^{2x} + e^{-2x}}{\sqrt{e^{2x} - e^{-2x}}},$$
$$= \frac{e^{2x} + e^{-2x}}{e^{2x} - e^{-2x}} \cdot$$

Example 21. Find Dy, D^2y, D^3y and D^4y for

$$y = 4x^5 + 4x^3 + 2x^2 + 6.$$
$$Dy = 20x^4 + 12x^2 + 4x,$$

$$D^2y = 80x^3 + 24x + 4,$$
$$D^3y = 240x^2 + 24,$$
$$D^4y = 480x.$$

Example 22. Find Dy, D^2y and D^5y for

$$y = e^{4x+3}.$$
$$Dy = 4e^{4x+3},$$
$$D^2y = 16e^{4x+3},$$
$$D^3y = 64e^{4x+3},$$
$$D^4y = 256e^{4x+3},$$
$$D^5y = 1024e^{4x+3}.$$

Example 23. Find D^2y and D^3y for

$$y = \frac{1}{x} = x^{-1}.$$

$$Dy = -x^{-2} = \frac{-1}{x^2},$$

$$D^2y = 2x^{-3} = \frac{+2}{x^3},$$

$$D^3y = -6x^{-4} = \frac{-6}{x^4}.$$

Example 24. Find D^2y and D^3y for $y = x(2x + 1)^2$.

$$Dy = (x)D(2x + 1)^2 + (2x + 1)^2 = 12x^2 + 8x + 1,$$
$$D^2y = 24x + 8,$$
$$D^3y = 24.$$

5.3 Complete Criteria for Maxima and Minima

It was made clear, and it is very important to know in economics, that the first derivative of a function measures the rate of change of the function. Further, we pointed out that the second derivative measures the rate of change of the first derivative. Let us have two simple examples from economics: (1) Suppose we have a function which purports to represent the total cost of a typical firm:

(5.3.1) $y = 4x^2 - 5x + 7,$ and $y = f(x)$

where y is the total cost and x stands for output. If we take the first derivative of the above function, we will have something which has been called *marginal cost* in economics. Our marginal cost, then, is

(5.3.2) $$\frac{dy}{dx} = 8x - 5.$$

If we obtain the derivative of expression (5.3.2), the rate of change of the marginal cost will be found, a phenomenon which is of great theoretical significance in economics.

Let us take another example from economics. Suppose the total revenue of a typical firm is represented by the following equation:

(5.3.3) $$R = -5x^2 + 2x.$$

The first derivative of (5.3.3) will give the marginal revenue, which is the rate of change of total revenue:

(5.3.4) $$\frac{dR}{dx} = -10x + 2,$$

which is the marginal revenue of our firm. The derivative of (5.3.4) is

(5.3.5) $$\frac{d^2R}{dx^2} = -10$$

which measures the rate of change of the marginal revenue.

In the light of the aforementioned explanations, we set up the following rules for maxima and minima. Let us assume that $y = f(x)$ for our purpose.

(1) If $\frac{dy}{dx} > 0$ and $\frac{d^2y}{dx^2} > 0$, the function evaluated at $x = a$ rises at an increasing rate as x increases and the graph of the function is convex from below as in Figure 5.1. Conversely, if the graph of a function is convex from below and slopes upward for a set of admissible values of x, as in Figure 5.1, the assumed function rises at an increasing rate for those values. In Figure 5.1, one notices that the actual value of the tangents increases as x increases.

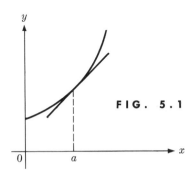

FIG. 5.1

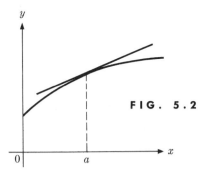

FIG. 5.2

(2) If $\frac{dy}{dx} > 0$ and $\frac{d^2y}{dx^2} < 0$, the function evaluated at $x = a$ rises at a decreasing rate as x increases and the graph of the function is concave from below as in Figure 5.2. Conversely, if the graph of a function is con-

cave from below and slopes upward for a set of admissible values of x, as in Figure 5.2, the given function rises at a decreasing rate for those values. In Figure 5.2, it is recognizable that the actual value of the tangents decreases as x increases. A very illustrative example of this case is when the law of the marginal diminishing returns is operative in the production of a given output for which the marginal output decreases gradually as more units of the variable input are employed and finally the production function reaches a point for which marginal product is zero.

(3) If $\dfrac{dy}{dx} > 0$ and $\dfrac{d^2y}{dx^2} = 0$, the function evaluated at $x = a$ rises at a

constant rate as x increases and the graph of the function is a straight line as in Figure 5.3. Conversely, if the graph of a function is a straight line and slopes upward for a set of acceptable values of x, as in Figure 5.3, the assumed function rises at a constant rate for those values. From Figure 5.3, it is clear that the slope of the graph is constant.

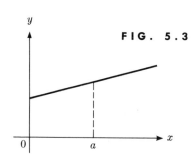

FIG. 5.3

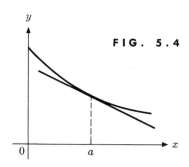

FIG. 5.4

(4) If $\dfrac{dy}{dx} < 0$ and $\dfrac{d^2y}{dx^2} > 0$, the function evaluated at $x = a$ falls at

an increasing rate as x increases and the graph of the function is convex from below as in Figure 5.4. Conversely, if the graph of a function is convex from below and slopes downward for a set of admissible values of x, as in Figure 5.4, the given function decreases at an increasing rate for those values. From Figure 5.4, it is recognizable that as x increases, the actual value (*not* the absolute value) of the tangents gets larger.

(5) If $\dfrac{dy}{dx} < 0$ and $\dfrac{d^2y}{dx^2} < 0$, the function, evaluated at $x = a$, decreases

at a decreasing rate as x increases and the graph of the function is concave from below as in Figure 5.5. Conversely, if the graph of a function is concave from below and slopes downward for a set of acceptable values of x, as in Figure 5.5, the assumed function falls at a decreasing rate for those values. By observing Figure 5.5, one can immediately take a mental note of the fact that the actual value, (*not* the absolute value), of the tangents gets smaller as x increases within its bound.

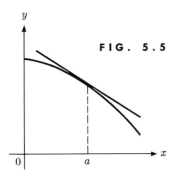

FIG. 5.5

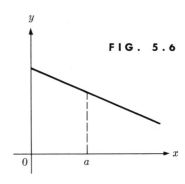

FIG. 5.6

(6) If $\dfrac{dy}{dx} < 0$ and $\dfrac{d^2y}{dx^2} = 0$, the function, evaluated at $x = a$, falls at a constant rate as x increases and the graph of the function is a straight line as in Figure 5.6. Conversely, if the graph of function is a straight line and slopes downward for a set of admissible values of x, as in Figure 5.6, the given function decreases at a constant rate for those values. It is obvious that the slope of the curve in Figure 5.6 is constant.

(7) If $f'(a) = 0$ and $f''(a) > 0$, the function has a minimum at $x = a$ and the graph of the function for that point and points before and after that is as depicted in Figure 5.7.

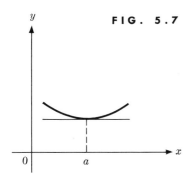

FIG. 5.7

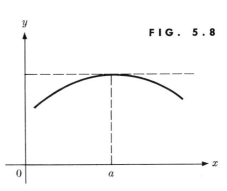

FIG. 5.8

(8) If $f'(a) = 0$ and $f''(a) < 0$, the function has a maximum at $x = a$ and the graph of the function for that point and the points before and after that is as shown in Figure 5.8.

(9) If $f'(a) = 0$ and $f''(a) = 0$, and $f'''(a) \neq 0$ the function has a point of inflection[1] at $x = a$ and the graph of the function for that point and the points before and after that is as depicted in Figure 5.9.

---

[1] A point of inflection is where a function alters its rate of change. At a point of inflection the tangent crosses the curve.

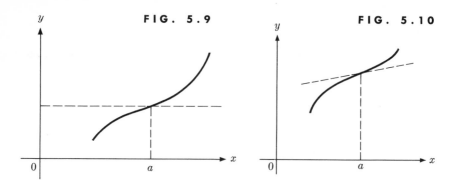

FIG. 5.9   FIG. 5.10

(10) If $f'(a) > 0$ and $f''(a) = 0$, the function has a point of inflection at $x = a$ and the graph for that point and the points before and after that is as depicted by Figure 5.10. In this case $f''(x) < 0$ for $x < a$ and $f''(x) > 0$ for $x > a$ which indicates that the function rises at a decreasing rate before the point of inflection and increases at an increasing rate thereafter. Of course, had we had $f''(x) > 0$ for $x < a$ and $f''(x) < 0$ for $x > a$, the function would have increased at an increasing rate before the point of inflection and a decreasing rate after that point; or the graph of the function would have been convex first and concave after $x = a$.

(11) If $f'(a) < 0$ and $f''(a) = 0$, the function has a point of inflection at $x = a$ and the graph of the function for that point and the points preceding and ensuing that point is as illustrated by Figure 5.11. It is clear that $f''(x) < 0$ for $x < a$ and $f''(x) > 0$ for $x > a$. If, on the other hand, we had $f''(x) > 0$ for $x < a$ and $f''(x) < 0$ for $x > a$, the function would have been convex before the point of inflection and concave after that point.

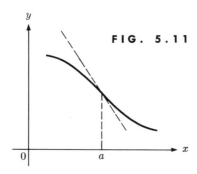

FIG. 5.11

We now apply the preceding rules to the following illustrative examples.

Example 1. For what values of x does the function

$$y = x^3 - x^2 - x + 6$$

increase and decrease? Let $\dfrac{d}{dx} = D$. In order to answer this question, we find the values of x for which the derivative is zero, *i.e.*, for which the function may change from increasing to decreasing or conversely. We have

$$Dy = 3x^2 - 2x - 1,$$

and $Dy = 0$ at $x = 1, -\frac{1}{3}$. Clearly, the sign of the derivative can change at $x = 1$ and $x = -\frac{1}{3}$ since Dy is continuous. Hence it has one sign in each of the intervals $x < -\frac{1}{3}$, $1 > x > -\frac{1}{3}$ and $x > 1$. We can now assign different values of these intervals to x in the equation of the derivative.

According to our rule, if for a given value of x the equation of the derivative is positive for that value, the function would rise and, conversely, the function falls if the derivative is negative. We may represent this by the following diagram.

	$x = -\frac{1}{3}$	$x = 1$	
$-\infty$			$+\infty$
$x < -\frac{1}{3}$	$-\frac{1}{3} < x < 1$	$x > 1$	
Dy is positive	Dy negative	Dy positive	
y increasing	y decreasing	y increasing	

The second derivative of the function should tell us whether the function is concave or convex. Now

$$D^2y = 6x - 2$$

and $D^2y = 0$ at $x = \frac{1}{3}$. Thus the second derivative is positive or negative respectively for $x \gtrless \frac{1}{3}$. Hence the graph of the function is concave from below to the left of $x = \frac{1}{3}$ and convex from below to the right of $x = \frac{1}{3}$.

Based on the above example and the rules given before, we will find the intervals of the variable x in which each of the following functions increases or decreases and their interval of concavity and convexity.

Example 2. Consider

$$y = 2x^3 - 3x^2.$$

We have

$$Dy = x(6x - 6).$$

Since at $x = 0, 1$, $Dy = 0$, hence y increases for $x < 0$ and $x > 1$ and decreases for $1 > x > 0$. Also

$$D^2y = 12x - 6$$

so that $D^2y = 0$ at $x = \frac{1}{2}$. Thus, for $1 > x > \frac{1}{2}$ the function y falls at an increasing rate, for $\frac{1}{2} > x > 0$ it decreases at a decreasing rate and for $x > 1$ it rises at an increasing rate.

Example 3. Consider

$$y = \tfrac{3}{4}x^4 + \tfrac{11}{3}x^3 - 2x^2.$$

We have

$$Dy = x(3x^2 + 11x - 4),$$
$$D^2y = 9x^2 + 22x - 4.$$

It is clear that $Dy = 0$ at $x = 0, -4, \tfrac{1}{3}$ and $D^2y = 0$ for $x = \tfrac{1}{6}$ and $x = -\tfrac{47}{18}$. Also, $Dy > 0$ for $x > \tfrac{1}{3}$, $0 > x > -4$ and $Dy < 0$ for $\tfrac{1}{3} > x > 0$ and $x < -4$. Hence, for the former set of the intervals of the variable x, Dy rises. Dy falls for the latter set of the intervals of the variable x. Furthermore, $D^2y > 0$ for $x > \tfrac{1}{6}$ and $x < -\tfrac{47}{18}$, but $D^2y < 0$ for $\tfrac{1}{6} > x > -\tfrac{47}{18}$. Whence, y rises at an increasing rate for $x > \tfrac{1}{3}$ and falls at an increasing rate for all $\tfrac{1}{3} > x > \tfrac{1}{6}$ and $x < -4$.

Example 4. Consider

$$12y = 3x^4 - 28x^3 - 48x^2 - 24.$$

We have

$$Dy = x(x^2 - 7x - 8),$$
$$D^2y = 3x^2 - 14x - 8.$$

Obviously, $Dy = 0$ at $x = 0, -1$ and 8 and $D^2y = 0$ at $x = \dfrac{14 \pm \sqrt{292}}{6}$.
Also, $Dy > 0$ for $x > 0$ and $0 > x > -1$ and $Dy < 0$ for $x < -1$ and $8 > x > 0$.

Whence, for the former set of intervals y increases and for the latter set of intervals it decreases. Moreover, $D^2y > 0$ for $x > \dfrac{14 + \sqrt{292}}{6}$ and $x < \dfrac{14 - \sqrt{292}}{6}$ but D^2y is negative for $\dfrac{14 + \sqrt{292}}{6} > x > \dfrac{14 - \sqrt{292}}{6}$.
Wherefrom, y rises at an increasing rate for all $x > \dfrac{14 + \sqrt{292}}{6}$ and $\dfrac{14 - \sqrt{292}}{6} > x > -1$. Further, y falls at an increasing rate for all $8 > x > \dfrac{14 + \sqrt{292}}{6}$.

Example 5. Consider

$$y = e^x.$$

We have

$$Dy = e^x,$$
$$D^2y = e^x.$$

Clearly, $Dy = 0$ at $x = -\infty$ and $D^2y = 0$ at $x = -\infty$. Also, $Dy > 0$ for all $x > -\infty$ and $D^2y > 0$ for all $x > -\infty$. However, since $Dy < 0$

and $D^2y < 0$ do not exist, then the function rises at an increasing rate for all $x > -\infty$.

Example 6. Find the points of inflection of

$$y = \tfrac{1}{12}x^4 - \tfrac{1}{3}x^3 - \tfrac{3}{2}x^2 + \tfrac{26}{12}x + \tfrac{51}{12}.$$

We have

$$Dy = \tfrac{1}{3}x^3 - x^2 - 3x + \tfrac{26}{12},$$
$$D^2y = x^2 - 2x - 3.$$

We notice that $D^2y = 0$ at $x = -1$ and 3. Setting these values in the original function, we obtain respectively $y = 1$ and -5. Then, $(-1, 1)$ and $(3, -5)$ are the points of inflection.

However, we notice $Dy > 0$ for $x = -1$ and $Dy < 0$ at $x = 3$, then at $x = -1$ the inflection point is of the kind depicted in Figure 5.10 and at $x = 3$ the inflection point is of the kind displayed in Figure 5.11 and the function is convex from below for $x < -1$, $x > 3$ and concave from below for $3 > x > -1$.

Example 7. Locate the extreme points, maxima and minima, and the points of inflection of

$$y = \tfrac{1}{3}x^3 - 3x^2 + 8x - 5.$$

We have

$$Dy = x^2 - 6x + 8,$$
$$D^2y = 2x - 6.$$

According to our rules, the extreme values are at $Dy = 0$ or at $x = 4$, and 2. Since at $x = 4$, $D^2y > 0$ the function y has a minimum at $x = 4$. On the other hand, at $x = 2$, $D^2y < 0$, then y has a maximum at $x = 2$. Moreover, $D^2y = 0$ at $x = 3$.

Substituting $x = 3$ in y, we obtain $y = 1$. Whence, the point of inflection is at $(3, 1)$.

Example 8. Locate the maximum and minimum points and the point of inflection of

$$y = 2x^3 - 3x^2 - 12x + 2.$$

We have

$$Dy = 6x^2 - 6x - 12,$$
$$D^2y = 12x - 6.$$

According to our rules, since $Dy = 0$ at $x = 2$ and -1, and $D^2y > 0$ at $x = 2$ and $D^2y < 0$ at $x = -1$, then at $x = 2$, y has a minimum and at $x = -1$ it has a maximum. Further, $D^2y = 0$ at $x = \tfrac{1}{2}$ for which $y = -4.5$ and $Dy < 0$, then at $(\tfrac{1}{2}, -4.5)$ there is a point of inflection of the kind depicted in Fig. 5.11.

Example 9. Find the extreme values of

$$y = xe^x.$$

We have

$$Dy = e^x(x + 1),$$
$$D^2y = e^x(x + 2).$$

Clearly, $Dy = 0$ at $x = -1$ and at this point $D^2y = e^{-1}(-1 + 2) = \dfrac{1}{e}$ which is positive and $y = \dfrac{-1}{e}$. Thus the function has a minimum $y = \dfrac{-1}{e}$ at $x = -1$.

Example 10. Find the extreme values of

$$y = \frac{3x}{2(\log x)}.$$

We have

$$Dy = \frac{6(\log x - 1)}{4(\log^2 x)},$$

$$D^2y = \frac{3[2 \log x - \log(x - 1)]}{(4x)(\log^3 x)}.$$

Obviously, $Dy = 0$ at $\log x = 1$ or $x = e$ and at this point $D^2y = \tfrac{3}{4}[2 - \log(2.718\ldots-1)] > 0$ and $y = \dfrac{3e}{2}$. Hence, the function has a minimum $y = \dfrac{3e}{2}$ at $x = e$.

Example 11. Finally, let us apply the rules to our firm's cost function

$$y = 4x^2 - 5x + 7,$$

where y is total cost and x output as before. The question is: At what level of output will total cost be either a maximum or a minimum? We have

$$Dy = 8x - 5.$$

We ought to place the first derivative equal to zero and find the value of x for which the first derivative is zero, *i.e.*,

$$8x - 5 = 0.$$

Therefrom we obtain

$$x = +\tfrac{5}{8}.$$

Now, we take the second derivative

$$\frac{d^2y}{dx^2} = 8.$$

Whereas the second derivative is positive, the function, according to rule (7), has a minimum at $x = +\tfrac{5}{8}$.

5.4 Keynes' Aggregate Supply Function[2]

All existing textbooks indicate that the equilibrium of national income is found at the point of intersection of aggregate effective demand and the 45° line. Accordingly, the 45° line is treated as though it were the Keynesian aggregate supply function. The purpose of this section is to deduce the shape of the aggregate supply function via those mathematical tools which have been explained in the previous sections of this chapter.

Let there be assumed: that pure competition prevails, *i.e.*, the economy is producing a homogeneous output (X); that technology is constant, *i.e.*, the law of the marginal diminishing returns is operative; that the homogeneous labor (N) is the only variable factor of production and that its price is constant. Accordingly, the production and cost functions can be expressed as follows:

(5.4.1) $$X = X(N),$$

(5.4.2) $$Z = Z(X).$$

If the law of the marginal diminishing returns is operative, then output (X) should increase but at a decreasing rate as the additional units of labor are employed up to the point of full employment where the marginal output would be zero, which implies that the production function is a parabola whose axis points downward. To put the matter into mathematical phraseology, we have

(5.4.3) $$\frac{dX}{dN} = X' > 0, \qquad \text{(marginal physical product)}$$

(5.4.4) $$\frac{d^2X}{dN^2} = X'' < 0, \qquad \text{(rate of change of the marginal physical product)}$$

(5.4.5) $$\frac{d^3X}{dN^3} = X''' = 0. \qquad \text{(rate of change of the rate of change of the marginal physical product)}$$

Under pure competition, the money wage rate w tends to be equal to the marginal value product which is the marginal physical product times price, (p), of the output. To express it mathematically

(5.4.6) $$w = pX',$$

or

(5.4.7) $$\frac{w}{X'} = p.$$

On the other hand, under pure competition, price tends to be equal to the marginal cost. Since the cost function is shown by (5.4.2), the marginal

---

[2] This section is based on my note: "Keynes' Aggregate Supply Function," *Economic Journal*, December 1961.

cost is

(5.4.8)
$$\frac{dZ}{dX} = Z'.$$

Thus, for the equality of the marginal cost and price we can write

(5.4.9)
$$Z' = p.$$

From (5.4.7) and (5.4.9) we obtain

(5.4.10)
$$Z' = \frac{w}{X'}.$$

The reader must not take (5.4.10) as an identity since the last equation is the result of the combination of two monotonic *conditional equations* which can express functionality. If, however, (5.4.7) and (5.4.9) were identically the same expressions, (5.4.10) would have been an identity.[3] Now that we are fairly convinced that (5.4.10) is not an identity, we can determine unambiguously its signs. (Incidentally, our relation is the famous and "familiar" Marshallian "cross" between the theory of production and the theory of value from which one can deduce the shape of the supply curve.[4])

Since $w > 0$ and $X' > 0$, then $Z' > 0$ which means that the aggregate supply function is an increasing function of the output. Differentiate (5.4.10) with respect to output to get[5]

(5.4.11)
$$Z'' = \frac{-wX''}{(X')^3}.$$

Since $w > 0$ and $X'' < 0$, then, the numerator is positive. The denominator is positive at any rate. Thus, (5.4.11) will be positive. That is,

---

[3] L. E. Dickson, *New First Course in the Theory of Equations*, New York, 1960, pp. 14–15. See also J. V. Uspensky, *Theory of Equations*, New York, 1948, pp. 52–53.

[4] P. Sraffa, "The Laws of Returns Under Competitive Conditions," pp. 180–197; J. Viner, "Cost Curves and Supply Curves," pp. 198–232; J. Robinson, "Rising Supply Curves," pp. 233–241, all in *Readings in Price Theory*, Chicago, 1952.

[5] The proof is as follows: We have

$$Z' = \frac{w}{X'} \quad \text{or} \quad \frac{dZ}{dX} = \frac{w}{\dfrac{dX}{dN}}$$

which on differentiation with respect to N gives

(1)
$$\frac{d}{dN}\left(\frac{dZ}{dX}\right) = \frac{d}{dN}\left(w \Big/ \frac{dX}{dN}\right) = \frac{-wX''}{(X')^2}.$$

But since $\dfrac{dZ}{dX}$ is a function of X, we write

$$\frac{d}{dN}\left(\frac{dZ}{dX}\right) = \frac{d}{dX}\left(\frac{dZ}{dX}\right)\frac{dX}{dN} = Z''X'$$

which on substitution in (1) will yield

$$Z''X' = \frac{-wX''}{(X')^2} \quad \text{or} \quad Z'' = \frac{-wX''}{(X')^3}. \qquad \text{Q.E.D.}$$

if $Z = Z(X)$ is graphed in a plane where Z is measured along the vertical axis and X along the horizontal, the function must rise at an increasing rate up to the level of full employment, where output will stop rising while cost will increase which, according to Keynes, is the point of true inflation.[6]

Having examined the signs of the successive derivatives of $Z = Z(X)$, we discerned that the aggregate supply function is convex from below and slopes upward, *i.e.*, that it rises at an increasing rate. It is to be noted that the deduced shape of the supply function is based on the assumptions that Keynes made.

5.5 Profit-Maximization Concept

This is a discussion from which many economic theorems emanate, yet it is often misunderstood. There seem to be some unclear views held by a few economists concerning the meaning and objective of the profit maximization principle.

There are many who suppose "profit-maximization" simply to mean that an entrepreneur wants to "take the blood out of the turnip" in the process of production; that it should be the tendency of an entrepreneur to make his profit of the next year more than what he could obtain this year. Or, in the process of economic activity, his profit should be escalated; otherwise, he presumably is not "maximizing his profit." This was the notion of some socialists who wanted to criticize the institutional framework of capitalism for promoting the unequal distribution of income due to the "natural" tendency of the entrepreneur for profit maximization; that those who own the means of production "get richer" in the process of production and allocation as though production were a two-person zero-sum game. This misconception was further implied by the Ricardian economics which had advanced the argument that a falling rate of profit was the cause of economic fluctuations.

Strangely enough, a group of anti-socialistic economists have tried hard, for many decades, to "prove" empirically[7] and theoretically that the typical

---

[6] *The General Theory of Employment, Interest and Money*, New York, 1936, p. 303.

[7] Recently a writer, on the basis of sample of interviews and in answering the charges raised against "big business" by the Subcommittee on Antitrust and Monopoly of the Committee on the Judiciary, United States Senate, 85th Congress, 1st Session, has remarked that "the large company has a fairly well-defined pricing goal that is related to a long-range profit horizon, its management seeks .... a simultaneous decision with respect to price, cost and product characteristics; and its pricing devices are handy devices for checking the internal consistency of the separate decisions as against the general company objectives. Under this hypothesis, no single theory of the firm — and certainly no single motivational hypothesis such as profit-maximization — is likely to impose an unambiguous course of action for any given situation; nor will it provide a satisfactory basis for valid and useful prediction of price behavior. It seems reasonable to conclude that the pricing policies are in almost every case equivalent to a company policy that represents an order of priorities and choice from among competing objectives rather than policies tested by any simple concept of 'profit-maximization.'" R. F. Lanzillotti, "Pricing Objectives in Large Companies," *American Economic Review*, December 1958.

modern entrepreneur does not any longer "maximize profit" when he considers his resource allocation. The literature is replete with "statistical findings" on the motives of the modern corporation in contrast to the "old-fashioned" entrepreneur in Keynes' and marginalist's arguments.

The meaning of "profit-maximization," according to traditional marginalists, has always been the case in which the entrepreneur should stop production exactly at the point where marginal cost and marginal revenue are equal and only when the marginal cost curve crosses the marginal revenue curve from below. If this principle is applied to the theory of investment programming, the firm continues to demand for investment up to the point where the equality of marginal cost and revenue is satisfied. The principle of "profit-maximization" or in general "maximum-value-criterion" is universal in application and can be used in different sections of economics. This is one of the meaningful theorems which runs through economics.[8] Let, then, the principle figuring in the dialogue of socialists vis-a-vis anti-socialists be called the principle of "taking the blood out of the turnip," for the sake of expository clarity.

There are some economists who think that "profit-maximization" is, and should be, a motivational objective for an entrepreneur in pursuing his goals. It is not so and it cannot be, at least according to the inventors of the notion. We should point out emphatically that the objective of the principle is to use it as a guide in production, as a test of performance at the point of equilibrium. The guide prescribes to the representative firm that if its activity generates an output for which marginal revenue is not equal to marginal cost, the firm should not go ahead and undertake the given activity. This is a good rule, but it may be disobeyed especially when the equality of marginal cost and marginal revenue corresponds with negative output.[9]

Let us suppose that a firm is engaged in the production of commodity X under known cost conditions represented by the total cost function $Z = Z(X)$. Let us further assume that pure competition prevails so that the demand for firm's output is known and is represented by the demand function $X = X(p)$, which indicates that the firm fixes its price and allows the demand conditions to determine the corresponding level of

---

[8] P. A. Samuelson, *Foundations of Economic Analysis*, 1960, Chapter 1.

[9] Recently Professor Baumol has suggested: "Like an electronic computer, marginal analysis is, by itself, incapable of taking account of non-negativity requirement. To return to the more familiar optimum output problem, for the competitive firm we note that the rule of the marginal analysis is that the output of any item should be at the level at which marginal cost is equal to price. But for *unprofitable* item marginal cost may be only equal to price at an impossible negative output level. . . . Of course, no moderately sane economist making a graphic analysis will ever recommend a negative output. But where a large number of interdependent decisions have to be made, the calculations may all have to be done with the help of mathematical reasoning. And a mathematical analysis based on marginal equalities like marginal cost equals price, must in such a case yield nonsense results." "Activity Analysis in One Lesson," *American Economic Review*, December 1958.

output. On these assumptions, the firm wishes to maximize its profit, defining profit as the difference between total revenue and total cost. We write all our relations as follows:

(5.5.1) $X = X(p)$ demand function

(5.5.2) $R = px$ total revenue

(5.5.3) $\dfrac{dR}{dX} =$ marginal revenue

(5.5.4) $\dfrac{dR}{dp} = \dfrac{dR}{dX}\dfrac{dX}{dp}$ function of function derivative

(5.5.5) $Z = Z(X)$ cost function

(5.5.6) $\dfrac{dZ}{dX} =$ marginal cost

(5.5.7) $\dfrac{dZ}{dp} = \dfrac{dZ}{dX}\dfrac{dX}{dp}$ function of function rule

(5.5.8) $R - Z =$ profit

The necessary and sufficient conditions for maximum profit are given by:

(5.5.9) $\dfrac{d}{dp}(R - Z) = 0 \quad \text{and} \quad \dfrac{d^2}{dp^2}(R - Z) < 0;$

the necessary condition gives

(5.5.10) $\dfrac{d}{dp}(R - Z) = \dfrac{dR}{dp} - \dfrac{dZ}{dp} = 0,$

or

(5.5.11) $\dfrac{dR}{dp} = \dfrac{dZ}{dp}.$

On substituting from (5.5.4) and (5.5.7) into (5.5.11), we obtain

$$\dfrac{dR}{dX}\dfrac{dX}{dp} = \dfrac{dZ}{dX}\dfrac{dX}{dp},$$

and by eliminating $\dfrac{dX}{dp}$ from both sides, we get

(5.5.12) $\dfrac{dR}{dX} = \dfrac{dZ}{dX}$

which is the equality of the marginal revenue and marginal cost.

The sufficient condition for maximum profit was given by

$$\dfrac{d^2}{dp^2}(R - Z) < 0$$

which by substituting from our definitions we have

(5.5.13)
$$\frac{d^2 R}{dX^2} < \frac{d^2 Z}{dX^2}$$

which indicates that the sufficient condition for a maximum profit is that marginal cost should increase faster than marginal revenue; or, more conventionally, marginal cost should cross marginal revenue from below.

5.6 The Concept of Elasticity

It has been made clear, in this and the previous chapters, that for a continuous function $y = y(x)$

$$\frac{\Delta y}{\Delta x}$$

is the average rate of change and

$$\frac{dy}{dx}$$

is the instantaneous rate of change and

$$\frac{\dfrac{dy}{dx}}{y} = \frac{1}{y}\frac{dy}{dx} = \frac{d(\log y)}{dy}\frac{dy}{dx} = \frac{d(\log y)}{dx}$$

is the proportional rate of change of y for absolute changes in x; and, finally, for the proportional change of y for the proportional change in x we have

$$\frac{\%\ \text{change in } y}{\%\ \text{change in } x} = \lim_{\Delta x \to 0}\left\{\frac{\dfrac{y(x + \Delta x) - y(x)}{y}}{\dfrac{x + \Delta x - x}{x}}\right\}$$

$$= \lim_{\Delta x \to 0}\left\{\frac{x}{y}\frac{y(x + \Delta x) - y(x)}{\Delta x}\right\}$$

$$= \frac{x}{y}\frac{dy}{dx}.$$

On the other hand, if we assume that

$$v = \log y,\ y = y(x),\ x = e^u \text{ where } u = \log x,$$

we can, according to the function of function rule, write

$$\frac{dv}{du} = \frac{dv}{dy}\frac{dy}{dx}\frac{dx}{du},$$

or

$$\frac{d(\log y)}{d(\log x)} = \frac{1}{y}\frac{dy}{dx}\frac{d}{du}(e^u) = \frac{1}{y}\frac{dy}{dx}x = \frac{x}{y}\frac{dy}{dx}.$$

Hence:

(5.6.1) $\dfrac{\% \text{ change of } y}{\% \text{ change of } x} = \dfrac{d(\log y)}{d(\log x)} = \dfrac{x}{y}\dfrac{dy}{dx} = \dfrac{\dfrac{dy}{dx}}{\dfrac{y}{x}} = \dfrac{\text{marginal ratio}}{\text{average ratio}}.$

According to the descriptive part of Section 1 of Chapter 3, the proportional change in quantity with respect to the proportional change in price was named the elasticity of demand. Hence, in general (5.6.1) is called the elasticity of a continuous function $y = y(x)$ at a point, e.g., $x = (a)$ and shown by

$$\frac{Ey}{Ex} = \frac{E}{Ex}y(x)$$

where the letter E stands for the elasticity.

Since the elasticity of a function $y = y(x)$ is a combined term composed of $\dfrac{dy}{dx}$ and $\dfrac{x}{y}$, it will follow all the laws of the derivatives. Accordingly, we have:

(1) the elasticity of a constant is zero

$$\frac{Ea}{Ex} = 0,$$

(2) the elasticity of two (or many) terms added to or subtracted from each other is given by

$$\frac{E(p \pm q)}{Ex} = \frac{p\dfrac{Ep}{Ex} \pm q\dfrac{Eq}{Ex}}{p \pm q}$$

where, of course, $p = p(x)$ and $q = q(x)$.

(3) The elasticity of a product is the sum of the individual terms:

$$\frac{E(pq)}{Ex} = \frac{Ep}{Ex} + \frac{Eq}{Ex}.$$

(4) The elasticity of a quotient is the difference between the two terms of the quotient:

$$\frac{E\left(\dfrac{p}{q}\right)}{Ex} = \frac{Ep}{Ex} - \frac{Eq}{Ex}.$$

(5) A special case of rule (2) is

$$\frac{E(p+a)}{Ex} = \frac{p\dfrac{Ep}{Ex} + 0}{p+a} = \frac{p}{p+a}\frac{Ep}{Ex}.$$

(6) And special cases of (3) are

$$\frac{E(ap)}{Ex} = \frac{Ep}{Ex},$$

$$\frac{E}{Ex}(ax+b) = \frac{ax}{ax+b}$$

$$\frac{E}{Ex}(ax) = 1,$$

$$\frac{E}{Ex}\left(\frac{a}{x}\right) = -1,$$

$$\frac{E}{Ex}(ax^\alpha) = \alpha,$$

$$\frac{E}{Ex}(ae^{\alpha x}) = \alpha x.$$

From the special cases of rule (6) one can immediately deduce that only power functions, and not linear functions, have constant elasticities. It means that if we graph a power function on two logarithmic scales, the slope of the curve of the function will be constant and remain the same for all points of the curve. But, the elasticity of a linear function, as we can see, changes for all points of the curve. Mention was made in Section 1 of Chapter 3 that usually we are encountered with the statement in many textbooks that a curve of a linear equation graphed on the natural scales has a constant elasticity. According to our mathematical intuition, this is *incorrect*.

It is also clear from the special cases of the last rule that the elasticity of a straight line $y = ax$ is unity, and of $y = \dfrac{a}{x}$ is minus unity all over the curve. Thus, if a demand function is approximated by a hyperbola of the first kind, its elasticity is unity and constant for all points of the curve. If the elasticity of a power function is a positive number, the proportional changes of the dependent variable for the proportional changes of the independent variable are in the same direction. On the other hand, if the elasticity of a power function is a negative number, the dependent variable changes proportionally in the opposite direction from the proportional changes of the independent variable. Hence, if the elasticity of a function is more (less) than $(+1)$, a proportional change in the independent variable results in a greater (lesser) proportional change, in the same direction, in the dependent variable. Conversely, when the elasticity is more than (-1)

but not positive, a proportional increase in the independent variable results in a greater proportional decrease in the dependent variable. If, however, the value of the elasticity is unity, the proportional change in one variable is the same as the proportional change in the other variable.

In economics, it is commonly accepted that if the absolute value of the elasticity of a function is more than unity, that function is called *elastic*. If, however, it is less than unity the function is called *inelastic*. And, in case the elasticity is equal to unity, the function is referred to as possessing *unitary elasticity*. The numerical value of the elasticity of demand is negative since its slope is negative. However, the elasticity of supply is positive since $\frac{dq_s}{dp}$ is positive.

We are, now, in a position to introduce and discuss a few concepts of individual elasticities in economics.

The Elasticity of Demand. It was pointed out earlier that a consumer's purchase plan summarizes the consumer's decision as to what goods and how much of each good to purchase at the prevailing market price, given his tastes and the prices of all other competitive and complementary goods. In Section 1 of Chapter 3, we described how a consumer behaves, in forming his purchase plan and quantity demanded, in relation to given prices of a commodity; that he wishes to buy more at the lower prices and less at the higher prices. We also explained how he revises his decision in response to some change in the pattern of market prices. The responsiveness that demonstrates the relation between a proportional change in price and the consequent proportional change in the quantity demanded is called the elasticity of demand for that given good. Or

$$\frac{Eq}{Ep} = \frac{p}{q}\frac{dq}{dp} = \frac{d(\log q)}{d(\log p)} < 0.$$

For convenience, we multiply both sides of the expression by (-1) to make the actual value of the elasticity positive:

$$\eta = \frac{Eq}{Ep} = -\frac{p}{q}\frac{dq}{dp} = -\frac{d(\log q)}{d(\log p)} > 0.$$

This conversion does not alter the basic definition of the elasticity of demand; *i.e.*, the proportional change in price results in an opposite proportional change in quantity.

There is a geometrical method, very convenient and invented by Marshall,[10] with which one can easily detect the elasticity of demand for each point of the curve. Let us suppose that the demand curve is given by the linear equation $q_d = a + bp$ and shown in Figure 5.12. Let us suppose that we wish to find out the elasticity of the demand curve at point T.

_____

[10] *Principles of Economics*, London, 1936, pp. 839–40.

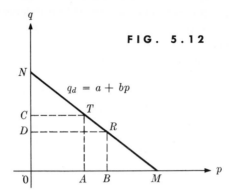

FIG. 5.12

For that, we let the price increase from A to B which means that

$$AB = \Delta p.$$

If the price moves from A to B, the quantity demanded will fall from C to D or

$$DC = \Delta q, \ CD = -\Delta q.$$

Now, we can approximately write the elasticity for T by

$$\eta = -\frac{\dfrac{\Delta q}{q}}{\dfrac{\Delta p}{p}} = \frac{\dfrac{AB}{0A}}{\dfrac{DC}{0C}} = \frac{AB}{DC}\frac{0C}{0A}.$$

And by a theorem of geometry on similar right triangles, we have

$$\frac{AB}{DC} = \frac{AM}{0C},$$

which by substituting in the preceding expression gives

$$\eta = \frac{AM}{0C}\frac{0C}{0A} = \frac{AM}{0A}.$$

Again, since

$$\frac{AM}{0A} = \frac{TM}{NT}$$

or, finally

$$\eta = \frac{TM}{NT}.$$

Whence, if the elasticity of a point of a demand curve, which is a straight line, is needed, we have only to divide the lower part of the line by the upper part of it and the resultant quotient will be the elasticity of the demand for that point. If, however, the demand curve is nonlinear, e.g. hyperbola, we should only draw a tangent to the curve at the point whose elasticity is needed. Again, the lower part of the tangent over the upper part of it will give the elasticity for the point of tangency.

For a normal demand, we write

$$x = x(p)$$

and

$$R = xp$$

also

$$\frac{dR}{dp} = x + p\frac{dx}{dp},$$

however

$$\frac{dR}{dp} = \frac{dR}{dx}\frac{dx}{dp};$$

then

$$\frac{dR}{dx} = \frac{dR}{dp}\bigg/\frac{dx}{dp}$$

$$= \frac{x + p\dfrac{dx}{dp}}{\dfrac{dx}{dp}} = p + x\frac{dp}{dx}$$

$$= p\left(1 + \frac{x}{p}\frac{dp}{dx}\right)$$

$$= p\left(1 - \frac{1}{\eta}\right).$$

In the last expression, we are connecting the marginal revenue, price (average revenue), and the elasticity. The reader can assign different values to the elasticity and notice the manipulations in marginal revenue.

The Elasticity of Supply. In Section 2 of Chapter 3, we demonstrated the sales plan of a firm. We analyzed that the decision to sell depends on the prices of the inputs, the price of the product, the firm's objective, and (*inter alia*) the production possibilities. We also explained when and how a sales plan is revised and implemented. By and large, we concluded that the higher the selling price, the more the firm wishes to sell, and the lower the selling price the less the firm wishes to sell. The responsiveness of a sales plan to changes in the expected price is called the elasticity of supply, and is measured by the proportionate changes in the quantity over the proportionate changes in the expected selling price,

$$K = \frac{\%\text{ change in quantity}}{\%\text{ change in price}} = \frac{\dfrac{\Delta q}{q}}{\dfrac{\Delta p}{p}} = \frac{d(\log q)}{d(\log p)} = \frac{\dfrac{dq}{dp}}{\dfrac{q}{p}}.$$

The elasticity of supply is positive under normal conditions for all points of the supply since the supply function is positive normally. Conventionally, supply is perfectly inelastic at a point when the numerical value of the elasticity at that point is zero. If the elasticity is infinitely large, the supply is being perfectly elastic. The supply is called relatively elastic when the value of its elasticity is greater than unity. If, however, the elasticity is less than unity, the supply is called relatively inelastic.

The reader can imagine an elasticity for any economic phenomenon. As long as there is an economic decision and there is a chance for its revision, one can design an elasticity to indicate the degree and extent of responsiveness of the variables.

EXERCISES 5

1. Find the derivative of each of the following functions:

$$y = x^3 - x^2 + 2x - 4. \qquad\qquad y = x^3 - 2x.$$

$$y = (x^2 + 2x - 3)^2. \qquad\qquad y = \left(x^3 + 2x - 3 + \frac{1}{x}\right)^2.$$

$$y = \frac{1}{x+3}. \qquad\qquad y = \frac{5x^2}{3 - 2x}.$$

$$x = 2 + \frac{3y}{y+5}. \qquad\qquad y = \frac{3}{x^2 + 6}.$$

$$y = \frac{(x^2 - 3)^4}{(x^3 + 3)}. \qquad\qquad y = \sqrt{1 - x}.$$

$$y = \sqrt{x - 1} + \sqrt{x + 2}. \qquad\qquad y = \sqrt[3]{(1 - x^2)(1 - 3x)}.$$

$$x = \frac{ay}{(y - a)}.$$

2. Find $\dfrac{dy}{dx}$ if

$$x = y(1 - y^2)^2. \qquad\qquad x = (y^2 - 2y)(1 - y^2)^2.$$

$$x = \frac{y^2 - 5}{3 + y}. \qquad\qquad x = y^3 - 3y.$$

$$x^2 + y^2 = a^2. \qquad\qquad x^{\frac{2}{3}} + y^{\frac{3}{4}} = a^{\frac{5}{6}}.$$

$$x^2 + xy = b^2. \qquad\qquad y^2(2a + x) = 3x^4.$$

$$y^2(x - 3y) = 2x + 5y. \qquad\qquad xy + 4a^2y + x + y = 0.$$

3. Find the derivative of the following functions:

$$y = 3\log(x - 3). \qquad\qquad y = \log\sqrt{(x - 2)(x + 1)}.$$

$$y = (\log x^2)^3. \qquad\qquad y = 3x^x.$$

$$y = \sqrt{3 + x} - 4\log\left(\frac{\sqrt{3 + x}}{x}\right). \qquad y = \log\frac{\sqrt{2x + 5}}{(x_2 - 2x)^2}.$$

$$y = e^{3x} - e^{3/2x}.$$

$$y = \frac{1 - e^{3x}}{e^{3x} - 1}.$$

$$y = e^{5x+3}(5x^3 + e^{3x} + 3).$$

$$y = e^{x^2}(\log x^3).$$

4. Differentiate each of the following functions with respect to its variable.

$$y = \cot\left(\frac{x}{4}\right).$$

$$y = \cos^2 x^3.$$

$$y = \tan^2 3x^2.$$

$$y = \sin(5x)\cos^2(3x).$$

$$y = e^{\sin^2 x} + e^{\cos^2 x}.$$

$$y = 3\sin\left(\frac{x}{2}\right) - 3x\cos\left(\frac{x}{3}\right).$$

$$y = x\csc^{-1}\sqrt{2x^2 - 3}.$$

$$y = 3x\cos^{-1}\sqrt{x + \frac{1}{x}} - \sqrt{1 + x^2}.$$

$$y = \sin^{-1}\sqrt{x^2 + 1} - \cos^{-1}\left(\sqrt{x^2 + \frac{1}{x}}\right).$$

$$y = x\tan^{-1} ax \frac{1}{a}\log\sqrt{3 - 2ax^2}.$$

5. Find the second and third derivative of each of the following functions:

$$y = 2xe^{3x}.$$

$$y = \log_2 3x.$$

$$y = 3x^{-2x}.$$

$$y = \frac{x^3}{12} + 3x + 5.$$

$$y = \frac{x}{2a + x^2}.$$

6. Find the points of inflection of each of the following functions:

$$y = \tfrac{1}{3}x^3 + \tfrac{1}{2}x^2.$$

$$y = 3x^4 + 4x^3 + 3x^2.$$

$$y = x^3 - 2x^2.$$

$$y = 5x^3 + 2x^2 + x.$$

$$y = xe^{-2x^2}.$$

$$y = \frac{x}{3 + x^2}.$$

$$y = \frac{2}{x(\log x)}.$$

7. Test each of the following functions for their extreme points and find their maximum and minimum values:

$$y = x^3 + 2x^2 + 3x - 6.$$

$$y = x(x^2 + 3).$$

$$y = \frac{2}{x} + \frac{x^3}{3}.$$

$$y = \frac{4x}{x^2 - 1}.$$

$$y = 3x^{1/2x}.$$

$$y = 3e^{5x} + 2e^{-4x}.$$

$$y = 4xe^{-2x}.$$

$$y = e^{5x+4}(\log x).$$

$$y = \frac{3x}{\log x}.$$

$$y = \frac{\sqrt{(2x - 4)}}{\sqrt[3]{(2x^2 - 4)}}.$$

8. Let us suppose that $Y = aI^2 + bI + c$ relates income to investment. Find the rate of change of income with respect to investment. Draw the curve of

the rate of change and income-investment-ratio, assuming $a = 5, b = -10$, and $c = 5$.

9. The sum of two positive numbers is 16. Find the two numbers if their product is a maximum.

10. The sum of two positive numbers is 18. Find the two numbers if the sum of their square is a minimum.

11. A company wants to install a machine which takes 150 sq. ft. of floor space. Also we must allow 2-foot margins on four sides. The company wants to use the least amount of floor space. What dimensions will require the least amount of floor space?

12. A telephone company wants to establish the telephone communication system between two places which are on both sides of a river which is 3 miles wide. It is known to the company that the cable line costs $\frac{2}{3}$ as much per mile on the land as under water. If the company wishes to minimize the cost of establishing the communication system, what line would be less expensive?

13. A baby furniture company finds that it makes a net profit of $6.00 per crib for 150 cribs or less in a week. If the profit decreases 5¢ per crib over 150, what number of cribs would yield the greatest profit?

14. A carboard box company wishes to minimize the cost of making boxes whose base has sides 3 by 2 and is to contain 460 cubic feet. If the bottom costs 6¢, top 8¢, and sides 9¢ per sq. ft. what dimensions would make the cost minimum? (The cost is inclusive of printing.)

15. A company produces 1000 tons of steel in a given period and sells it at $2.00 per pound. What level of output would give the best value if the demand for steel is so that 80 tons' rise in output per period causes a drop of 30¢ in price per pound?

6 PARTIAL DERIVATIVES AND ECONOMIC APPLICATION

6.1 Functions of More Than Two Variables in Economics

What has been said and analyzed in the preceding chapters was based on the notion that any section of our economic system consists of only two variables, dependent and independent. Indeed, and viewed realistically, the economic system is so organized that there are many variables influencing one dependent variable. In fact, a multivariable analysis lurked behind some of our discussions in Chapter 3, especially in relation to the models of Lang and Kaldor where the economy is supposed to consist of m firms producing n commodities x_1, x_2, ... x_n with p_1, p_2, ... p_n as their prices.

Following the traditional economic theory, we suggested in Chapter 3 that the decision to obtain a certain quantity of a commodity, q_1, by a household depends, *inter alia*, on consumer taste for q_1, its price p_1, consumer income y, and the prices of all other goods which are related to this commodity somehow. Or, mathematically

(6.1.1)
$$q_1 = q_1(y, T, p_1, p_2, \ldots p_n),$$

where $y, T, p_2, \ldots p_n$ are the parameters of the system.

Since income and taste are usually taken as given, the market demand for each good can be explicitly written as

(6.1.2)
$$q_1 = q_1(p_1, \ldots p_n),$$
$$q_2 = q_2(p_1, \ldots p_n),$$
$$\cdots \cdots \cdots,$$
$$q_n = q_n(p_1, \ldots p_n).$$

If $p_1, \ldots p_n$ are the independent variables so that one price may not be expressed as a function of the other one(s), then (6.1.2) would consist of n independent and consistent equations in n independent unknowns q_i, which renders the system determinate according to the rule considered in Chapter 1.

In distinguishing an implicit function from an explicit one, we ought to be cognizant of the fact that the dependent variable of any one equation of the system of equations (6.1.2) is connected arbitrarily to its independent variables. Any equation of (6.1.2) is an explicit statement which is found as a result of formulating certain original assumptions made deductively and submitted to empirical observations for either refutation or confirmation. Each equation of (6.1.2) is related to an implicit function which is wide in scope and generality, and for the ith equation we have

(6.1.3) $$f_i(q_1, q_2, \ldots q_n; p_1, p_2, \ldots p_n) = 0$$

which are the original assumptions of the system.

Related to each equation of (6.1.2) there exists an $(n + 1)$-dimensional space: one dimension for the demand and n dimensions for the prices. It is not possible to visualize an $n + 1$ dimensional space, though it exists theoretically. It is possible, however, to assume that there are no more than two goods produced. Although there is no loss of generality, our system of equations (6.1.2) will be simplified by

(6.1.4) $$q_1 = q_1(p_1, p_2)$$
$$q_2 = q_2(p_1, p_2)$$

each of which is depicted by a three-dimensional diagram.

The geometrical configuration of an equation of (6.1.4) is called a *surface*. Let us take $q_1 = q_1(p_1, p_2)$ for analysis. If p_1, p_2, and q_1 are continuous variables and if $0p_1p_2q_1$ represents three axes intersecting at right angles at 0 in space, where q_1 is measured along the vertical axis $0q_1$ and p_1 and p_2 are measured along the horizontal axes $0p_1$ and $0p_2$ in easterly and southwesterly directions, the set of values of the single-valued function $q_1 = q_1(p_1, p_2)$ constitutes a configuration in the space known as the *surface* of $q_1 = q_1(p_1, p_2)$. Let the surface of the equation be illustrated in Figure 6.1.

The surface may be cut by infinite planes, but of all planes there are three planes which are of utmost interest to us. These planes are: (1) parallel to $0p_1q_1$ and perpendicular to $0p_2q_1$; (2) parallel to $0p_2q_1$ but perpendicular to $0p_1q_1$; and finally (3) parallel to $0p_1p_2$ and perpendicular to $0q_1$. In Figure 6.1, the surface is crossed by a plane parallel to $0p_1q_1$ and its section MNQ presents an interesting case. It demonstrates that when p_2 is kept constant at $0N$, the quantity demanded q_1 decreases as p_1 increases. For instance, when p_1 is expected to be $0A$, the quantity demanded is BC; and when p_1 is $0D > 0A$, the quantity demanded will be $EF < BC$.

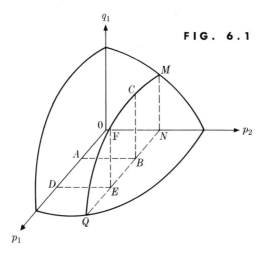

FIG. 6.1

We may also cross the surface of our equation by a plane parallel to $0p_1p_2$ or $0p_2q_1$ in order to notice the variation of either p_2 or q_1 when the other variable is constant. By crossing the surface by two vertical planes parallel to $0p_1q_1$ and $0p_2q_1$, we can examine *partially* the variations of the dependent variable with respect to the changes in one of the independent variables while the other independent variable is kept constant. Mathematically, the incremental changes are shown by

$$\frac{\Delta q_1}{\Delta p_1}\bigg|_{p_2=\text{constant}} \qquad \text{and} \qquad \frac{\Delta q_1}{\Delta p_2}\bigg|_{p_1=\text{constant}}.$$

A generalized production function provides a second and interesting case to illustrate the function of more than two independent variables in economics. We find it increasingly realistic to treat output Y as a function of its inputs $X_1, X_2, \ldots X_n$; or

(6.1.5) $$y = y(x_1, x_2, \ldots x_n).$$

To confine ourselves to visible dimensions, we are told that output Y depends on labor N and capital K; or symbolically,

(6.1.6) $$Y = Y(N, K).$$

Let the surface of this function be shown in Figure 6.2. It is to be noticed that there are infinite sections, or curves, which are found as a result of crossing the surface by planes parallel to $0NK$ and perpendicular to $0Y$. One may draw a few sections, curves, on the diagram. Each curve, called a contour, is a locus of the point of all combinations of N and K that yield the same quantity of output called an *isoquant* or a *constant-product* curve.

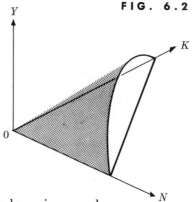

FIG. 6.2

For each contour, we have, in general,

$$Y(N, K) = \text{constant}.$$

And by allotting different values to the constant, various isoquants will be found. (Consult a macro theory text.) Therefore, for each level of output there will be only one isoquant, and for different levels of output there are various isoquants, so that infinite curves describe all levels of output. Higher contours generally belong to higher levels of output and lower contours are for lower levels of output. Moreover, it is to be recognized that the contours cannot be intersecting.

Now, let us cross the surface of the production function by a plane parallel to $0NY$ and perpendicular to $0KY$. We can examine, from the cross-section, the *partial* variation of Y with respect to changes in N while K is kept constant. For the partial incremental change we have

$$\frac{\Delta Y}{\Delta N}\bigg|_{K=\text{constant}}.$$

The partial variation of Y due to incremental changes in K, while N remaining unaltered may be shown by

$$\frac{\Delta Y}{\Delta K}\bigg|_{N=\text{constant}}.$$

6.2 The Meaning of Partial Derivatives

In Chapter 5, we were concerned exclusively with the application of derivatives of functions of a single variable, but there is nothing to prevent us from applying the notion of differentiation to functions of several variables. A function of two or more independent variables can be differentiated with respect to any one of the variables if the others are considered to be constants during the operations. In Section 6.1 of this chapter, we entertained two examples and invited the reader to examine the incremental rate of change of the dependent variable, say, income, with respect to one related independent variable, say, labor, while the other independent variable, capital, was kept constant. The instantaneous value of such a rate is called a *partial derivative* or a *partial differential coefficient,* of the function.

If we consider $z = f(x, y)$, the first partial derivative of z with respect to x is defined by

(6.2.1)
$$\lim_{\Delta x \to 0} \frac{f(x + \Delta x, y) - f(x, y)}{\Delta x};$$

and we denote the same expression by one of the symbols

$$\frac{\partial z}{\partial x} = \frac{\partial f(x, y)}{\partial x} = f'_x(x, y).$$

Likewise, for the first partial derivative of z with respect to y, we have

(6.2.2)
$$\frac{\partial z}{\partial y} = \lim_{\Delta y \to 0} \frac{f(x, y + \Delta y) - f(x, y)}{\Delta y}.$$

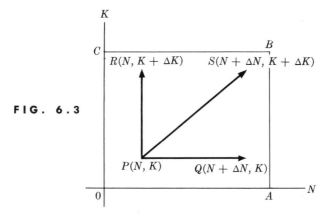

FIG. 6.3

The reader should recognize (6.2.1) as the definition of the derivative of a function of one variable x; that is what it really means, since y is assumed to be constant. To illustrate this, let the rectangle $0ABC$ of Figure 6.3 be the horizontal section, contour, of the surface of an output Y where the output at any point of the contour is given by some function of N and K standing for labor and capital. If $Y_P = f(N, K)$, then $Y_Q = f(N + \Delta N, K)$ as P and Q have the same ordinate. Hence the output changes in going from P to Q by the amount

$$Y_Q - Y_P = f(N + \Delta N, K) - f(N, K).$$

As this difference is due to a change in N alone, the output along the line PQ has as its instantaneous rate of change at P the following limit

$$\lim_{\Delta N \to 0} \frac{Y_Q - Y_P}{\Delta N} = \lim_{\Delta N \to 0} \frac{f(N + \Delta N, K) - f(N, K)}{\Delta N}$$

which is exactly an illustration of a first partial derivative of a function of two variables and is accordingly $\dfrac{\partial Y}{\partial N}$. Similarly, the rate of change of output in the direction PR is $\dfrac{\partial Y}{\partial K}$. It is to be recognized that a partial derivative, say, $\dfrac{\partial Y}{\partial N}$, depends not only on N which defines the partial derivative but also on K which was kept constant during the operation. To emphasize the point, a partial derivative is a *partial derived function* and is

$$\frac{\partial Y}{\partial N} = f_N(N, K).$$

For another example, if the quantity of a commodity demanded is a function of its own price and income of the household, the price and income elasticities of demand involved can be written as

$$\frac{Eq_d}{Ep} = \frac{p}{q_d} \frac{\partial q_d}{\partial p} = \frac{\partial(\log q_d)}{\partial(\log p)},$$

and

$$\frac{Eq_d}{EY} = \frac{Y}{q_d} \frac{\partial q_d}{\partial Y} = \frac{\partial(\log q_d)}{\partial(\log Y)}.$$

Higher Partial Derivatives. If $z = f(x, y)$ is differentiated partially twice with respect to x or y; or once with respect to each x and y, we have *second order partial derivatives*. The second partial derivatives are denoted by the symbols:

$$\frac{\partial}{\partial x}\left(\frac{\partial z}{\partial x}\right) = \frac{\partial^2 z}{\partial x^2} = f_{xx}(x, y),$$

$$\frac{\partial}{\partial x}\left(\frac{\partial z}{\partial y}\right) = \frac{\partial^2 z}{\partial x \, \partial y} = f_{yx}(x, y),$$

$$\frac{\partial}{\partial y}\left(\frac{\partial z}{\partial x}\right) = \frac{\partial^2 z}{\partial y \, \partial x} = f_{xy}(x, y),$$

$$\frac{\partial}{\partial y}\left(\frac{\partial z}{\partial y}\right) = \frac{\partial^2 z}{\partial y^2} = f_{yy}(x, y).$$

According to Young's Theorem, the proof of which is not given here, if $f(x, y)$ is a continuous function with continuous partial derivative, we have

$$\frac{\partial^2 z}{\partial x \, \partial y} = \frac{\partial^2 z}{\partial y \, \partial x}$$

which means that the "cross" partial derivatives are equal for a continuous function.

A similar notation is used for partial derivatives higher than the second partials of functions of two or more independent variables. Thus,

$$\frac{\partial}{\partial x}\left(\frac{\partial^2 z}{\partial x^2}\right) = \frac{\partial^3 z}{\partial x^3} = f_{xxx}(x, y),$$

$$\frac{\partial}{\partial y}\left(\frac{\partial^2 z}{\partial x^2}\right) = \frac{\partial^3 z}{\partial y\,\partial x^2} = f_{xxy}(x, y),$$

$$\frac{\partial}{\partial x}\left(\frac{\partial^2 z}{\partial x\,\partial y}\right) = \frac{\partial^3 z}{\partial x^2\,\partial y} = f_{yxx}(x, y),$$

$$\frac{\partial}{\partial y}\left(\frac{\partial^2 z}{\partial y\,\partial x}\right) = \frac{\partial^3 z}{\partial y^2\,\partial x} = f_{xyy}(x, y),$$

$$\frac{\partial}{\partial y}\left(\frac{\partial^2 z}{\partial y^2}\right) = \frac{\partial^3 z}{\partial y^3} = f_{yyy}(x, y),$$

$$\frac{\partial}{\partial x}\left(\frac{\partial^2 z}{\partial y^2}\right) = \frac{\partial^3 z}{\partial x\,\partial y^2} = f_{yyx}(x, y),$$

and likewise for the fourth and higher derivatives.

If we have a function of more than two independent variables, the first and succeeding partial derivatives of the function with respect to each variable are defined and denoted just as in the case of $f(x, y)$ described above. In this case, all variables are treated as constants except the one with respect to which the derivative is taken. For

$$y = f(x_1, x_2, \ldots x_n)$$

we have

$$\frac{\partial y}{\partial x_i}, \; \frac{\partial^2 y}{\partial x_1\,\partial x_i}, \; \frac{\partial^2 y}{\partial x_2\,\partial x_i}, \; \ldots \; \frac{\partial^2 y}{\partial x_n\,\partial x_i},$$

for the first and "cross" partial derivatives of the function with respect to the ith variable.

Geometric Representation of Partials—Tangent Plane.

In Section 6.1 of this chapter, we demonstrated that a three-dimensional function $z = f(x, y)$ depicts a surface.

Let us consider the surface S whose equation is

$$q_1 = q_1(p_1, p_2)$$

where q_1 is a three-dimensional function the partial derivatives of which exist at (p_1^0, p_2^0), and let C be the curve on S that lies in the plane $p_2 = p_2^0$. Then, the slope of the tangent line to C at the point D is given by the partial derivative of q_1 with respect to p_1. See Figure 6.4. Similarly, if the surface is crossed by a plane parallel to $0p_2q_1$, the slope of the tangent line to this section at any point gives the partial derivative of q_1 with respect to p_2, while p_1 is constant.

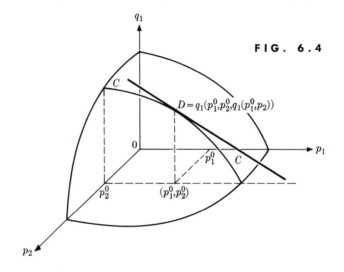

FIG. 6.4

Hence, the first partial derivatives of, say, $z = f(x, y)$ are the slopes of the curves cut from the surface by planes which are parallel to the $0yz$ and $0xz$ planes respectively. The equation of the tangent lines to the surface to any point of the surface is

(6.2.3)
$$z - z_1 = \frac{\partial z_1}{\partial y_1} (y - y_1)$$

if $x - x_1 = 0$, and

(6.2.4)
$$z - z_1 = \frac{\partial z_1}{\partial x_1} (x - x_1)$$

if $y - y_1 = 0$. The equation of any plane through an arbitrary point is given by

(6.2.5)
$$A(x - x_1) + B(y - y_1) + C(z - z_1) = 0.$$

If, however, we substitute $(y - y_1) = 1$ in (6.2.3), we will have

$$z - z_1 = \frac{\partial z_1}{\partial y_1},$$

and for (6.2.4), we get

$$z - z_1 = \frac{\partial z_1}{\partial x_1}$$

if we set $x - x_1 = 1$. Now, if the tangent lines (6.2.3) and (6.2.4) are contained in the plane, then we must have

$$B + C \frac{\partial z_1}{\partial y_1} = 0$$

where we substituted $(x - x_1) = 0$, $(y - y_1) = 1$ and $(z - z_1) = \dfrac{\partial z_1}{\partial y_1}$ in (6.2.5) and

$$A + C \frac{\partial z_1}{\partial x_1} = 0$$

where we put $(x - x_1) = 1$, $(y - y_1) = 0$ and $(z - z_1) = \dfrac{\partial z_1}{\partial x_1}$. Hence

$$\frac{\partial z_1}{\partial x_1} = -\frac{A}{C}, \quad \text{and} \quad \frac{\partial z_1}{\partial y_1} = -\frac{B}{C}.$$

Solving (6.2.5) for $z - z_1$ and substituting the above values, the *equation of the tangent plane* will be

(6.2.6) $$z - z_1 = \frac{\partial z_1}{\partial x_1} (x - x_1) + \frac{\partial z_1}{\partial y_1} (y - y_1).$$

6.3 Some Criteria for Maxima and Minima

In the light of our advancement in the three-dimensional space, we may set up new criteria for maxima and minima.

(1) There exists a maximum value in all directions of the function $z = f(x, y)$ at a point $x = a$, $y = b$ if

(6.3.1) $$\frac{\partial z}{\partial x} = \frac{\partial z}{\partial y} = 0,$$

(6.3.2) $$\frac{\partial^2 z}{\partial x^2} < 0 \quad \text{and} \quad \frac{\partial^2 z}{\partial y^2} < 0,$$

(6.3.3) $$\left(\frac{\partial^2 z}{\partial x^2}\right)\left(\frac{\partial^2 z}{\partial y^2}\right) > \left(\frac{\partial^2 z}{\partial x \, \partial y}\right)^2.$$

(2) There will be a minimum in all directions of the function $z = f(x, y)$ at a point $x = a$ and $y = b$ if, in addition to satisfying (6.3.1) and (6.3.3) we have

(6.3.4) $$\frac{\partial^2 z}{\partial x^2} > 0 \quad \text{and} \quad \frac{\partial^2 z}{\partial y^2} > 0.$$

Condition (6.3.1) is the *necessary* one for a maximum as well as for a minimum. Conditions (6.3.2) and (6.3.3) are the *sufficient* conditions for a maximum, while (6.3.3), in addition to (6.3.4), are the sufficient conditions for a minimum. If, however,

(6.3.5) $$\left(\frac{\partial^2 z}{\partial x^2}\right)\left(\frac{\partial^2 z}{\partial y^2}\right) < \left(\frac{\partial^2 z}{\partial x \, \partial y}\right)^2$$

the given stationary point is a *saddle point.*

(3) The function $z = f(x, y)$ at the point (a, b) increases as x increases from the value of a if $\dfrac{\partial z}{\partial x} > 0$, y remaining equal to b. If $\dfrac{\partial z}{\partial x} < 0$ the function decreases as x increases from the value of a while y remains constant at b. For the function $z = f(x, y)$ at the point (a, b). $\dfrac{\partial^2 z}{\partial x^2} > 0$ indicates that the function changes at an increasing rate if x increases from a while y is kept at b. On the other hand, for the same function at (a, b), $\dfrac{\partial^2 z}{\partial x^2} < 0$ indicates that the function is changing at a decreasing rate. The same interpretations can be offered for $\dfrac{\partial z}{\partial y}$ and $\dfrac{\partial^2 z}{\partial y^2}$ for the variations of y from b while x remains stationary at a.

Extremal Problems with Constraints. Many economic and mathematical problems are cast in such a mold that their variables are restricted by some "side-relation" or "constraint." For instance, we may speak of a utility function

$$U = U(q_1, \ldots q_n)$$

being restricted by income constraint

$$y = p_1 q_1 + \cdots + p_n q_n = \sum_{i=1}^{n} p_i q_i,$$

or

$$\left(y - \sum_{i=1}^{n} p_i q_i \right) = 0$$

of the consumer. It is clear that when the variables of a function are being constrained by some relation existing among them, they will not be independent of each other. Let x, y, z be three variables and let $F(x, y, z)$ stand for a function whose extremal value is to be sought. Further, let x, y, z be restricted by a "side-relation" being expressed by $G(x, y, z) = 0$.

In what ensues, we give three methods for examining and solving the minimum and maximum problems with constraints. First, there is the *method of direct elimination.* According to this method, we express one of the variables of the constraint equation in terms of the other variables. Then, we will substitute the obtained result into the function and assume that the remaining variables are independent of each other. Having done so, the solution is then obtained by (6.3.1).

Let us evaluate the extremal values of

$$F(x, y, z) = 3x^2 - 4x - 6y + z^2 - 2z + 4$$

subject to

$$G(x, y, z) = 2x + 4y - 2z + 4 = 0.$$

According to the rule, we will eliminate z in the latter and substitute its value in the former expression. Or

$$z = x + 2y + 2$$

and

$$F(x, y, z) = 4x^2 - 2x + 4y^2 - 2y + 4xy + 4.$$

Then

$$\frac{\partial F}{\partial x} = 8x - 2 + 4y = 0$$

$$\frac{\partial F}{\partial y} = 8y - 2 + 4x = 0$$

the simultaneous solution of which yields $x = \frac{1}{6}$ and $y = \frac{1}{6}$. On substituting these values in the constraint equation, we will find $z = \frac{15}{6}$. Hence, the function $F(x, y, z)$ has a relative extreme at $x = \frac{1}{6}$, $y = \frac{1}{6}$ and $z = \frac{15}{6}$. Needless to say, an extremal point may occur with any number of variables and there may be more than one constraint equation.

The method of implicit functions is another method for coping with extremal problems of a function, say, $F(x, y, z)$ which is constrained by a restriction, say, $G(x, y, z) = 0$. Similar to the previous method, we must express one of the variables, say, z in terms of the other variables and for definiteness we assume that $\dfrac{\partial G}{\partial z} \neq 0$ and that $G(x, y, z) = 0$ has a solution $z = f(x, y)$. Now, we can write

$$U = F[x, y, f(x, y)]$$

and solve the equations

$$\frac{\partial U}{\partial x} = 0 \quad \text{and} \quad \frac{\partial U}{\partial y} = 0.$$

But

$$\frac{\partial U}{\partial x} = \frac{\partial F}{\partial x} + \frac{\partial F}{\partial z}\frac{\partial f}{\partial x},$$

$$\frac{\partial U}{\partial y} = \frac{\partial F}{\partial y} + \frac{\partial F}{\partial z}\frac{\partial f}{\partial y}.$$

We also have the identity $G(x, y, z) = 0$ from which we have

$$0 = \frac{\partial G}{\partial x} + \frac{\partial G}{\partial z}\frac{\partial f}{\partial x}$$

$$0 = \frac{\partial G}{\partial y} + \frac{\partial G}{\partial z}\frac{\partial f}{\partial y}.$$

We solve the last two equations for $\dfrac{\partial f}{\partial x}$ and $\dfrac{\partial f}{\partial y}$ and substitute them in $\dfrac{\partial U}{\partial x}$ and $\dfrac{\partial U}{\partial y}$ to have

$$\frac{\partial U}{\partial x} = \frac{\dfrac{\partial F}{\partial x}\dfrac{\partial G}{\partial z} - \dfrac{\partial F}{\partial z}\dfrac{\partial G}{\partial x}}{\dfrac{\partial G}{\partial z}},$$

$$\frac{\partial U}{\partial y} = \frac{\dfrac{\partial F}{\partial y}\dfrac{\partial G}{\partial z} - \dfrac{\partial F}{\partial z}\dfrac{\partial G}{\partial y}}{\dfrac{\partial G}{\partial z}}.$$

But if the extremal conditions ought to be satisfied, then

$$\frac{\partial F}{\partial x}\frac{\partial G}{\partial z} - \frac{\partial F}{\partial z}\frac{\partial G}{\partial x} = 0$$

$$\frac{\partial F}{\partial y}\frac{\partial G}{\partial z} - \frac{\partial F}{\partial z}\frac{\partial G}{\partial y} = 0.$$

Now these two equations in addition to the constraint equation $G(x, y, z) = 0$ will give us three equations the simultaneous solution of which for x, y, z will give us the extremal point.

Let a utility function be defined by $U = q_1 q_2 q_3$ which is to be maximized subject to income constraint

$$288 = 2q_1 q_3 + 4q_1 q_2 + 3q_2 q_3.$$

For convenience let us write the utility function as $F(q_1, q_2, q_3)$ and the budget equation as $G(q_1, q_2, q_3)$. Then

$$\frac{\partial F}{\partial q_1} = q_2 q_3 \qquad \frac{\partial F}{\partial q_2} = q_1 q_3 \qquad \frac{\partial F}{\partial q_3} = q_1 q_2$$

$$\frac{\partial G}{\partial q_1} = 2q_3 + 4q_2 \qquad \frac{\partial G}{\partial q_2} = 4q_1 + 3q_3 \qquad \frac{\partial G}{\partial q_3} = 2q_1 + 3q_2.$$

Next, we write

$$\begin{cases} (q_2 q_3)(2q_1 + 3q_2) - (q_1 q_2)(2q_3 + 4q_2) = 0 \\ (q_1 q_3)(2q_1 + 3q_2) - (q_1 q_2)(4q_1 + 3q_3) = 0 \\ \qquad\qquad 2q_1 q_3 + 4q_1 q_2 + 3q_2 q_3 = 288 \end{cases}$$

where $q_1 = 6$, $q_2 = 4$ and $q_3 = 8$.

Thus, when the consumer purchases 6 units of q_1, 4 units of q_2 and 8 units of q_3 he would maximize his utility function subject to the income equation. (We have omitted the negative values of the example since negative consumption is meaningless.)

The two preceding methods for dealing with the extremals of restricted functions have one basic disadvantage. That is, we must always make one variable arbitrarily dependent on other variables of a function. This choice may not be desirable in some cases. Finally, the *method of* *Lagrange*, which is aimed at answering the same problems solved by the two preceding methods, is the third method that enables us to avoid a choice of independent variables.

The method is as follows. Given $F(x, y, z)$ and $\bar{G}(x, y, z) = 0$ form

$$U = F(x, y, z) - \lambda[G(x, y, z)]$$

where λ is called Lagrange's multiplier. Then solve

$$\frac{\partial U}{\partial x} = 0 \quad \frac{\partial U}{\partial y} = 0 \quad \frac{\partial U}{\partial z} = 0 \quad \frac{\partial U}{\partial \lambda} = 0$$

simultaneously to find the values of four quantities x, y, z, λ. There is a possibility that there might be more than one point which could be found this way. However, the points of extremal values are among the points found by this method.

In the sequel, we find the extremal values of the two previous illustrative examples. Let, again, the utility function and the income constraint be given

$$U = q_1 q_2 q_3$$
$$288 = 2q_1 q_3 + 4q_1 q_2 + 3q_2 q_3.$$

Then

$$U = q_1 q_2 q_3 - \lambda[2q_1 q_3 + 4q_1 q_2 + 3q_2 q_3 - 288],$$

and

$$\frac{\partial U}{\partial q_1} = q_2 q_3 - 2\lambda q_3 - 4\lambda q_2 = 0$$

$$\frac{\partial U}{\partial q_2} = q_1 q_3 - 4\lambda q_1 - 3\lambda q_3 = 0$$

$$\frac{\partial U}{\partial q_3} = q_1 q_2 - 2\lambda q_1 - 3\lambda q_2 = 0$$

$$\frac{\partial U}{\partial \lambda} = 2q_1 q_3 + 4q_1 q_2 + 3q_2 q_3 - 288 = 0$$

the simultaneous solution of which gives $q_1 = 6$, $q_2 = 4$ and $q_3 = 8$.

Also, let $F = 3x^2 - 4x - 6y + z^2 - 2z + 4$ subject to $G = 2x + 4y - 2z + 4 = 0$ be given. Then

$$U = (3x^2 - 4x - 6y + z^2 - 2z + 4) - \lambda[(2x + 4y - 2z + 4)]$$

and

$$\frac{\partial U}{\partial x} = 6x - 4 - 2\lambda = 0$$

$$\frac{\partial U}{\partial y} = -6 - 4\lambda = 0$$

$$\frac{\partial U}{\partial z} = 2z - 2 + 2\lambda = 0$$

$$\frac{\partial U}{\partial \lambda} = 2x + 4y - 2z = 0$$

the simultaneous solution of which gives $x = y = \frac{1}{6}$, $z = \frac{15}{6}$.

Economic Examples of Maxima and Minima.[1] Let us suppose that the demand curve facing a firm and the total cost function associated with that demand are both given and known. Further, suppose that we wish to explore the effect of a tax increase on output. It is obvious that the total profit is equal to total revenue minus total production cost and total tax payment or

(6.3.6) $$\pi = xp(x) - C(x) - tx,$$

where π is the profit, $xp(x)$ is the total revenue, $C(x)$ is the total cost and tx the total tax payment with t as the tax per unit of output. It is clear that $\pi = \pi(x, t)$ where $x = x(t)$.

If we assume that the firm seeks that output for which the profit is to be a maximum, we should have

(6.3.7) $$\frac{\partial \pi(x, t)}{\partial x} = 0,$$

(6.3.8) $$\frac{\partial^2 \pi(x, t)}{\partial x^2} < 0,$$

which are the necessary and sufficient conditions for a maximum. Substituting from (6.3.6) into (6.3.7) we have

$$\frac{\partial}{\partial x} [xp(x) - C(x) - tx] = 0,$$

or

(6.3.9) $$\frac{\partial}{\partial x} [xp(x) - C(x)] - t = 0.$$

Differentiating (6.3.9) with respect to t and using the function of function rule, we have

(6.3.10) $$\frac{\partial^2}{\partial x^2} [xp(x) - C(x)] \left(\frac{\partial x}{\partial t} \right) = 1,$$

or

(6.3.11) $$\left(\frac{\partial x}{\partial t} \right) = \frac{1}{\dfrac{\partial^2}{\partial x^2} [xp(x) - C(x)]}.$$

---

[1] This example is from Samuelson's *Foundations*, pp. 14–16.

On the other hand, the denominator of (6.3.11) must, according to (6.3.8), be negative if the function is to be a maximum, or

$$\frac{\partial^2}{\partial x^2} [xp(x) - C(x)] < 0,$$

therefore,

(6.3.12) $\left(\dfrac{\partial x}{\partial t}\right) < 0,$

which clearly indicates that as the tax per unit of output rises, the output demanded will fall. One could intuitively arrive at this conclusion.

It can be shown[2] that the criterion for a maximum for a function, say $z = f(x, \alpha)$, involving a single variable and a parameter becomes

$$f_{x\alpha} \frac{\partial x}{\partial \alpha} > 0,$$

where $f_{x\alpha} = \dfrac{\partial}{\partial \alpha}\left(\dfrac{\partial z}{\partial x}\right)$. If the profit after tax is shown by

$$\pi = \pi(x, t) = [xp(x) - C(x)] - tx$$

the corresponding criterion for a maximum can be computed easily. Since

$$\frac{\partial \pi}{\partial x} = \frac{\partial}{\partial x} [xp(x) - C(x)] - t,$$

and

$$\frac{\partial}{\partial t}\left(\frac{\partial \pi}{\partial x}\right) = \pi_{xt} = -1,$$

the criterion becomes

$$(-1) \frac{\partial x}{\partial t} > 0,$$

or

$$\frac{\partial x}{\partial t} < 0,$$

which is the same as (6.3.12).

6.4 Homogeneous Functions and Euler's Theorem

Consider the following functions

(1) $X = AL^a K^{1-a}$ (2) $X = \dfrac{LK}{L + K}$

[2] *Ibid.*, pp. 30–33.

(3) $X = AL^2 + BK^2$ (4) $X = 2ALK - BL^2 - CK^2$

(5) $X = (L^2K) \log \left(\dfrac{L}{K}\right).$

We assume that $X = X(L, K)$ in all the functions. On examination, we notice that in all these functions if L is replaced by λL and K by λK, where λ is a parameter, each function is being multiplied by a power of λ. That is

(1) $A(\lambda L)^a (\lambda K)^{1-a} = A\lambda^a L^a \lambda^{1-a} K^{1-a} = \lambda X,$

(2) $\dfrac{(\lambda L)(\lambda K)}{(\lambda L) + (\lambda K)} = \lambda \dfrac{LK}{(L + K)} = \lambda X,$

(3) $A(\lambda L)^2 + B(\lambda K)^2 = \lambda^2 (AL^2 + BK^2) = \lambda^2 X$

(4) $2A(\lambda L)(\lambda K) - B(\lambda L)^2 - C(\lambda K)^2$
$$= \lambda^2 (2ALK - BL^2 - CK^2) = \lambda^2 X,$$

and

(5) $(\lambda L)^2 (\lambda K) \log \dfrac{\lambda L}{\lambda K} = \lambda^3 \left(L^2 K \log \dfrac{L}{K}\right) = \lambda^3 X.$

Formally, we can write

$$\lambda^n X = X(\lambda L, \lambda K).$$

For the first and the second functions $n = 1$. For the third and the fourth functions $n = 2$, and for the last functional equation $n = 3$. All functions which have this interesting property are called *homogeneous of degree* n. Obviously, n is a constant and may be any positive or negative number.

Moreover,

$$\frac{L}{L^2 + K^2}$$

is homogeneous of degree -1 and

$$\frac{L^2 - K^2}{L^2 + K^2}$$

is homogeneous of degree zero. In particular, if $n = 1$ the function is called *linear* and *homogeneous*. (1) and (2) are linear and homogeneous functions. Most functions in economics are *positively homogeneous*, *i.e.*, $n > 0$. In general, if there is a function of n variables $y = f(x_1, x_2, \ldots x_n)$ and if

$$f(\lambda x_1, \ldots \lambda x_n) = \lambda^r f(x_1, \ldots x_n)$$

then $y = f(x_1, \ldots x_n)$ is homogeneous of the rth degree.

Let $X = X(L, K)$ be positively homogeneous of degree n. Further, assume that $\dfrac{\partial X}{\partial L}$, $\dfrac{\partial X}{\partial K}$, $\dfrac{\partial X}{\partial (\lambda L)}$ and $\dfrac{\partial X}{\partial (\lambda K)}$ exist. Then

$$L \frac{\partial X}{\partial L} + K \frac{\partial X}{\partial K} \equiv nX(L, K).$$

This is called the *Euler's Theorem* for a homogeneous function of degree n. In particular, if $n = 1$ we will have

$$L \frac{\partial X}{\partial L} + K \frac{\partial X}{\partial K} \equiv X(L, K)$$

which is the *Euler's Theorem* for a linear homogeneous function.

The proof is as follows: It is obvious that $\dfrac{\partial (\lambda L)}{\partial \lambda} = L$ and $\dfrac{\partial (\lambda K)}{\partial \lambda} = K$. Since $X(\lambda L, \lambda K) = \lambda^n X(L, K)$, then

$$\frac{\partial X(\lambda L, \lambda K)}{\partial \lambda} \equiv \frac{\partial [\lambda^n X(L, K)]}{\partial \lambda} = n\lambda^{n-1} X(L, K).$$

In addition

$$\begin{aligned}
\frac{\partial X(\lambda L, \lambda K)}{\partial \lambda} &= \frac{\partial X(\lambda L, \lambda K)}{\partial (\lambda L)} \frac{\partial (\lambda L)}{\partial \lambda} + \frac{\partial X(\lambda L, \lambda K)}{\partial (\lambda K)} \frac{\partial (\lambda K)}{\partial \lambda} \\
&= \frac{\partial X(\lambda L, \lambda K)}{\partial (\lambda L)} L + \frac{\partial X(\lambda L, \lambda K)}{\partial (\lambda K)} K,
\end{aligned}$$

or

$$n\lambda^{n-1} X(L, K) = \frac{\partial X(\lambda L, \lambda K)}{\partial (\lambda L)} L + \frac{\partial X(\lambda L, \lambda K)}{\partial (\lambda K)} K.$$

If we set $\lambda = 1$, then

$$nX(L, K) \equiv \frac{\partial X}{\partial L} L + \frac{\partial X}{\partial K} K. \qquad\qquad \text{Q.E.D.}$$

Moreover, if $n = 1$, for a linear case, then

$$X(L, K) \equiv \frac{\partial X}{\partial L} L + \frac{\partial X}{\partial K} K.$$

For a linear homogeneous function the following properties, one of which was just proved, are given without proof. Let $z = f(x, y)$:

$$(1) \quad \begin{cases} \dfrac{z}{x} = \phi\left(\dfrac{y}{x}\right); \\[2ex] \dfrac{z}{y} = \psi\left(\dfrac{x}{y}\right); \end{cases}$$

$$(2) \quad \begin{cases} \dfrac{\partial z}{\partial x} = g_1\left(\dfrac{y}{x}\right); \\[2ex] \dfrac{\partial z}{\partial y} = g_2\left(\dfrac{x}{y}\right); \end{cases}$$

$$(3) \quad z \equiv \frac{\partial z}{\partial x}\,x + \frac{\partial z}{\partial y}\,y; \quad \text{Euler's Theorem}$$

$$(4) \quad \begin{cases} \dfrac{\partial^2 z}{\partial x^2} = -\dfrac{y}{x}\dfrac{\partial^2 z}{\partial x\,\partial y}; \\[2ex] \dfrac{\partial^2 z}{\partial y^2} = -\dfrac{x}{y}\dfrac{\partial^2 z}{\partial x\,\partial y}. \end{cases}$$

We pointed out before that no matter how the variables of an identity vary, the derivatives of each side of it will hold. Let us consider the partial derivatives of property (3) with respect to x. We have

$$\frac{\partial}{\partial x}\left(x\frac{\partial z}{\partial x} + y\frac{\partial z}{\partial y}\right) \equiv \frac{\partial z}{\partial x}$$

or

$$\frac{\partial z}{\partial x} + x\frac{\partial^2 z}{\partial x^2} + y\frac{\partial^2 z}{\partial x\,\partial y} \equiv \frac{\partial z}{\partial x}$$

hence

$$\frac{\partial^2 z}{\partial x^2} \equiv -\frac{y}{x}\frac{\partial^2 z}{\partial x\,\partial y},$$

which is the property (4) of a two-variable linear homogeneous function.

It was noted that if for $y = f(x_1, x_2, \ldots x_n)$ there exists

$$f(\lambda x_1, \lambda x_2, \ldots \lambda x_n) = \lambda^r f(x_1, x_2, \ldots x_n),$$

the given function is of degree r. Moreover, it can be shown that

$$x_1\frac{\partial y}{\partial x_1} + x_2\frac{\partial y}{\partial x_2} + \cdots + x_n\frac{\partial y}{\partial x_n} = ry$$

which is an identity.

Thus far we have been concerned with pure mathematics which sometimes appears "dry and dull" to some economists. Let us suppose that a given output x is produced with the aid of n factors $v_1, v_2, \ldots v_n$ so that the production is of the form

(6.4.1) $$x = \varphi(v_1, v_2, \ldots v_n),$$

with the continuous partial derivatives

(6.4.2) $$\frac{\partial x}{\partial v_i} = \frac{\partial \varphi}{\partial v_i} = \varphi_i.$$

The cost that is to be incurred in order to produce x is given by

(6.4.3)
$$C = F + \sum_{i=1}^{n} w_i v_i$$

where C stands for total cost, F for fixed cost and w_i the price of the ith variable factor v_i. It is quite clear that (6.4.1) can be written as

$$\varphi(v_1, v_2, \ldots v_n) - x = 0,$$

or

(6.4.4)
$$\lambda[\varphi(v_1, v_2, \ldots v_n) - x] = 0.$$

If we add (6.4.4) to, or subtract it from, any expression, say (6.4.3), the given expression will not alter in value. We have

(6.4.5)
$$M = F + \sum_{i=1}^{n} w_i v_i - \lambda[\varphi(v_1, v_2, \ldots v_n) - x],$$

which is equivalent to (6.4.3). λ is called the Lagrangean Multiplier. If we wish to minimize cost, indicated by either (6.4.3) or (6.4.5), we must have

$$\frac{\partial M}{\partial v_i} = w_i - \lambda \frac{\partial x}{\partial v_i} = w_i - \lambda \varphi_i = 0,$$

or in general

(6.4.6)
$$w_i = \lambda \frac{\partial x}{\partial v_i} = \lambda \varphi_i.$$

One can deduce from (6.4.6)

$$\lambda = \frac{w_i}{\varphi_i},$$

that is, in equilibrium the price of a factor is proportional to its productivity, and in general

(6.4.7)
$$\lambda = \frac{w_1}{\varphi_1} = \frac{w_2}{\varphi_2} = \cdots = \frac{w_n}{\varphi_n}.$$

This is the well-known economic rule that the price-marginal productivity ratio of all factors, for the production of a given output, must be the same in equilibrium. Or, if the prices of all factors changed *pari passu* in the same direction, factor employment would not be affected; which reveals that with given prices of productive factors and a given level of output, the demand for factors

(6.4.8)
$$v_i = v_i(x, w_1, w_2, \ldots w_n)$$

is homogeneous of zero order, and according to Euler's Theorem we have

(6.4.9)
$$0 \equiv \sum_{i=1}^{n} w_j \frac{\partial v_i}{\partial w_j} \quad (j = 1, 2, \ldots n),$$

and specifically

(6.4.10)
$$\frac{\partial v_i}{\partial w_i} < 0$$

which dictates that as the price of the ith factor changes with the prices of all other factors remaining unchanged, the demand for the ith factor will change in the opposite direction.

On the other hand, from (6.4.5) we have

(6.4.11)
$$\frac{\partial M}{\partial x} = \frac{\partial C}{\partial x} = \lambda.$$

Thus, λ in (6.4.6), (6.4.7) and (6.4.11) is marginal cost or

(6.4.12)
$$w_i = \frac{\partial C}{\partial x} \varphi_i.$$

Also, we are told that under pure competition the price of output is equal to its marginal cost, or

(6.4.13)
$$w_i = p\varphi_i.$$

This last expression is the law of productivity under pure competition; *i.e.*, the price of a factor, under pure competition, is equal to the value of marginal product. We shall use (6.4.13) immediately in the succeeding section.

6.5 Income Distribution Model

We have continued to claim that mathematical economics has much to contribute to the refinement of implications and the clarification of assumptions. The productivity theory of distribution, which is a lineal descendant of the older theories of productivity of capital by the application of the productivity of different factors, bears the stamp of the mathematical method. J. B. Clark hailed the theory as a newly discovered "law of nature"; the law which prescribes to each according to his productivity, that the rule of competition gives "to each factor of production the equivalent of what it creates."

Although few economists today take the marginal productivity theory of distribution as a "natural law," a significant number of economists would subscribe to the view enunciated in the preceding paragraph. Nevertheless, if a theory of distribution is to *explain* the origin of the distributive shares, a fundamental question which preoccupied Ricardo all through his writings, it would hardly be incorrect to say that modern economics contains no theory of distribution worthy of the name if one wishes reluctantly to disregard Kaldor's Keynesian theory of distribution described in Chapter 3.

In order to refine the implications and clarify the assumptions of the productivity theory of distribution, let us suppose that total output is produced with two homogeneous factors,

(6.5.1) $$X(N, K).$$

National income is, then, divided into the returns to labor and capital or

(6.5.2) $$Y \equiv W + P,$$

and

$$W = Nw,$$
$$P = K\pi,$$

where

$$Y = \text{national income,}$$
$$W = \text{wage-bill}$$
$$P = \text{returns to capital,}$$
$$N = \text{labor force,}$$
$$K = \text{stock of capital,}$$
$$w = \text{money wage rate,}$$
$$\pi = \text{the rate of profit.}$$

According to the marginal productivity theory of distribution, the price of a factor of production (whether land, labor, or capital) is equal, under pure competition, to the value of the marginal product, a result which was deduced in the last paragraph of Section 6.4, or

(6.5.3) $$w = p \frac{\partial X}{\partial N},$$

(6.5.4) $$\pi = p \frac{\partial X}{\partial K},$$

where p is the price of the output, and

$$\frac{\partial X}{\partial N} = \text{marginal product with respect to labor,}$$

$$\frac{\partial X}{\partial K} = \text{marginal product with respect to capital.}$$

On substitution, we have $\quad W = pN \dfrac{\partial X}{\partial N},$

$$P = pK \frac{\partial X}{\partial K},$$

and

(6.5.5)
$$Y \equiv pN \frac{\partial X}{\partial N} + pK \frac{\partial X}{\partial K},$$

or

$$Y \equiv p \left(N \frac{\partial X}{\partial N} + K \frac{\partial X}{\partial K} \right),$$

therefore

$$\frac{Y}{p} = X \equiv N \frac{\partial X}{\partial N} + K \frac{\partial X}{\partial K}$$

which is Euler's theorem for two independent variables and indicates that $X = X(N, K)$ is a linear homogeneous function.

In mathematical economics, a linear homogeneous production function is erected on the assumption of constant returns to scale so that total output is being exhausted between inputs. An expression which is deduced from an identity (or if an identity is derived from an expression) can hardly claim that it would *explain* a given phenomenon. And as Marshall hastened to point out, the marginal productivity theory could not constitute a theory of distribution since it left unanswered the problem as to the nature and determination of the distributive shares.

What is instructive, and we should make a note of it, is that the theory of marginal productivity has been used as an answer to the type of problem to which Ricardo's theory of rent was framed as an answer and hence as a refutation, or at least a sufficient substitute for the latter. Wicksteed, who traced so much of the mathematical refinement of the theory, tried very hard to demonstrate that any concept of "residual" or surplus-value is untenable. Wicksteed pointed out that the Ricardian theory of rent, expressed in mathematical terms, states that "the whole produce being $F(x)$, and $F'(x)$ being the rate of remuneration per unit which satisfied capital-plus-labor, the whole amount which capital-plus-labor will draw out will be rent. Now this is simply a statement that when all other factors of production have been paid off, the 'surplus' or residuum can be claimed by the landowner."[3]

If $Y = W + P + R$ defines the distribution of national income among the factors of production, and if $W + P$ is given by exogenous elements, rent, R, would be the difference between national income and $W + P$. Wicksteed, on the same line of reasoning, suggested that the price of labor or of capital can be subjected to the same rule. If this is the case, he said, it is all an arbitrary matter of taking some factor as "given" and another factor as residual. So the advocates of the marginal productivity theory declared that each factor must receive according to its productivity. But if each factor is to receive a share equal to the value of its marginal product, the economy, as we have shown, must operate

---

[3] P. H. Wicksteed, *Coordination of the Laws of Production and Distribution*, pp. 17–18.

under constant returns to scale which is the case of a stationary economy. Then, what Wicksteed failed to emphasize, apparently was the fact that the conditions surrounding stationary constant returns to scale is different from the ones embodying a growing economy subject to increasing returns to scale.

If mathematical technique is to retain its applicability, it must reveal rather than veil reality; it must, to repeat, contribute to the refinement of implications and the clarification of assumptions.

EXERCISES 6

1. Find $\dfrac{\partial z}{\partial x}, \dfrac{\partial z}{\partial y}, \dfrac{\partial^2 z}{\partial x\, \partial y}, \dfrac{\partial^2 z}{\partial y\, \partial x}, \dfrac{\partial^2 z}{\partial x^2}$ and $\dfrac{\partial^2 z}{\partial y^2}$ of the following functions:

$z = 13 + 2x^2 - 3y^3$. $\qquad\qquad$ $z = 2x^3 + 5x^2y$.

$z = x^2y^3 - 3xy^2 + 2x^2y + y^2 - 5x^4$.

$z = e^x \sin y$. $\qquad\qquad$ $z = 2xe^{3x} \cos 3y$.

$z = \log\sqrt{2x^2 - 3y^2}$. $\qquad\qquad$ $z = xe^{-y^2} \cos x^2$.

$z = e^{2y}(\cos^2 x + \sin^2 x)$. $\qquad\qquad$ $z = y \sin x + 2xe^{3y}$.

$z = x^2 e^{-3y^2} + y \log(\sin y - \csc x)$.

2. Find the maximum or minimum values of each of the following functions of two variables. Which ones have max. or min. in all directions?

$z = 2x^2 + 5x + 4y + 5$. $\qquad$ $z = x^2 - 4x - 2y^2 + y - 5$.

$z = 6x - 1 + 12y - 3x^2 + 4y^2$. $\quad$ $z = 3x^2 - 5xy + 6y^2 - x + 3y - 5$,

$z = 2y^2 - 3xy + 5x - 3y + 2x^2 + 3$.

$z = 4x^2 - 3xy - 4y^2 - 2x + 3y$. $\quad$ $z = 3 - (x + 2)^2 - (y - 3)^2$.

$z = x^2 - 2y^2 - 3x + 5y - 7$.

3. Find the equation of the tangent plane to each of the following surfaces at the point indicated.

$$2x^2 + 3y^2 - z^2 = 6 \text{ at } (2, 0, -2).$$
$$\tfrac{1}{2}x^2 + \tfrac{1}{4}y^2 + \tfrac{1}{4}z^2 = 0 \text{ at } (-1, 3, 2).$$
$$x - 4x^2 + 3y + z = 0 \text{ at } (2, 1, 5).$$
$$x^2 + y^2 - z^2 + 2y = 0 \text{ at } (3, 2, 4).$$
$$3x + 2x^2 + y - 4y^2 + z - z^2 - 5 = 0 \text{ at } (2, -3, 4).$$

4. Let $F(x, y)$ be positively homogeneous of the nth degree and assume that $F, \dfrac{\partial F}{\partial x}, \dfrac{\partial F}{\partial y}$ are differentiable, show that

$$x^2 \frac{\partial^2 F}{\partial x^2} + 2xy \frac{\partial^2 F}{\partial x\, \partial y} + y^2 \frac{\partial^2 F}{\partial y^2} = n(n - 1)F(x, y).$$

Show the result for third and fourth derivatives.

5. If $F(x, y)$ is positively homogeneous of degree r, and differentiable, show that its first partial derivatives are positively homogeneous of degree $(r - 1)$. Generalize this result to the case when $y = y(x_1, x_2, \ldots x_n)$.

6. Let us suppose that a firm is producing a given homogeneous product with three factors x, y, z and that its budget constraint is $250 = 4x + 3y + 6z$ and its output is given by $Q = 3xyz$. For what amounts of inputs can the firm maximize its output while not violating the budget constraint? Use the method of Lagrange.

7. We stated in the text that there might be more than one restricting equation. For what values of x, y, z will $F(x, y, z) = 2x^2 + 3y^2 + 2z^2$ be a maximum if it is restricted by $2x - 3y + 5z = 0$ and

$$\frac{x^2}{2} + 3y^2 - \frac{z^2}{6} = 1?$$

Use the method of Lagrange.

8. For what values of x, y, z will

$$\frac{3xyz}{3x + 4y + 6z}$$

be a maximum? The function is subject to the following conditions:

$$x, y, z > 0,$$
$$xyz = 8.$$

(Use the method of Lagrange.)

9. Solve the problems in Exercises 6, 7, and 8 by the method of direct elimination.

10. Solve the problems posed in Exercises 6, 7, and 8 by the method of implicit functions.

7 DIFFERENTIALS AND DIFFERENTIATION IN ECONOMICS

7.1 The Variation and Differential of Two or More Variables

We have noticed that for a linear relation $y = f(x)$ we could write

(7.1.1)
$$\frac{\Delta y}{\Delta x} = \frac{dy}{dx},$$

or

$$\Delta y = \frac{dy}{dx} \cdot \Delta x.$$

This is true for the derivative of a linear function, measuring the slope of the function which is constant for all values of the independent variable; the same as the ratio of increments. For nonlinear functions, on the other hand, the rate of increments is approximately equal to the derivative of the function. However, we gathered from the definition of derivatives that as Δx approaches zero, the difference between the derivative and the rate of increments narrows down, or at any point we have exactly

(7.1.2)
$$\frac{\Delta y}{\Delta x} = \frac{dy}{dx} + e,$$

where e is the possible error between the derivative and the rate of increments. We can rearrange (7.1.2) and write

(7.1.3)
$$\Delta y = \frac{dy}{dx} \cdot \Delta x + (e \cdot \Delta x).$$

Since e depends on Δx, for sufficiently small values of Δx, the term $(e \cdot \Delta x)$ becomes very small and negligible. Thus, for sufficiently small values of Δx of a nonlinear function we may have

(7.1.4) $$\Delta y = \frac{dy}{dx} \cdot \Delta x.$$

If the increment of each variable is called *differential* and is shown by $\Delta y = dy$ and $\Delta x = dx$, (7.1.4) can be rewritten approximately

(7.1.5) $$dy = \frac{dy}{dx} \, dx.$$

Now let us suppose that $z = f(x, y)$ is given and that z and all its partial derivatives are continuous functions. If Δx and Δy are given increments of x and y, the resulting increment of z is

(7.1.6) $$\Delta z = f(x + \Delta x, y + \Delta y) - f(x, y).$$

By analogy with the function of one variable, we may write

$$\frac{\Delta_x z}{\Delta x} = \frac{\partial z}{\partial x} + e_1,$$

and

$$\frac{\Delta_y z}{\Delta y} = \frac{\partial z}{\partial y} + e_2.$$

Or

$$\Delta_x z = \left(\frac{\partial z}{\partial x} + e_1\right) \Delta x,$$

and

$$\Delta_y z = \left(\frac{\partial z}{\partial y} + e_2\right) \Delta y.$$

Since

$$\Delta z = \Delta_x z + \Delta_y z,$$

then

(7.1.7) $$\Delta z = \frac{\partial z}{\partial x} \cdot \Delta x + \frac{\partial z}{\partial y} \cdot \Delta y + e_1 \cdot \Delta x + e_2 \cdot \Delta y.$$

However, if we take a mental note of the fact that e_1 and e_2 depend on Δx and Δy for sufficiently small values of Δx and Δy, the two terms $(e_1 \cdot \Delta x)$ and $(e_2 \cdot \Delta y)$ become extremely small. Hence, the remaining two terms of z may be used to approximate the change in z. If we put $\Delta z = dz$ and call it the differential of z, $\Delta y = dy$ and name it the differential of y and $\Delta x = dx$ and refer to it as the differential of x, expression (7.1.7) can be converted into the following neat form:

(7.1.8) $$dz = \frac{\partial z}{\partial x} \, dx + \frac{\partial z}{\partial y} \, dy$$

which represents the *approximate change* or *error in z* for given changes or errors in x and y.

Since the partial derivatives and increments are readily combined to give approximate changes in the function of two variables, (7.1.8) is a useful formula. As dx and dy are increments, we have,

$$d_x z = \frac{\partial z}{\partial x}\, dx,$$

$$d_y z = \frac{\partial z}{\partial y}\, dy,$$

where $d_x z$ and $d_y z$ represent the *partial differentials* of z with respect to x and y respectively. We notice that dz becomes $d_x z$ when $dy = 0$, and it becomes $d_y z$ if $dx = 0$. Therefore the differential of z is the sum of the partial differentials of z with respect to each x and y.

The process of obtaining the differentials, small increments, of a function is called *differentiation*. The most obvious method of differentiating a function, such as $z = f(x, y)$, is to evaluate the partial derivatives of the function and substitute those partial derivatives in the fundamental expression

$$dz = \frac{\partial z}{\partial x}\, dx + \frac{\partial z}{\partial y}\, dy.$$

The expressions for Δz and dz are readily extended to the cases of three or more variables. Hence if $y = f(x_1, x_2, \ldots x_n)$, by the same line of reasoning given for two variables, we have

$$\Delta y = \frac{\partial y}{\partial x_1}\, \Delta x_1 + \frac{\partial y}{\partial x_2}\, \Delta x_2 + \cdots + \frac{\partial y}{\partial x_n}\, \Delta x_n$$
$$+ e_1 \cdot \Delta x_1 + e_2 \cdot \Delta x_2 + \cdots + e_n \cdot \Delta x_n,$$

and the differential of y is defined as

$$dy = \frac{\partial y}{\partial x_1}\, dx_1 + \frac{\partial y}{\partial x_2}\, dx_2 + \cdots + \frac{\partial y}{\partial x_n}\, dx_n,$$

and is used to measure approximately the value of Δy, just as dz was used to measure Δz.

For the production function $X = X(N, K)$ a change in output is measured by

$$dX = \frac{\partial X}{\partial N}\, dN + \frac{\partial X}{\partial K}\, dK,$$

and the differential of $z = x^2 + 2xy + y^2$ is

$$dz = (2x + 2y)\, dx + (2x + 2y)\, dy$$

since

$$\frac{\partial z}{\partial x} = (2x + 2y) \qquad \text{and} \qquad \frac{\partial z}{\partial y} = (2x + 2y).$$

The Derivative of $z = f(x, y)$ with Respect to Some Other Variable. Thus far we have been considering the case where x and y of $z = f(x, y)$ were two independent variables. x and y are often related to each other or another variable somehow. Under these conditions, the result of differentiation changes slightly. If, for instance, one desires to find the rate of change of z with respect to some other variable, say, t, one must obviously presuppose that $x = \phi(t)$ and $y = \psi(t)$ and that $\dfrac{dx}{dt}$ and $\dfrac{dy}{dt}$ exist. If so

$$\frac{dz}{dt} = \lim_{\Delta t \to 0} \left(\frac{\partial z}{\partial x} \frac{\Delta x}{\Delta t} + \frac{\partial z}{\partial y} \frac{\Delta y}{\Delta t} + e_1 \frac{\Delta x}{\Delta t} + e_2 \frac{\Delta y}{\Delta t} \right)$$

or

(7.1.9)
$$\frac{dz}{dt} = \frac{\partial z}{\partial x} \frac{dx}{dt} + \frac{\partial z}{\partial y} \frac{dy}{dt},$$

where Δx and Δy approach zero as a limit as $\Delta t \to 0$, and whence e_1 and $e_2 \to 0$. Of course, a short-cut method for writing (7.1.9) is to write the complete differential of $z = f(x, y)$

$$dz = \frac{\partial z}{\partial x} dx + \frac{\partial z}{\partial y} dy$$

and then divide both sides of it by dt to obtain (7.1.9).

In general, if $y = f(x_1, x_2, \ldots x_n)$ and if $x_1 = f_1(t)$, $x_2 = f_2(t)$, $\ldots x_n = f_n(t)$, the derivative of y with respect to t is given by

$$\frac{dy}{dt} = \frac{\partial y}{\partial x_1} \frac{dx_1}{dt} + \frac{\partial y}{\partial x_2} \frac{dx_2}{dt} + \cdots + \frac{\partial y}{\partial x_n} \frac{dx_n}{dt}.$$

As the reader notices, we are treating the ratio of differentials as the derivative of two variables.

If $z = f(x, y)$ so that $y = g(x)$, and if $\dfrac{dy}{dx}$ exists so that z is a continuous function of x alone, we may find the rate of change of z with respect to x as in the previous case, that is:

$$\frac{dz}{dx} = \lim_{\Delta x \to 0} \frac{\Delta z}{\Delta x} = \lim_{\Delta x \to 0} \left(\frac{\partial z}{\partial x} \frac{\Delta x}{\Delta x} + \frac{\partial z}{\partial y} \frac{\Delta y}{\Delta x} + e_1 \frac{\Delta x}{\Delta x} + e_2 \frac{\Delta y}{\Delta x} \right).$$

Thus, if Δy, e_1 and $e_2 \to 0$ when $\Delta x \to 0$ we have

(7.1.10)
$$\frac{dz}{dx} = \frac{\partial z}{\partial x} + \frac{\partial z}{\partial y} \frac{dy}{dx},$$

which is again as though we divided both sides of the complete differential of $z = f(x, y)$ by dx to get (7.1.10). Likewise, by considering $z = f(x, y)$

and $x = h(y)$ so that z being a continuous function of y alone, we get

$$\frac{dz}{dy} = \frac{\partial z}{\partial x} \frac{dx}{dy} + \frac{\partial z}{\partial y}.$$

Another situation is where z is a continuous function of, say, u and v such that

$$z = f(x, y), \quad x = \phi(u, v) \text{ and } y = \psi(u, v).$$

We have

$$dz = \frac{\partial z}{\partial x} dx + \frac{\partial z}{\partial y} dy,$$

$$dx = \frac{\partial x}{\partial u} du + \frac{\partial x}{\partial v} dv,$$

$$dy = \frac{\partial y}{\partial u} du + \frac{\partial y}{\partial v} dv,$$

or

$$dz = \frac{\partial z}{\partial x} \left(\frac{\partial z}{\partial u} du + \frac{\partial z}{\partial v} dv \right) + \frac{\partial z}{\partial y} \left(\frac{\partial y}{\partial u} du + \frac{\partial y}{\partial v} dv \right),$$

and by rearranging for du and dv, we have

$$dz = \left(\frac{\partial z}{\partial x} \frac{\partial x}{\partial u} + \frac{\partial z}{\partial y} \frac{\partial y}{\partial u} \right) du + \left(\frac{\partial z}{\partial x} \frac{\partial x}{\partial v} + \frac{\partial z}{\partial y} \frac{\partial y}{\partial v} \right) dv.$$

If we desire the partial of z with respect to u, since dv would be zero, we ought to have

$$\frac{\partial z}{\partial u} = \frac{\partial z}{\partial x} \frac{\partial x}{\partial u} + \frac{\partial z}{\partial y} \frac{\partial y}{\partial u}.$$

Similarly, the partial derivative of z with respect to v, since du has to be zero, must be

$$\frac{\partial z}{\partial v} = \frac{\partial z}{\partial x} \frac{\partial x}{\partial v} + \frac{\partial z}{\partial y} \frac{\partial y}{\partial v}.$$

The Differential of a Partial. Let us suppose that $z = f(x, y)$ and the partials of z with respect to x and y exist. Of course, since $\dfrac{\partial z}{\partial x} = g_1(x, y)$ and $\dfrac{\partial z}{\partial y} = g_2(x, y)$, the differential of a partial is given by

$$d\left(\frac{\partial z}{\partial x} \right) = \frac{\partial}{\partial x} \left(\frac{\partial z}{\partial x} \right) dx + \frac{\partial}{\partial y} \left(\frac{\partial z}{\partial x} \right) dy,$$

$$= \frac{\partial^2 z}{\partial x^2} dx + \frac{\partial^2 z}{\partial y \partial x} dy.$$

Also,

$$d\left(\frac{\partial z}{\partial y} \right) = \frac{\partial}{\partial x} \left(\frac{\partial z}{\partial y} \right) dx + \frac{\partial}{\partial y} \left(\frac{\partial z}{\partial y} \right) dy,$$

$$= \frac{\partial^2 z}{\partial x \partial y} dx + \frac{\partial^2 z}{\partial y^2} dy.$$

7.2 The Rules of Differentiation

The rules of differentiation are exactly the same as those for derivatives. We give the following rules because they are often used and are significant in economics.

(1) The differential of the sum (or difference) of two (or more) variables is the sum (or difference) of the individual variables:

$$d(u \pm v) = du \pm dv.$$

(2) The differential of the product of two (or more) variables is the sum of the first variable times the differential of the second variable and the product of the second variable times the differential of the first variable:

$$d(uv) = u\,dv + v\,du.$$

Utilizing this rule, we can write the differential of a differential. Specifically, for $z = f(x, y)$ we have

$$dz = \frac{\partial z}{\partial x}\,dx + \frac{\partial z}{\partial y}\,dy,$$

then

$$d(dz) = d^2 z = d\left(\frac{\partial z}{\partial x}\,dx + \frac{\partial z}{\partial y}\,dy\right)$$

$$= d\left(\frac{\partial z}{\partial x}\right)dx + d\left(\frac{\partial z}{\partial y}\right)dy$$

$$= \left\{\frac{\partial}{\partial x}\left(\frac{\partial z}{\partial x}\right)dx + \frac{\partial}{\partial y}\left(\frac{\partial z}{\partial x}\right)dy\right\}dx$$

$$+ \left\{\frac{\partial}{\partial x}\left(\frac{\partial z}{\partial y}\right)dx + \frac{\partial}{\partial y}\left(\frac{\partial z}{\partial y}\right)dy\right\}dy,$$

or

$$d^2 z = \frac{\partial^2 z}{\partial x^2}\,dx^2 + 2\frac{\partial^2 z}{\partial x\,\partial y}\,dx \cdot dy + \frac{\partial^2 z}{\partial y^2}\,dy^2,$$

where x and y are two independent variables.

(3) The differential of a quotient is exactly similar to the derivative of a quotient:

$$d\left(\frac{u}{v}\right) = \frac{v\,du - u\,dv}{v^2}.$$

(4) The differential of a power function u^n is given by

$$d(u^n) = nu^{n-1}\,du.$$

(5) The differential of an exponential function e^u is the product of the exponential function and the differential of the index of the function:

$$d(e^u) = e^u\,du.$$

(6) The differential of a logarithm, log u, is the product of the reciprocal of the variable and the differential of the variable:

$$d(\log u) = \frac{1}{u}\, du.$$

Economic Examples. So far we have been in our mathematical whirlpool. Now, we may apply the tool to economics. There is a "general proposition" which Professor Hicks "overlooked" in the first edition of his book *Value and Capital* but later added to Chapter III pp. 51–2 of the second edition of that book. Consequently, he made certain adjustments in other chapters. According to Hicks, the proposition is important because it "is probably the ultimate generalization of the theory of demand, since it relates, not to a particular price change, but to any change in the system of prices confronting a consumer. Any such price-change will set up an income effect and a substitution effect; about the income effect nothing in general can be said, but there is something to be said in general about the substitution effect." In Professor Hicks' words, the proposition is as follows: "When we consider a change in prices, which is such that it leaves the consumer on the same indifference level, we can always say that the new collection of goods purchased must have a higher value in terms of the old prices than the old collection had. For the old collection was the only collection of goods on this indifference level which was available to him at the old prices. Similarly the old collection of goods must have a higher value in terms of the new prices than the new collection of goods has.

"It follows from the first of these inequalities that the sum of the increments in amounts purchased (due attention being paid to sign) must be positive when valued at the old prices. It follows from the second inequality that the sum of the same increments, valued at the new prices, must be negative. These two statements can only be consistent with one another if the sum of the increments, valued at the *increment* of the corresponding price in each case, is negative. This is the sense in which the most generalized change in prices must set up a change in demands in the opposite direction."

The mathematical translation of the proposition is as follows. Let us suppose that there are two goods and such that the old collection of goods are x_1 and x_2 with their respective prices p_1 and p_2. The new collection of goods are x_1' and x_2' with their prices p_1' and p_2'. According to the first part of the proposition, "the new collection of goods purchased must have a higher value in terms of the old prices than the old collection of goods had." Or

(7.2.1) $$x_1'p_1 + x_2'p_2 > x_1p_1 + x_2p_2.$$

And according to the second part of the proposition, we have

(7.2.2) $$x_1p_1' + x_2p_2' > x_1'p_1' + x_2'p_2'.$$

From (7.2.1) we get

$$(x_1' - x_1)p_1 + (x_2' - x_2)p_2 > 0,$$

or

(7.2.3) $$\Delta x_1 p_1 + \Delta x_2 p_2 > 0.$$

From (7.2.2) we obtain

$$(x_1' - x_1)p_1' + (x_2' - x_2)p_2' < 0,$$

or

(7.2.4) $$\Delta x_1 p_1' + \Delta x_2 p_2' < 0.$$

If we multiply (7.2.3) by (-1) and add it to (7.2.4), we have

$$\Delta x_i \, \Delta p_i < 0.$$

Let us call Δx_i and Δp_i the differential of x and p and denote them by dx and dp so as to have

$$dx \cdot dp < 0,$$

which is the law of demand.

The determination of marginal cost can be another example for using the differentials. Let us suppose, as we did in Chapter 6, that the demand for the productive factors necessary for the production of output x is given by

(7.2.5) $$x = \varphi(v_1, v_2, \ldots v_n),$$

and the cost for undertaking the production is given by

(7.2.6) $$C = F + \sum_{i=2}^{n} w_i v_i,$$

where w_i is the price of the ith input and is assumed to be fixed. Further, we assume that the partials of (7.2.5) exist and are continuous and shown by φ_i for the ith factor. According to the method of the Lagrangean Multiplier, which we mentioned in Chapter 6, we have

$$M = F + \sum_{i=1}^{n} w_i v_i - \lambda[\varphi(v_1, v_2, \ldots v_n) - x].$$

If we are to minimize the cost, we should have

$$\frac{\partial M}{\partial v_i} = w_i - \lambda \varphi_i = 0,$$

or

(7.2.7) $$w_i = \lambda \varphi_i$$

where λ is the marginal cost. Why? The proof follows. Utilizing rule (2) of differentiation, the differentials of (7.2.6) and (7.2.5) will be respectively

$$dC = \sum_{i=1}^{n} w_i \, dv_i,$$

and

$$dx = \sum_{i=1}^{n} \varphi_i \, dv_i.$$

Dividing the first by the second expression we have

(7.2.8)
$$\frac{dC}{dx} = \frac{\displaystyle\sum_{i=1}^{n} w_i \, dv_i}{\displaystyle\sum_{i=1}^{n} \varphi_i \, dv_i}.$$

Substituting from (7.2.7) into (7.2.8) we have

(7.2.9)
$$\frac{dC}{dx} = \frac{\displaystyle\sum_{i=1}^{n} \lambda\varphi_i \, dv_i}{\displaystyle\sum_{i=1}^{n} \varphi_i \, dv_i} = \lambda,$$

which completes the proof.[1]

7.3 Differentiation of Implicit Functions

Let us suppose that we have the following implicit function

$$f(x, y) = 0,$$

where x is a multi-valued function of y and y is a multi-valued function of x. If we assume that $z = 0$, from which we get

$$dz = 0,$$

we can also write

(7.3.1)
$$f(x, y) = z = 0.$$

The differential of (7.3.1) is

$$dz = \frac{\partial z}{\partial x} \, dx + \frac{\partial z}{\partial y} \, dy = 0,$$

or

$$\frac{dy}{dx} = -\frac{\dfrac{\partial z}{\partial x}}{\dfrac{\partial z}{\partial y}},$$

---

[1] For a more rigorous proof, see Samuelson's *Foundations*, 64–68.

where the ratios of the differentials $\dfrac{dy}{dx}$ and $\dfrac{dx}{dy}$ are to be interpreted as the derivatives of y with respect to x and x with respect to y respectively. The implicit function $f(x, y) = 0$ gives y as a function of x with derivative $\dfrac{dy}{dx} = -\dfrac{f_x}{f_y}$ at the point (x, y); and it gives x as a function of y with derivative $\dfrac{dx}{dy} = -\dfrac{f_y}{f_x}$, where

$$f_x = \frac{\partial z}{\partial x},$$

and

$$f_y = \frac{\partial z}{\partial y}.$$

A very interesting example of the differentiation of implicit functions in economics is seen in Samuelson's income determination model.[2]

In a closed economy, the value of net national income is composed of the value of goods for domestic consumption and net private investment. Thus, by definition

(7.3.2) $Y = C + I.$

This equation by itself is indeterminate because there are two unknowns (C, I) and only one equation. Therefore Keynes wrote

$$C = C(Y)$$
$$I = \bar{I}$$

which indicate that consumption is a function of income and investment is made autonomous of income change. With these changes, (7.3.2) can be rewritten

(7.3.3) $Y = C(Y) + \bar{I}$

where $Y = Y(I)$ and the extent of dependence is measured by the value of the multiplier.

Equation (7.3.3) can be rearranged and made into an implicit function

(7.3.4) $F[Y - C(Y) - I] = 0.$

Now, according to the rules of implicit differentiation we have

$$\frac{dY}{dI} = -\frac{\dfrac{\partial}{\partial I}[Y - C(Y) - I]}{\dfrac{\partial}{\partial Y}[Y - C(Y) - I]},$$

---

[2] P. A. Samuelson "Simple Mathematics of Income Determination," in *Income, Employment and Public Policy: Essays in Honor of Alvin H. Hansen*, pp. 133–155.

or

(7.3.5)
$$\frac{dY}{dI} = \frac{1}{1 - C'(Y)},$$

since

$$\frac{\partial}{\partial I}[Y - C(Y) - I] = -1,$$

and

$$\frac{\partial}{\partial Y}[Y - C(Y) - I] = 1 - C'(Y)$$

where

$$C'(Y) = \frac{dC}{dY}$$

and is the value of the marginal propensity to consume. Then, by taking dY and dI as the differentials of income and investment, we have

(7.3.6)
$$dY = \frac{1}{1 - C'(Y)} \, dI.$$

That is, "investment dollars are high-powered dollars." The larger the value of the marginal propensity to consume, the greater the value of the multiplier, which is $\dfrac{1}{1 - C'(Y)}$, and hence more powerful investment dollars.

Next, we assume that $I = I(Y)$ so that

$$Y = C(Y) + I(Y),$$

and if we approximate the consumption function by a linear function of the form

$$C(Y) = \alpha + \beta Y$$

where α is the intercept representing fixed minimal consumption without income and $\beta = \dfrac{dC}{dY}$ known as the marginal propensity to consume, we can write

(7.3.7)
$$Y = \alpha + \beta Y + I(Y).$$

Let us transform (7.3.7) into an implicit function

(7.3.8)
$$F[Y - \alpha - \beta Y - I(Y)] = 0$$

and, according to the rule of differentials, have

$$\frac{dY}{d\alpha} = -\frac{\dfrac{\partial}{\partial \alpha}[Y - \alpha - \beta Y - I(Y)]}{\dfrac{\partial}{\partial Y}[Y - \alpha - \beta Y - I(Y)]},$$

or

$$\frac{dY}{d\alpha} = \frac{1}{1 - \dfrac{dC}{dY} - \dfrac{dI}{dY}}$$

since

$$\frac{\partial}{\partial \alpha} [Y - \alpha - \beta Y - I(Y)] = -1$$

and

$$\frac{\partial}{\partial Y} [Y - \alpha - \beta Y - I(Y)] = 1 - \beta - \frac{dI}{dY}$$

$$= 1 - \frac{dC}{dY} - \frac{dI}{dY}.$$

Then, by taking dY and $d\alpha$ as the differentials of income and shift parameter α, we have

(7.3.9)
$$dY = \frac{1}{1 - \dfrac{dC}{dY} - \dfrac{dI}{dY}} \, d\alpha.$$

That is, an autonomous change in either consumption or investment schedules will change income.

So far government taxes and expenditures have been disregarded. In a closed economy, the value of net national product is equal to

(7.3.10)
$$Y = C + I + G$$

where

$G = \overline{G}$:   aggregate government expenditures and net of relief and transfer payments,

$I = \overline{I}$:   private investment and net of depreciation,

$W = \overline{W}$:   taxes,

$C = C(Y - \overline{W})$:   consumption is a function of the disposable income, or

(7.3.11)
$$Y = C(Y - \overline{W}) + \overline{I} + \overline{G}$$

to make (7.3.10) determinate. An implicit function of (7.3.11) is

(7.3.12)
$$F[Y - C(Y - \overline{W}) - \overline{I} - \overline{G}] = 0.$$

According to the rule of differentials of implicit functions we have

$$\frac{dY}{dG} = \frac{dY}{dI} = \frac{1}{1 - C'(Y - W)}$$

since

$$\frac{\partial}{\partial I} [Y - C(Y - W) - I - G] = -1,$$

$$\frac{\partial}{\partial G} [Y - C(Y - W) - I - G] = -1,$$

and

$$\frac{\partial}{\partial Y} [Y - C(Y - W) - I - G] = 1 - C'(Y - W)$$

where $C'(Y - W)$ is the marginal propensity to consume for disposable income. If dY, dI, and dG are regarded as the differentials of income, investment, and government expenditures, we can write

(7.3.13) $dY = \dfrac{1}{1 - C'(Y - W)} dG = \dfrac{1}{1 - C'(Y - W)} dI.$

In other words, Samuelson says, "government expenditure has the same favorable effect on income as does private investment; both effects being equal to the reciprocal of the marginal propensity to save out of disposable income."

Finally, we wish to explore the case where the economy is open for foreign trade. Here we are examining the value of multiplier in the case of international trade. According to the definition of national income account, we have

(7.3.14) $Y = C(Y) + I + X$

where

C = value of consumption goods produced domestically,

X = value of exports,

M = value of foreign produced consumption goods.

By adding M to and subtracting it from the right hand side of equation (7.3.14), we have

(7.3.15) $Y = C(Y) + M(Y) + I + (X - M).$

If it is assumed that I and $(X - M)$ are autonomous, (7.3.15) would be determinate and its implicit function will be

$$F[Y - C(Y) - M(Y) - I - (X - M)] = 0$$

and according to the rule of the differentials of implicit functions we have

$$\frac{dY}{\cdot} = \frac{dY}{(X - M)} = \frac{1}{1 - C'(Y) - M'(Y)}$$

since

$$\frac{\partial F}{\partial I} = -1,$$

$$\frac{\partial F}{\partial Y} = 1 - C'(Y) - M'(Y),$$

$$\frac{\partial F}{\partial(X - M)} = -1.$$

If we take dY, dI, and $d(X - M)$ as the differentials of income, investment, and "net foreign investment," we have

$$dY = \frac{1}{1 - C'(Y) - M'(Y)} \, dI = \frac{1}{1 - C'(Y) - M'(Y)} \, d(X - M).$$

Thus, the influence of the "net foreign investment" on national income is as effective as the private domestic investment.

7.4 The Neo-Classical Growth Model

On the relation of capital accumulation to economic growth, Professor Hicks, at the Corfu Conference on economic growth and capital accumulation, expressed his doubts about the "maintenance of the neo-classical assumption of constant returns to scale." The assumption of a linear homogeneous production function, he added, "is a weakness that runs right through linear programming, when it is lifted up from the 'micro' level, where it does such good work, and applied to the 'macro' problems of the economy as a whole. In the days of marginal productivity we needed a constant-returns-to-scale assumption in order to make it possible for the factors to get their marginal products; but how do we know that the factors do get their marginal products? For my own part I find it hard to believe that increasing returns and growth by capital accumulation are not tied very closely together. . . . If one assumes a production function with increasing returns to scale, the marginal productivity theory goes by the board."[3]

Under pure competition where factor payments are equal to the value of their marginal products, constant returns to scale is consequential.[4] The condition

(7.4.1) $$w = p \, \frac{\partial Q}{\partial N}$$

presupposes the neo-classical production function

(7.4.2) $$Q = Q(N, K),$$

---

[3] "Thoughts on the Theory of Capital — the Corfu Conference, "*Oxford Economic Papers*, June 1960, pp. 128–29.

[4] See pp. 151–152. It should be noted in passing that the assumption of constant returns to scale implies the rule of pure competition where factor payments are equal to the value of their marginal products.

where w is the money wage rate, p the price of output, Q is output depending on inputs labor, N, and capital, K.[5] The partial derivatives of Q with respect to N and K are the respective marginal products. According to Euler's theorem, we can deduce

(7.4.3)
$$Q \equiv \frac{\partial Q}{\partial N} N + \frac{\partial Q}{\partial K} K,$$

which conveys

$$\lambda Q = Q(\lambda K, \lambda N).$$

Further, the differential of (7.4.2) gives

(7.4.4)
$$dQ = \frac{\partial Q}{\partial K} dK + \frac{\partial Q}{\partial N} dN.$$

Dividing both sides of (7.4.4) by Q, also dividing and multiplying both terms of the right hand side of (7.4.4) by K and N respectively, we have

(7.4.5)
$$\frac{dQ}{Q} = \frac{\partial Q}{\partial K} \frac{K}{Q} \frac{dK}{K} + \frac{\partial Q}{\partial N} \frac{N}{Q} \frac{dN}{N}.$$

Since

$$\frac{\partial Q}{\partial N} \frac{N}{Q} = \frac{\partial(\log Q)}{\partial(\log N)} = \frac{EQ}{EN},$$

and

$$\frac{\partial Q}{\partial K} \frac{K}{Q} = \frac{\partial(\log Q)}{\partial(\log K)} = \frac{EQ}{EK},$$

therefore

(7.4.6)
$$\frac{dQ}{Q} = \frac{\partial(\log Q)}{\partial(\log K)} \frac{dK}{K} + \frac{\partial(\log Q)}{\partial(\log N)} \frac{dN}{N},$$

where $\frac{dQ}{Q}$ is the proportionate rate of growth of output, $\frac{dK}{K}$ is the proportionate rate of growth of the stock of capital, and $\frac{dN}{N}$ is the proportionate rate of growth of the labor force all for a given period of time, say, annually.

The elasticity of output with respect to capital is the proportion of the output which would be paid in net profit; and the elasticity of output with respect to labor is the proportion of output going to the labor force. If $\frac{EQ}{EK} = .12$, we can say that if the owners of the stock of capital received

---

[5] To avoid all definitional and controversial issues relating to capital, we prefer to use K as an "index-number" of the stock of capital, a term used by D. Champernowne, "A Dynamic Growth Model Involving a Production Function," *The Theory of Capital*, Ed. D. C. Hague, New York, 1961, p. 223. Meanwhile, mention should be made that equation (7.4.2) assumes, not only pure competition, but technology, the rate of growth of population, propensity to save, and land are all constant. *Ibid.*, p. 225.

returns equal to the value of their marginal product, 12 per cent of output would go to the owners of the stock of capital. Another way of making the same statement is to say that a 1 per cent increase in the stock of capital would increase a .12 of 1 per cent rise in output. If the proportionate rate of growth of output is, say, 15%, and the proportionate rates of growth of capital and labor are 15% each, it is obvious that the economy is experiencing constant returns to scale. In this case

$$\frac{\partial(\log Q)}{\partial(\log K)} + \frac{\partial(\log Q)}{\partial(\log N)} = 1.$$

"Now it is a familiar proposition in classical economic analysis . . . that a fully competitive equilibrium in which all factors of production are paid rewards equal to the value of their marginal social net products is possible only in conditions of constant returns to scale. If there are increasing returns to scale, either there will be elements of monopoly somewhere in the economy or else there will be elements of external economy which will mean that marginal social product exceeds marginal private product in some parts of the economic system. Closely allied to this familiar proposition is the proposition . . . that in conditions of constant returns to scale, the payments of a reward to each factor equal to its marginal product will absorb the whole, and neither more nor less than the whole, of the available product."[6] It means, mathematically, that the sum of the elasticities of output with respect to inputs must be unity in the case of constant returns to scale. If we write

$$\frac{\partial(\log Q)}{\partial(\log K)} = \alpha,$$

and

$$\frac{\partial(\log Q)}{\partial(\log N)} = \beta,$$

then

(7.4.7)
$$\frac{dQ}{Q} = \alpha \frac{dK}{K} + \beta \frac{dN}{N}.$$

If it is assumed that α and β are constant and that (7.4.7) is independent of its initial conditions, (7.4.7) can, by differential equations which will be explained in Chapter 9, be reduced to

(7.4.8)
$$Q = AK^\alpha N^\beta$$

where $A = e^{-C}$, C being a constant number. (7.4.8) is the Cobb-Douglas neo-classical production function which makes the sum of partial elasticities of output with respect to an "index number" of the stock of capital and labor equal to unity with the elasticities of substitution between

---

[6] J. E. Meade, *A Neo-Classical Theory of Economic Growth*, New York, 1961, pp. 13–14.

K and N in the production of Q being[7]

$$\sigma = -\frac{\left(\frac{dN}{N}\right) - \left(\frac{dK}{K}\right)}{\dfrac{d\left(\frac{\partial Q}{\partial N}\right)}{\frac{\partial Q}{\partial N}} - \dfrac{d\left(\frac{\partial Q}{\partial K}\right)}{\frac{\partial Q}{\partial K}}}$$

$$\sigma = -\frac{\left(\frac{dN}{N}\right) - \left(\frac{dK}{K}\right)}{\dfrac{\frac{\partial^2 Q}{\partial N^2}\,dN + \frac{\partial^2 Q}{\partial K\,\partial N}\,dK}{\frac{\partial Q}{\partial N}} - \dfrac{\frac{\partial^2 Q}{\partial K^2}\,dK + \frac{\partial^2 Q}{\partial N\,\partial K}\,dN}{\frac{\partial Q}{\partial K}}}$$

The differential of (7.4.3) gives

(7.4.9)
$$dQ = dK\left(\frac{\partial Q}{\partial K} + \frac{\partial^2 Q}{\partial K^2}\,K + \frac{\partial^2 Q}{\partial N\,\partial K}\,N\right)$$
$$+ dN\left(\frac{\partial Q}{\partial N} + \frac{\partial^2 Q}{\partial N^2}\,N + \frac{\partial^2 Q}{\partial K\,\partial N}\,K\right).$$

Subtracting (7.4.4) from (7.4.9) yields

$$0 = dK\left(\frac{\partial^2 Q}{\partial K^2}\,K + \frac{\partial^2 Q}{\partial N\,\partial K}\,N\right)$$
$$+ dN\left(\frac{\partial^2 Q}{\partial N^2}\,N + \frac{\partial^2 Q}{\partial K\,\partial N}\,K\right).$$

Since dK and dN, the differentials of capital and labor, are constant, it follows that

$$\frac{\partial^2 Q}{\partial K^2}\,K + \frac{\partial^2 Q}{\partial N\,\partial K}\,N = 0,$$

and

$$\frac{\partial^2 Q}{\partial N^2}\,N + \frac{\partial^2 Q}{\partial K\,\partial N}\,K = 0.$$

According to Young's theorem, which was explained in Chapter 6, for a continuous function with continuous partials, we have

$$\frac{\partial^2 Q}{\partial K\,\partial N} = \frac{\partial^2 Q}{\partial N\,\partial K},$$

that is to say,

$$\frac{\partial^2 Q}{\partial N^2} = -\frac{K}{N}\frac{\partial^2 Q}{\partial N\,\partial K}$$

$$\frac{\partial^2 Q}{\partial K^2} = -\frac{\partial^2 Q}{\partial N\,\partial K}\frac{N}{K}.$$

---

[7] *Ibid.*, pp. 89–93.

By substituting in the expression for the elasticity of substitution we get

(7.4.10)
$$\sigma = \frac{\left(\dfrac{\partial Q}{\partial N}\right)\left(\dfrac{\partial Q}{\partial K}\right)}{Q\,\dfrac{\partial^2 Q}{\partial N\,\partial K}}.$$

There is one question which is fundamental and should be raised: Why should pure competition, which is the foundation of neo-classical economic analysis and its consequential constant returns to scale be assumed as many economists nowadays tend to do? The answer is quite simple. The assumptions of pure competition and constant returns to scale determine all variables of the system and make the system altogether consistent. That is, given the money wage rate, the level of output would be determined by equations (7.4.1) and (7.4.2). The output, having been determined thus, would determine the rate of change of capital accumulation and economic growth via (7.4.6) and the Cobb-Douglas production function, with capital and labor/output ratios being determined by equation (7.4.10). It is recognizable that income and growth determination are linked, in this analysis, to income distribution; viz., given the money wage rate, (assuming that wages are functional and profits are residual), the growth rate of output is determined.

EXERCISES 7

1. Find dz, $d_x z$ and $d_y z$ of the following functions:

$z = 2x^2 - 3xy + y^2.$ $\qquad$ $z = 5x^2 + 3x + 2xy - 6y - 5y^2 + 4.$

$z = e^{ax}\cos(ay).$ $\qquad$ $z = \log\sqrt{3x - 2y^2}.$

$z = e^{-v^2}\sin x.$ $\qquad$ $z = e^{ax}\tan^{-1} y.$

$z = e^{x^2/3y}\cos(3x).$ $\qquad$ $z = e^x \sin y + (\tfrac{1}{3})e^{-3x}\cos y.$

$z = \log(x^2 + y^2)\sin(x + y).$ $\qquad$ $z = \dfrac{1}{x^2 + y^2}.$

2. Find dy/dx of the following functions. (Use the method of differentials.)

$y = e^{4x} - 3e^{3/x}.$ $\qquad$ $e^{xy} = \dfrac{1 + e^{3x}}{1 - e^{2y}}.$

$e^{xy} = 6xy^2 + 2e^v.$ $\qquad$ $3xy = y + e^{-x} + e^{3x/v}.$

$e^{x^2 y} = \dfrac{\log x^2}{y}.$ $\qquad$ $y = \log\sqrt{(e^{2x} - e^{-2x})(e^{2x} + e^{-2x})}.$

$y = \dfrac{x}{x - \sqrt{e^x - 4}}.$ $\qquad$ $x(\log y^2) = 2y(\log x^2) + 3.$

$xy = e^{x^2}\log(xe^{3x}).$ $\qquad$ $y = e^{1-x}\log\sqrt{x^2 - 9}.$

3. Find dy/dx of the following functions: (Use the method of implicit differentiation. Do *not* solve the equations for y.)

$x^4 y = 2.$ $y + 2x^{\frac{1}{2}} = 0.$

$3xy + 3y + 4x = 3x^2.$ $x^3 + y^3 = 2.$

$2x^2 + 3y^3 = 5x + 6.$ $x^3 y^2 + x^2 = y^2.$

$(x^2 + y)x = y.$ $y - x^{\frac{3}{4}} = 0.$

$y - x^{\frac{1}{2}} + x^{-\frac{1}{2}} = 0.$ $2x^{\frac{4}{5}} - e^{xy} = 0.$

4. Let output Y be related to labor, L, capital, K, and technology t, *i.e.*, $Y = F(L, K, t)$. Relate the proportionate rate of growth of output to the proportionate rates of change of labor, capital and technology. Let $Y = Y(x_1, \ldots x_n)$. Relate the proportionate rate of growth of Y to the proportionate rates of growth of x_i.

5. Let $Y = F(L, K, t)$ as in exercise 4. Show that

$$y = Uk + Q1 + r$$

where U and Q are the elasticities of output with respect to capital and labor respectively. Y, k, and l are the proportionate rates of growth of income, capital and labor. R is the proportionate rate of growth of output due solely to technical progress which is usually called the rate of technical progress. Discuss the economic implications of this derivation. (J. E. Meade, *A Neoclassical Theory of Economic Growth*, pp. 10–18). It is assumed that net output would rise in any one period because of technical progress denoted by dy'.

6. Consider a constant-returns-to-scale production function

$$Y = F(K, L, N)$$

where Y, K, L, and N stand for output, capital, labor, and land. It is known that under constant returns to scale the marginal products of the factors are equal to their rates of return. (Why? Show.) Find an expression which could relate the growth rate in the share of income which is going to a factor as a result of changes in the supply of the other two factors. (See J. E. Meade, *op. cit.* pp. 77–82.)

7. It has been suggested that the underdeveloped economies must use those techniques which are less capital intensive and more labor intensive since the marginal product of labor tends to be zero — so is the money wage rate — in those economies. Show that these arguments are based on the marriage of Harrod-Domar growth model to the marginal productivity theory of distribution.

8. Show that under normal conditions and for any homogeneous production function, the marginal rate of substitution between the factors depends on the ratio of the factors used.

9. Show that under normal conditions the constant product curves of a linear homogeneous production function of the Cobb-Douglas type are downward sloping and convex to the origin at all points in the positive quadrant. Is the property true for any homogeneous production function?

10. Show that under normal conditions the indifference curves of a utility surface decrease at an increasing rate at all points in the positive quadrant.

11. Does diminishing marginal untility imply the convexity of indifference curves? Reversely, does the convexity of indifference curves imply diminishing marginal utility? (See G. Stigler, *The Theory of Price*, 1953, pp. 81 and 301.)

12. Let there be two markets with two independent demand curves; *i.e.*, the demand curve of one market does not depend on the price of the other market. It is said that a monopolist will maximize his receipts from the sale of a given quantity of his product if and only if the marginal revenue in each separate market is equal. Show that the same result can be had for interdependent markets if and only when the demand curves are linear. (See G. Stigler, *op. cit.* pp. 216–17 and 303–304.)

8 INTEGRALS AND INTEGRATIONS

8.1 The Meaning and the Technique of Integration

In the preceding chapters of this part, we were interested in the rate of change of a function with respect to its variable(s), *e.g.* the rate of change of income over time or the rate of change of employment with respect to income. However, it is desirable, often imperative, to be able to reverse the process of differentiation in order to find the function whose rate of change has been given. For instance, we wish to know the total accumulated capital over a definite period when its rate of change is specified. This inverse of the operation of differentiation is called *integration*. Let us suppose that there are two variables x, y so that

$$y = f(x)$$

and

$$dy = f'(x)\,dx.$$

If the process is reversed, that is to say, if we want to start from $f'(x)$ in order to obtain $y = f(x)$, the operation is called *integration*.

In the preceding example, y is called an indefinite integral of $f'(x)$ and the relation between $f'(x)$, $f(x)$ is denoted by the symbol

(8.1.1)
$$y = \int dy = \int f'(x)\,dx$$
$$= f(x) + C.$$

Here C is a constant whose value may be anything from positive or negative, and we add it because the derivative of a constant, according to our rule, is zero. Expression (8.1.1) is read: the integral of $f'(x)$ is $f(x) + C$. In (8.1.1) the phrase $f'(x)$ is named the *integrand*, C the *constant of integration*, and $\int$ the *integral* sign.

175

In the following paragraph, we would like to solve a few examples. Let us suppose $y = y(c)$ which is the consumption function and we are only given the marginal propensity to consume $\dfrac{dy}{dc} = 5$. We wish to solve $y = \int 5 \, dc$. (Here, we wish to find the value of y whose derivative is 5.) The solution is simply

$$y = 5c + C.$$

Again, the marginal cost of an operation is approximated by $\dfrac{dy}{dx} = x^3 + 2x^2 - 7$. Here, we wish to find the value of total cost

$$y = \int (x^3 + 2x^2 - 7) \, dx.$$

If we find a function whose first derivative is $x^3 + 2x^2 - 7$, that function is our solution; *viz.*

$$y = \tfrac{1}{4}x^4 + \tfrac{2}{3}x^3 - 7x + C.$$

There are an infinite number of examples that one can arrange and solve. Perhaps, practice can make the reader an expert in solving integrals. However, there are some rules which, while incomplete by themselves, nevertheless, may be of some help to the reader;

(1) In integration, if the integrand is multiplied or divided by a constant, the constant can be placed before the integral sign:

$$y = \int au \, du = a \int u \, du,$$

$$y = \int 5x \, dx = 5 \int x \, dx.$$

(2) If the integrand is given in the form

$$y = \int [f_1'(x) + f_2'(x) + \cdots + f_n'(x)] \, dx,$$

we can write

$$y = \int f_1'(x) \, dx + \int f_2'(x) \, dx + \cdots + \int f_n'(x) \, dx.$$

Specifically, if

$$y = \int (x^3 + 2x^2 - 7) \, dx,$$

we can note that

$$y = \int x^3 \, dx + \int 2x^2 \, dx - \int 7 \, dx.$$

(3) Integral of exponential functions:

$$\int a^u \, du = \frac{a^u}{\log a} + C,$$

$$\int e^u \, du = e^u + C.$$

In these formulas the differential factor du is the differential of u which represents any function of one variable and occurs as the exponent only of a or e. With these formulas, let us evaluate

$$\int 3xe^{x^2-1} \, dx.$$

Thus

$$u = x^2 - 1,$$

$$du = d(x^2 - 1) = 2x \, dx,$$

$$x \, dx = \frac{du}{2}.$$

We can write our example in the form

$$\int 3e^u \frac{du}{2} = \frac{3}{2} \int e^u \, du$$

$$= \frac{3}{2} e^{x^2-1} + C.$$

(4) Many integral examples can and should be solved by substitution. Let us evaluate

$$\int 8^{1-x} \, dx.$$

We make the substitution

$$u = 1 - x,$$

$$du = d(1 - x),$$

$$= -dx.$$

Our function can then be rearranged in the form

$$\int 8^u(-du) = -\int 8^u \, du$$

$$= -\frac{8^u}{\log 8} + C$$

$$= -\frac{8^{1-x}}{\log 8} + C.$$

(5) Integration by parts: The most frequently used forms of integration by parts are

$$\int u \, dv = uv - \int v \, du,$$

$$\int v \, du = uv - \int u \, dv.$$

Evaluate

$$\int xe^{2x} \, dx.$$

Let

$$u = x \quad \text{and} \quad dv = e^{2x} \, dx.$$

It follows directly that

$$du = dx \quad \text{and} \quad v = \tfrac{1}{2}e^{2x}$$

or

$$\int xe^{2x} \, dx = \int u \, dv = uv - \int v \, du,$$

$$= \tfrac{1}{2}xe^{2x} - \tfrac{1}{2}\int e^{2x} \, dx,$$

$$= \tfrac{1}{2}xe^{2x} - \tfrac{1}{4}e^{2x} + C.$$

(6) In Chapter 1, it was pointed out that the logarithms of each side of a relation of any form always hold. We also emphasized in Chapter 5 that only the derivatives of each side of an identity always hold and the derivatives of each side of a conditional equation hold only for those values of the variables for which the equation holds. With respect to integrals, we should note that the integrals of each side of a conditional equation, as well as an identity, always hold for all values of the variables.

Mathematically, any phenomenon whose instantaneous rate of change with respect to time is proportional to itself is subject to the *law of natural growth*. On the economic front, let us suppose that the rate of change of income per time is proportional to itself; *i.e.,*

$$\frac{dY}{dt} = kY,$$

where k is the constant of proportionality and Y income, therefore,

$$\frac{dY}{Y} = k \, dt.$$

Integrating, we find $\quad \log Y = kt + \log Y_0$

where the constant of integration is taken as $\log Y_0$ so as to simplify the next operations. Then

$$\log Y - \log Y_0 = kt$$

$$\log\left(\frac{Y}{Y_0}\right) = kt$$

and hence

$$\frac{Y}{Y_0} = e^{kt}$$

or

$$Y = Y_0 e^{kt}$$

which is the *law of natural growth* of income.

This law has also been applied to investment decision. Let us assume that a sum of money A at the compounded interest rate i is changing. Moreover, let us assume that A, i, and the time rate of change of A are given by

$$\frac{dA}{dt} = iA,$$

therefore,

$$\frac{dA}{A} = i\, dt.$$

Integrating, we find

$$\log A = it + \log 'A_0$$

where $\log A_0$ is taken as the constant of integration so as to simplify the following operations. (In economics, A_0 is the initial sum invested in order to obtain A t-years hence. Mathematically, A_0 is also the value of the initial condition which is also assumed to be independent of the rest of the values of the variable otherwise the original function cannot be integrated.) Then,

$$\log A - \log A_0 = \log \frac{A}{A_0} = it,$$

and hence

$$\frac{A}{A_0} = e^{it},$$

or

$$A = A_0 e^{it}.$$

The reader who has read Chapter 2 pages 25–27 is to be quite familiar with this last relation.

The law of natural growth has been applied to bacteriology, physics, and mechanics.

Definite Integral. Usually, as in the case of capital accumulation, we are not interested in the whole process of capital accumulation so much as in the amount of capital accumulated over a definite interval, given the rate of capital accumulation. To find the function from its rate of change over a specific period is called the *definite integral*.

Take

(8.1.2) $$dy = f'(x)\, dx,$$

from which we acquire

$$y = \int f'(x)\, dx,$$

(8.1.3)
$$= f(x) + C.$$

For $x = a$ this function has the value $f(a) + C$, and for $x = b$ its value is $f(b) + C$. Hence, if x changes continuously from the value a to the value b, the total change in the function will be

$$[f(b) + C] - [f(a) + C] = f(b) - f(a).$$

The difference of the values of the indefinite integral for $x = a$ and $x = b$ is called the definite integral of $f'(x)\, dx$ between the limits a and b. It is written

$$\int_a^b f'(x)\, dx = f(x)\bigg]_a^b = f(b) - f(a).$$

Notice that since the constant of integration disappears in taking the difference of the two values of the indefinite integral, it is not written when the integral has limits. We shall solve two examples to illustrate the meaning of the definite integral. Evaluate

$$\int_{x=2}^{x=4} 2x^2\, dx.$$

We, on the balance of the integration rules, can write

$$\int_{x=2}^{x=4} 2x^2\, dx = \frac{2x^3}{3}\bigg]_2^4 = \frac{128}{3} - \frac{16}{3} = 37\tfrac{1}{3}.$$

Evaluate

$$y = \int_2^5 x\sqrt{x - 2}\, dx.$$

Let us set

$$\sqrt{x - 2} = u$$

$$u^2 = x - 2 \qquad u^2 + 2 = x.$$

Now, our original integral can be written as

$$y = \int_2^5 2(u^2 + 2)u^2\, du = 2\left(\frac{u^5}{5} + \frac{2u^3}{3}\right)\bigg]_2^5$$

$$= 2\left\{\frac{1}{5}(x - 2)^{\frac{5}{2}} + \frac{2}{3}(x - 2)^{\frac{3}{2}}\right\}\bigg]_2^5$$

8.2 Some Properties of Definite Integrals

The following properties are derived, and can be deduced, from the definition of integrals.

$$\int_a^b f'(x)\, dx = f(b) - f(a),$$

$$\int_b^a f'(x)\, dx = f(a) - f(b),$$

$$\int_a^b f'(x)\, dx = -\int_b^a f'(x)\, dx,$$

$$\int_a^c f'(x)\, dx = \int_a^b f'(x)\, dx + \int_b^c f'(x)\, dx, \quad \text{if} \quad a < b < c,$$

$$\int_a^b \{-f'(x)\}\, dx = -\int_a^b f'(x)\, dx,$$

$$\int_a^b k\{f'(x)\}\, dx = k\int_a^b f'(x)\, dx,$$

$$\int_a^b \frac{f'(x)}{k}\, dx = \frac{1}{k}\int_a^b f'(x)\, dx.$$

The Definite Integral as the Limit of a Sum. The following is called the Fundamental Theorem of the Integral Calculus:

Let $f(x)$ and its derivative $f'(x)$ be continuous functions of x in the interval $a \le x \le b$.   Divide this interval into n sub-intervals Δx_1, $\Delta x_2, \ldots, \Delta x_n$ where $\Delta x_i > 0$. Let x_i be any value of the variable in the corresponding sub-interval Δx_i.   Then:

$$\lim_{\substack{n \to \infty \\ \Delta x_i \to 0}} \sum_{i=1}^{n} f'(x_i)\, \Delta x_i = \int_a^b f'(x)\, dx = f(b) - f(a).$$

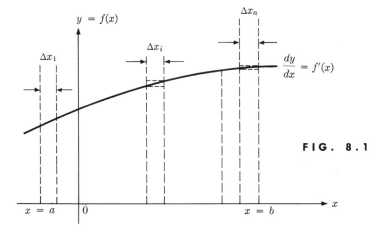

FIG. 8.1

The definite integrals and the areas under the curve in Figure 8.1 give us the idea that the definite integral is the limit of a sum which, in turn, permits us to set up the expression for the area bounded by given curves as the limit of the sum of elements of the area. Each element is a rectangle if the bounding curves are given in rectangular coordinates.

We can immediately apply the results of this section to deriving total revenue if the related marginal revenue is given. Let us assume that the marginal revenue from undertaking a project is

(8.2.1) $$\frac{dR}{dx} = V$$

where $V = V(x)$ is nonlinear and its curve is illustrated in Figure 8.2.

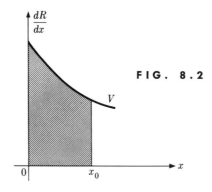

FIG. 8.2

Now, suppose that it is desired to obtain the total revenue from 0 to x_0 of output. From (8.2.1) we can have $dR = V\,dx$, or

$$R = \int_0^{x_0} dR = \int_0^{x_0} V \cdot dx$$

which gives the area above the x-axis and under the marginal revenue curve and closed by the ordinates at 0 and x_0. Since the area is above the x-axis total revenue is positive.

If specifically $V = -2x + 3$, our corresponding total revenue will be

$$R = \int_0^{x_0} (-2x + 3) \cdot dx = -x^2 + 3x + C$$

which is a parabola opening downward with a constant element.

Multiple Integration. By virtue of the fundamental theorem of the definite integral, a double integral is the limit of a double sum and a triple integral is the limit of a triple sum. In general, a multiple integral is the limit of a multiple sum. In order to explain what we intend to convey, let us suppose that an area which is enclosed between two curves is to be calculated. The total area may be divided into small areas of dimensions Δx by Δy. Of course, the sum of these small areas of dimensions Δx by Δy can be used as an approximation of the enclosed area. Furthermore, by virtue of the fundamental theorem, the limit of such a sum as both Δx and Δy approach zero is the enclosed area. If the area between two curves is shown by R, then

$$R = \lim_{\substack{\Delta y \to 0 \\ \Delta x \to 0}} \sum\sum \Delta y \cdot \Delta x = \lim_{\substack{m \to \infty \\ \Delta x \to 0}} \sum (\lim_{\substack{n \to \infty \\ \Delta y \to 0}} \sum \Delta y) \, \Delta x,$$

$$R = \lim_{\substack{m \to \infty \\ \Delta x \to 0}} \sum \left(\int_{y_1}^{y_2} dy \right) \Delta x = \int_{x_1}^{x_2} \int_{y_1}^{y_2} dy \cdot dx$$

which is a double sum. It has to be well remembered that the second integral sign belongs to the first differential in such double integrals. It must also be noted that during the first integration, $\int_{y_1}^{y_2} dy$, x is constant. We solve an example presently to explain this. The rule is that the function should be integrated with respect to y first, then with respect to x. Of course, if the fundamental theorem is applied in reverse order to the double sum, we have

$$R = \lim_{\substack{\Delta x \to 0 \\ \Delta y \to 0}} \sum\sum \Delta x \cdot \Delta y = \int_{y_1}^{y_2} \int_{x_1}^{x_2} dx \cdot dy.$$

Let us suppose that the marginal revenue of a firm for the production of X is given by $y = 4 - x$ and its marginal cost by $y = x + \dfrac{1}{x}$. We wish to find the area bounded by these two curves. First, we should solve these two equations simultaneously to find out for what values of X these two curves are equal. The simultaneous solution of them gives two values for X, namely, $x_1 = .3$ and $x_2 = 1.7$. Now, the area between the two curves is given by

$$V = \int_{.3}^{1.7} \int_{x+1/x}^{4-x} dy \cdot dx = \int_{.3}^{1.7} y \Big]_{x+1/x}^{4-x} dx,$$

$$= \int_{.3}^{1.7} \left(4 - 2x - \frac{1}{x} \right) dx = 4x - x^2 - \log x \Big]_{.3}^{1.7} = .98.$$

8.3 Expansions: MacLaurin and Taylor's Theorems

Towards the end of Chapter 2, we defined a *sequence* as a function whose domain is the set J^+ of all positive integers. If U is a sequence and $n \in J^+$, then we shall denote the value of U at n by U_n. That is, $U_n = U(n)$. If U is a sequence, then U_1 is the *first term* of U, U_2 the *second term* of U, and so on. In general, U_n is the nth term of U. For example, if U is defined by

$$U(n) = (\tfrac{1}{2})^n$$

such that $n \in J^+$, then the first term of the sequence is $\tfrac{1}{2}$, and the second term is $\tfrac{1}{4}$ and, say, the fifth term is $\tfrac{1}{32}$.

The sequence

$$U(n) = \frac{1}{n} : n \in J^+$$

is *monotone-decreasing* because if i and j are positive integers such that $i > j$, then

$$\frac{1}{i} < \frac{1}{j}.$$

But the sequence

$$U(n) = \frac{n}{n+1} : n \in J^+$$

is *monotone-increasing* because

$$\frac{n}{n+1} = 1 - \frac{1}{n+1}$$

and for $i > j$

$$\frac{1}{i+1} < \frac{1}{j+1}.$$

We have pointed out before that if $U(n)$ is monotone-increasing and if the set $\{U_n\}$ is bounded above, then $U(n)$ is a convergent sequence. For example

$$U(n) = \frac{n}{n+1} = 1 - \frac{1}{n+1} : n \in J^+$$

is bounded above, monotone-increasing, convergent and its limit is 1. Also, if a sequence is monotone-decreasing and the set $\{U_n\}$ is bounded below, then $U(n)$ is a convergent sequence.

In Chapter 2, we defined a series as the formal sum of the terms of a sequence. We need not repeat here the conditions under which a series can be convergent or divergent. However, there are a number of tests available for determining the behavior of a series. One which is used quite often and is called Cauchy's Ratio Test is applied here for determining the nature of a series. According to the ratio test, if in a series of positive terms the ratio of the $(n+1)$st term to the nth term has a limit R as n increases without bound, the series is convergent if $R < 1$ and divergent if $R > 1$ and the test fails if $R = 1$. Let us consider the series of positive terms

$$U_1 + U_2 + \cdots + U_n + U_{n+1} + \cdots$$

where

$$\lim_{n \to \infty} \frac{U_{n+1}}{U_n} = R: n \in J^+.$$

Formally, if $R < 1$ the given series is convergent and it would be divergent if $R > 1$.

The failure of the test is illustrated by the following series

$$1 + \frac{1}{2} + \frac{1}{3} + \cdots + \frac{1}{n} + \cdots$$

and

$$+ \frac{1}{1^2} + \frac{1}{2^2} + \frac{1}{3^2} + \cdots + \frac{1}{n^2} + \cdots$$

For the first series the ratio test yields

$$\lim_{n \to \infty} \left(\frac{\dfrac{1}{n+1}}{\dfrac{1}{n}} \right) = \lim_{n \to \infty} \left(1 - \frac{1}{n+1} \right) = 1.$$

Accordingly, we are unable to state as to whether the given series is divergent or convergent. However, we can intuitively say that the series is divergent. With respect to the second series we have

$$\lim_{n \to \infty} \left(\frac{\dfrac{1}{(n+1)^2}}{\dfrac{1}{n^2}} \right) = \lim_{n \to \infty} \frac{1}{\left(1 + \dfrac{1}{n} \right)^2} = 1.$$

Therefore, since $R = 1$, the test fails to determine whether the given series is convergent or divergent. However, the given series is known to be convergent.

As the extension of the Cauchy's ratio test, if in a series whose terms are not all of the same sign the *absolute value* of the ratio of the $(n + 1)$st term to the nth term has a limit R as n approaches infinity, then the series is convergent if $R < 1$ and divergent if $R > 1$. If $R = 1$ the test will not determine whether the series is convergent or divergent. Moreover, a series whose terms are not all of the same sign is convergent if the series whose terms are the absolute values of its terms is convergent.

Let us consider the following two series:

$$1 + \frac{1}{2^2} + \frac{1}{3^2} + \cdots + \frac{1}{n^2} + \frac{1}{(n+1)^2} + \cdots$$

$$1 + \frac{1}{2^2} - \frac{1}{3^2} - \frac{1}{4^2} + \frac{1}{5^2} + \frac{1}{6^2} - \cdots$$

Although we know that the first series is convergent, the ratio test fails to determine its behavior. In addition to the fact that the first series is convergent, we have

$$\lim_{n \to \infty} \frac{\dfrac{1}{(n+1)^2}}{\dfrac{1}{n^2}} = \lim_{n \to \infty} \frac{1}{\left(1 + \dfrac{1}{n}\right)^2} = 1$$

$$\lim_{n \to \infty} \frac{\dfrac{1}{|n+1|^2}}{\left|\dfrac{1}{n^2}\right|} = \lim_{n \to \infty} \frac{1}{|n+1|^2} = 1,$$

then the second series is convergent.

Power Series. Let us take the convergent sequence

$$U(n) = \frac{1}{2^n} : n \in J^+$$

and its corresponding infinite series

$$\sum_{n=1}^{\infty} \frac{1}{2^n}.$$

Next, we replace 2 by a variable x such that

$$\sum_{n=1}^{\infty} \frac{1}{x^n} : n \in J^+$$

It is obvious that the value of this series depends on both x and n. A series of this nature is called an *infinite series of functions*.

Formally, let $\{U_n : n \in J^+\}$ be a set of functions and the domain of each of these functions be a certain subset M such that $Do(U_n) = M$ for all $n \in J^+$. Then

$$\sum_{n=1}^{\infty} U_n = U_1 + U_2 + \cdots + U_n + \cdots$$

is called an *infinite series of functions*. Of course, for certain values of $x \in M$ an infinite series of functions may be divergent or convergent. For example for all $x \in M : |x| > 1$,

$$\sum_{n=1}^{\infty} \frac{1}{x^n} : n \in J^+$$

is convergent, and it is divergent for all $x \in M : |x| < 1$. The subset C of M for which

$$C = \left\{ x \in M : \sum_{n=1}^{\infty} U_n(x) \text{ converges} \right\}$$

is called the domain, or interval, of convergence of $\sum\limits_{n=1}^{\infty} U_n(x)$. Clearly, the domain of convergence of $\sum\limits_{n=1}^{\infty} \dfrac{1}{x^n}$ is

$$\{x \in M : |x| > 1\}.$$

A particularly important kind of infinite series of functions is *power-series*. An infinite series of functions

$$a_0 + \sum_{n=1}^{\infty} a_n x^n = \sum_{n=0}^{\infty} a_n x^n$$

or

$$a_0 + \sum_{n=1}^{\infty} a_n (x - h)^n = \sum_{n=0}^{\infty} a_n (x - h)^n ,$$

where $a_0, a_1, a_2, \ldots, a_n, \ldots$ are all constants, are called *power series*. The number h is referred to as the *center* of the power series.

We need the *Abel's Theorem* which we state without proof. If a power series converges for $x = c$, it converges for any $\{x \in M : |x| < c\}$. In other words, if there is a real number L such that

$$\lim_{n \to \infty} \frac{|a_{n+1}|}{|a_n|} = L \neq 0$$

then the domain of convergence of the power series

$$\sum_{n=0}^{\infty} a_n (x - h)^n$$

is an interval from $h - \dfrac{L}{1}$ to $h + \dfrac{L}{1}$. If

$$\lim_{n \to \infty} \frac{|a_{n+1}|}{|a_n|} = 0$$

then the domain of convergence of $\sum\limits_{n=0}^{\infty} a_n (x - h)^n$ is the set R of all real numbers.

The ratio test may be used to find the interval of convergence in most cases. Consider the power series

$$1 + \sum_{n=1}^{\infty} \frac{x^n}{n^2}$$

for which we have

$$\lim_{n \to \infty} \frac{|x^{n+1}|}{|x^n|} \frac{n^2}{(n + 1)^2} = \lim_{n \to \infty} \frac{n^2}{(n + 1)^2} |x| = |x|.$$

so the given power series converges for all $x \in R: |x| < 1$ and diverges for all $x \in R: |x| > 1$. If $x = 1$, then

$$\sum_{n=1}^{\infty} \frac{x^n}{n^2} = \sum_{n=1}^{\infty} \frac{1}{n^2}$$

which converges. Hence the domain of $1 + \sum_{n=1}^{\infty} \frac{x^n}{n^2}$ is the closed interval $1 \geq x \geq -1$. The values of the variable for which

$$\lim_{n \to \infty} \frac{|U_{n+1}|}{|U_n|} = 1$$

are called the *end-points* of the domain or interval of convergence; and to determine whether the series is convergent or not for them we must use some other constant-term series test.

Let us find the interval of convergence of

$$x + \frac{x^3}{3!} + \frac{x^5}{5!} + \frac{x^7}{7!} + \cdots .$$

Since

$$|U_n| = \left| \frac{x^{2n-1}}{(2n-1)!} \right|$$

we write

$$\lim_{n \to \infty} \frac{|U_{n+1}|}{|U_n|} = \lim_{n \to \infty} \left| \frac{x^{2n+1}}{(2n+1)!} \middle/ \frac{x^{2n-1}}{(2n-1)!} \right| = x^2 \lim_{n \to \infty} \frac{1}{2n(2n+1)} = 0$$

for all finite values of x. Therefore, the series converges for all finite values of x or $+\infty > x > -\infty$.

It can be shown that the sum function defined by

$$f(x) = \sum_{n=0}^{\infty} b_n(x-a)^n$$

whose domain of convergence contains the interval $\beta > a > \alpha$ is continuous and differentiable at every $\beta > x > \alpha$ and that the power series can be differentiated term by term and the resulting series will converge for all $\beta > x > \alpha$, i.e.,

$$\frac{d}{dx} f(x) = f'(x) = \sum_{n=1}^{\infty} n \cdot b_n \cdot (x-a)^{n-1},$$

and in general

$$f^{(k)}(x) = \sum_{n=k}^{\infty} n(n-1) \ldots (n-k+1)b_n(x-a)^{n-k}.$$

exist for all $\beta > x > \alpha$.

Consider the power series

$$1 + \sum_{n=1}^{\infty} \frac{(x-1)^n}{n}$$

for which we have

$$\lim_{n \to \infty} \left| \frac{U_{n+1}}{U_n} \right| = \lim_{n \to \infty} \left(\frac{n}{n+1} \right) \frac{|(x-1)^{n+1}|}{|(x-1)^n|} = |x-1|.$$

Hence, if $|x-1| < 1$ or $2 > x > 0$ the given power series is convergent, and if $|x-1| > 1$ the series is divergent. However, if $(x-1) = 1$, the given series will be divergent and if $(x-1) = -1$ or $x = 0$ then the series is convergent. Whence, the domain of convergence of the series is $2 > x \geq 0$.

Since $2 > x > 0$ is a subset of $2 > x \geq 0$, our series is continuous and differentiable for all x of the interval $2 > x > 0$ and that

$$f'(x) = \sum_{n=1}^{\infty} (x-1)^{n-1}$$

exists and converges for all x in its interval $2 > x > 0$.

Taylor and Maclaurin Series. We are often asked to calculate the value of a function at a given real number. This is not an easy task. For instance, for calculating, say, $\log 3$ or $\sin \frac{1}{4}$, we may consult Tables on logarithm and trigonometric functions. Nevertheless, the values in all tables are given with certain degree of accuracy. So, by referring to a table, one may not be really satisfied with the values given in the table. Furthermore, the tables did not fall from the heavens; after all someone had to prepare them. It should be noted that what ensues is not a treatise on numerical analysis, although we will develop some of the more elementary techniques of numerical approximation which is part of the *Expansion of Functions*. Actually, the latter concept is our main concern in the sequel.

We have already practiced and learned how to *condense*, say,

$$b_0 + b_1(x-a) + b_2(x-a)^2 + \cdots + b_n(x-a)^n + \cdots$$

to $\displaystyle\sum_{n=0}^{\infty} b_n(x-a)^n$ and even to a simpler form $f(x)$. *Expansion* is the converse of the act of condensation. The expansion of a function is not an easy task. There are at least three ways to expand a function. In what ensues we only give the *method of undetermined coefficients*.

Let us consider the power series

(8.3.1)

$$b_0 + b_1(x-a) + \cdots + b_n(x-a)^n + \cdots = \sum_{n=0}^{\infty} b_n(x-a)^n = f(x)$$

which is convergent and its domain of convergence is the interval $\beta > a > \alpha$ for all $\beta > x > \alpha$. According to the last paragraph of the preceding section, it is deduced that $f^{(n)}(x)$ exists for all $\beta > x > \alpha$ where $n \in J^+$. Specifically,

$$f'(x) = \sum_{n=1}^{\infty} n \cdot b_n(x - a)^{n-1},$$

$$f''(x) = \sum_{n=2}^{\infty} n(n - 1) \cdot b_n \cdot (x - a)^{n-2},$$

$$\cdots \cdots \cdots \cdots \cdots \cdots$$

$$f^{(k)}(x) = \sum_{n=k}^{\infty} n(n - 1)(n - 2) \ldots (n - k + 1)b_n(x - a)^{n-k},$$

$$\cdots \cdots \cdots \cdots \cdots \cdots \cdots \cdots \cdots$$

$$f^{(n)}(x) = \sum_{n=n}^{\infty} n(n - 1) \ldots 3 \cdot 2 \cdot 1 \cdot b_n(x - a)^{n-n},$$

all exist for all $\beta > x > \alpha$ and $n \in J^+$.

Moreover, the equations

(8.3.2)

$$f(x) = \sum_{n=0}^{\infty} b_n(x - a)^n = b_0 + b_1(x - a) + \cdots + b_n(x - a)^n + \cdots$$

and

(8.3.3)

$$f^{(k)}(x) = \sum_{n=k}^{\infty} n(n - 1) \ldots (n - k + 1)b_n(x - a)^{n-k}$$

$$= k(k - 1) \ldots 3 \cdot 2 \cdot 1 \cdot b_k$$

$$+ \sum_{n=k+1}^{\infty} n(n - 1) \ldots (n - k + 1)b_n(x - a)^{n-k}$$

upon substituting $x = a$ imply that

(8.3.4) $$f(a) = b_0$$

and

$$f^{(k)}(x) = k(k - 1) \ldots 2 \cdot 1 \cdot b_k = k!b_k$$

or

(8.3.5) $$\frac{f^{(k)}(a)}{k!} = b_k.$$

By substituting (8.3.4), (8.3.5), the definitional notation $0! = 1$ and $f^0(x) = f(x)$ — zero derivative of a function is itself — in (8.3.2), we can rewrite it as

(8.3.6) $\quad f(x) = f(a) + \dfrac{f'(a)}{1!} (x - a) + \cdots + \dfrac{f^{(n)}(a)}{n!} (x - a)^n + \cdots$

$$= \sum_{n=0}^{\infty} \frac{f^{(n)}(a)}{n!} (x - a)^n$$

or

(8.3.6′) $\quad f(x + a) = f(a) + \dfrac{f'(a)}{1!} x + \cdots + \dfrac{f^{(n)}(a)}{n!} x^n + \cdots$

$$= \sum_{n=0}^{\infty} \frac{f^{(n)}(a)}{n!} x^n.$$

Notice that the equations (8.3.2) and (8.3.3) or (8.3.6′) on substituting $x = a = 0$ imply that

(8.3.7) $\quad f(x) = f(0) + \dfrac{f'(0)}{1!} x + \cdots + \dfrac{f^{(n)}(0)}{n!} x^n + \cdots$

$$= \sum_{n=0}^{\infty} \frac{f^{(n)}(0)}{n!} x^n.$$

The right-hand side members of (8.3.6) and (8.3.7) are the expansions of $f(x)$. (8.3.6) or (8.3.6′) is called the *Taylor's series* of $f(x)$ at $x = a$ and (8.3.7) is named the *Maclaurin's series* of $f(x)$ at $x = a = 0$. The expressions (8.3.6) and (8.3.7) are being used in numerical analysis and in the stability conditions of an equilibrium. We shall solve a few examples in the following. But before embarking on that enterprise, we must answer the question as for what values of x the series (8.3.6), (8.3.6′) and (8.3.7) converge to $f(x)$.

Since (8.3.6) conveys generality, we shall use it to answer the question. Let the first n terms of (8.3.6) be shown by

(8.3.8) $\quad T_n(x) = f(a) + \dfrac{f'(a)}{1!} (x - a) + \cdots + \dfrac{f^{(n)}(a)}{n!} (x - a)^n.$

Equation (8.3.8) is called the *Taylor's Polynomial*. Let the remainder of (8.3.6) after the nth term be represented by

(8.3.9) $\quad\quad\quad\quad\quad R_n(x) = \dfrac{f^{(n)}(x_n)}{(n + 1)!} (x - a)^{n+1}.$

Whence, we may rewrite (8.3.6) as

(8.3.10) $\quad\quad\quad\quad\quad f(x) = T_n(x) + R_n(x).$

Previously, we have demonstrated that the sum of the first terms of a convergent series is the sum of the series. Hence

(8.3.11) $$\lim_{n\to\infty} T_n(x) = \lim_{n\to\infty}\left[\sum_{n=0}^{n} \frac{f^{(n)}(a)}{n!}(x-a)^n\right]$$

$$= \sum_{n=0}^{\infty} \frac{f^{(n)}(a)}{n!}(x-a)^n$$

if (8.3.2) is convergent. However, from (8.3.10) we get

(8.3.12) $$\lim_{n\to\infty} T_n(x) = f(x) - \lim_{n\to\infty} R_n(x).$$

On substituting (8.3.11) in (8.3.12) we obtain

(8.3.13) $$f(x) = \sum_{n=0}^{\infty} \frac{f^{(n)}(a)}{n!}(x-a)^n$$

if $\lim_{n\to\infty} R_n(x) = 0$. That is, the Taylor's series of $f(x)$ converges at $x = a$ for all $\beta > x > \alpha$ in the interval $\beta > a > \alpha$ if $f(x)$ is continuous such that $f^{(k)}(x)$ exists for $k \in J^+$ and $\beta > x > \alpha$ and if the limit of the Lagrange Remainder $R_n(x)$ is zero as n approaches infinity. This completes the answer.

Example 1. Expand $f(x) = e^x$. It is obvious that

$$f(x) = e^x, f'(x) = e^x, \ldots, f^{(n)}(x) = e^x.$$

Setting $x = a = 0$, we get

$$f(0) = 1, f'(0) = 1, \ldots, f^{(n)}(0) = 1$$

and according to (8.3.7)

$$e^x = 1 + x + \frac{1}{2!}x^2 + \cdots + \frac{1}{n!}x^n$$

provided that the Lagrange Remainder for this function is zero in its limit. The expansion of an exponential function gives rise to an *exponential series*. If one wishes to compute e^x to six decimals for $x = 1$, then one has

$$e = 1 + 1 + \frac{1}{2!} + \frac{1}{3!} + \frac{1}{4!} + \frac{1}{5!} + \frac{1}{6!} + \frac{1}{7!} + \frac{1}{9!} + \cdots$$

$$= 2.718282.\ldots$$

It is readily noticed that one may evaluate the result to any degree of accuracy which is needed.

Example 2. Expand $\log(x)$ and find the Taylor's series at $a = 1 = x$.
We have

$$f(x) = \log(x), f'(x) = \frac{1}{x}, \ldots, f^{(n)}(x) = \frac{(-1)^{n-1}(n-1)!}{x^n}.$$

Since $x = a = 1$, we have

$$f(1) = 0, \ f'(1) = 1, \ldots, f^{(n)}(1) = (-1)^{n-1}(n-1)!$$

and according to (8.3.6')

$$\log(x + 1) = x - \frac{x^2}{2} + \frac{x^3}{3} - \frac{x^4}{4} + \cdots + (-1)^{n-1}\frac{x^n}{n} + \cdots.$$

If $x = a = 0$, then $\log(1) = 0$. If $x = .10$ but $a = 1$, then

$$\log(1.1) = \tfrac{1}{10} - \tfrac{1}{200} + \tfrac{1}{3000} - \tfrac{1}{40000} + \cdots$$
$$= .095305$$

to six decimals.

Example 3. Expand $\sin(x)$ and $\cos(x)$.
   We know

$$f(x) = \sin x, \ f'(x) = \cos x, \ f''(x) = -\sin x, \ldots$$

and since $x = a = 0$, then

$$f(0) = 0, \ f'(0) = 1, \ f''(0) = 0, \ldots$$

Substituting these values in (8.3.7) it yields

$$\sin x = x - \frac{x^3}{3!} + \frac{x^5}{5!} - \frac{x^7}{7!} + \cdots.$$

Likewise, if $f(x) = \cos x$, we must have

$$f(x) = \cos x, \ f'(x) = -\sin x, \ f''(x) = -\cos x, \ldots$$

and putting $x = a = 0$ in (8.3.7) it yields

$$f(0) = 1, \ f'(0) = 0, \ f''(0) = -1, \ f'''(0) = 0, \ldots$$

and

$$\cos x = 1 - \frac{x^2}{2!} + \frac{x^4}{4!} - \frac{x^6}{6!} + \cdots.$$

The expansions of $\cos x$ and $\sin x$ will be used in Section 8.4.
   In the closing paragraph of this section, we give a theorem related to extremal problems. This theorem is advanced here without proof. The proof is available in any book on advanced calculus. Let

$$f(x) = \sum_{n=0}^{\omega} \frac{f^{(n)}(a)}{n!} x^n$$

be continuous and that $f^{(n)}(a)$ exists. If $f'(a) = 0$ and $f''(a) < 0$, the point $x = a$ gives a maximum value of $f(x)$; and if $f'(a) = 0$ and $f''(a) > 0$, the point $x = a$ gives a minimum value of $f(x)$. In general, if $f'(a) =$

$f''(a) = \cdots = f^{(n-1)}(a) = 0$ but $f^{(n)}(a) < 0$ and n is even then the point $x = a$ gives a maximum value of $f(x)$. However, $f^{(n)}(a) > 0$ would yield a minimum value of $f(x)$.

8.4 Complex Numbers

There is a group of non-zero numbers which is called *imaginary*. There is nothing imaginary about them. They are neither negative nor positive and are shown by the letter i and defined as

$$i^2 = -1 \quad \text{or} \quad i = \sqrt{-1}.$$

Take a number $3 + 2i$ or $5 + 6i$ and in general $a + ib$ where a and b like 3, 2, 5, and 6 are real numbers and $i = \sqrt{-1}$. The numbers $3 + 2i$, $5 + 6i$ and in general $a + bi$ are called *complex numbers* in which 3, 5, and a respectively are called the *real part* and 2, 6, and b are the *imaginary parts* and i in all three cases is the *imaginary number*.

We can safely say that all real numbers can be regarded as *complex numbers* for which the imaginary part is zero. A complex number $a + bi$ is zero if and only if

$$a = b = 0.$$

Two complex numbers $a_1 + b_1 i$ and $a_2 + b_2 i$ are equal if and only if

$$a_1 = a_2 \quad \text{and} \quad b_1 = b_2.$$

Find the values of x and y if

$$(2x - 3y - 1) + (x - 2y)i = 0.$$

According to our definition

$$\begin{cases} 2x - 3y - 1 = 0 \\ x - 2y = 0, \end{cases}$$

the simultaneous solution of which will yield

$$y = 1$$
$$x = 2.$$

Find the values of x and y for

$$(x^2 - y) + (2x - y)i = (y - x) + i.$$

According to our definition

$$\begin{cases} x^2 - y = y - x \\ 2x - y = 1, \end{cases}$$

whose simultaneous solution will yield

$$x_1 = 1 \qquad x_2 = 2$$
$$y_1 = 1 \qquad y_2 = 3.$$

Graphical Presentation of Complex Numbers. The complex number $a + bi$ which depends on a and b, the two real numbers, can be represented as a point on a rectangular coordinate. Assuming a and bi as the coordinates of a point, the complex number $a + bi$ can be shown in the following manner. Suppose XX' and YY' (Fig. 8.3) are two arbitrary fixed lines intersecting at right angles at the point 0. Let XX' be the axis along which the real numbers will be represented. XX' is called the *axis of real numbers* or *the axis of reals*. Let YY' be the axis along which the pure imaginary numbers will be represented. That is to say, one unit above 0 will show the imaginary unit i and a distance of b units from 0 should represent the pure imaginary number bi. YY' is called the *axis of pure imaginary numbers* or the *axis of imaginaries*.

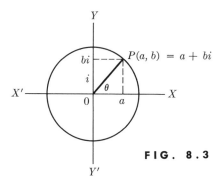

FIG. 8.3

P in Figure 8.3 represents complex number $a + bi$ where a and b are positive. $0P$ is called the vector distance of the complex number $a + bi$ whose length, the *modulus*, is defined by

$$r = \sqrt{a^2 + b^2}.$$

Complex numbers can conveniently be represented by *polar* or *trigonometric* form. Having denoted the length of $0P$ by r and the angle that $0P$ makes with XX' by θ, the *argument* of the complex number, from the right triangle $0aP$ we can write

$$a = r \cos \theta$$
$$b = r \sin \theta$$

(8.4.1) $$a + bi = r(\cos \theta + i \sin \theta).$$

(8.4.1) is called the polar or trigonometric form of the complex number $a + bi$. It can be shown in a different way which is more convenient. According to Taylor's series,

(8.4.2) $$\cos \theta = 1 - \frac{\theta^2}{2!} + \frac{\theta^4}{4!} - \frac{\theta^6}{6!} + \cdots,$$

(8.4.3)
$$\sin \theta = \theta - \frac{\theta^3}{3!} + \frac{\theta^5}{5!} - \frac{\theta^7}{7!} + \cdots .$$

Multiplying (8.4.3) by i and then adding to (8.4.2) will yield

(8.4.4)
$$\cos \theta + i \sin \theta = 1 + i\theta + \frac{i^2}{2!} \theta^2 + \frac{i^3}{3!} \theta^3 + \cdots .$$

Also

(8.4.5)
$$e^{i\theta} = 1 + i\theta + \frac{i^2}{2!} \theta^2 + \frac{i^3}{3!} \theta^3 + \cdots .$$

Since the right-hand sides of (8.4.4) and (8.4.5) are equal, thus

(8.4.6)
$$\cos \theta + i \sin \theta = e^{i\theta},$$

and

(8.4.7)
$$a + bi = (\cos \theta + i \sin \theta)r = re^{i\theta}.$$

Equation (8.4.7) demonstrates complex numbers in terms of trigonometric and exponential forms, a result of great importance. From (8.4.7) we can get the following properties

$$r = \sqrt{a^2 + b^2} \text{ is the } Modulus \text{ of the complex number}$$

$$\theta = argument = \tan^{-1} \frac{b}{a}.$$

Hence, if a and b are given, the modulus and argument will be known. In a special case where $b = r = 1$ and $a = 0$, $\theta = \frac{\pi}{2}$ the complex number

(8.4.8)
$$z = i = e^{i\pi/2}.$$

A Few Unrelated Definitions. (1) *Scalar.* A scalar is a multiplier, or a number of any form, which is used in Abstract Algebra. If there is a complex number z and a scalar i, the *scalar multiplication* is given by

$$iz = e^{i\pi/2}re^{i\theta} = re^{i(\theta+\pi/2)}.$$

(2) *Conjugate Complex Numbers.* Two complex numbers (vectors) $a + bi$ and $a - bi$, which come to our attention almost frequently, are called *conjugate complex numbers.* They can be shown in two different forms;

(8.4.9)
$$r(\cos \theta + i \sin \theta),$$

(8.4.10)
$$r(\cos \theta - i \sin \theta).$$

By Taylor's series

(8.4.11)
$$\cos \theta - i \sin \theta = 1 - i\theta + \frac{i^2}{2!} \theta^2 - \frac{i^3}{3!} \theta^3 + \cdots .$$

Also, Taylor's expansion will provide

(8.4.12) $$e^{-i\theta} = 1 - i\theta + \frac{i^2}{2!}\theta^2 - \frac{i^3}{3!}\theta + \cdots.$$

Since the right-hand sides of (8.4.4) and (8.4.3) are equal, thus

$$r(\cos\theta - i\sin\theta) = re^{-i\theta}$$

and (8.4.9) and (8.4.10) can be shown by

(8.4.13) $$r(\cos\theta + i\sin\theta) = re^{i\theta}$$

(8.4.14) $$r(\cos\theta - i\sin\theta) = re^{-i\theta}.$$

The Four Fundamental Operations with Complex Numbers. Addition, subtraction, multiplication, and division follow from the essentials of complex numbers given above.

I, II. Addition and Subtraction: To add (or subtract) two complex numbers (vectors) $a + bi$ and $c + di$, the real and imaginary parts should be added (or subtracted) separately.

$$(a + ib) \pm (c + id) = (a \pm c) + i(b \pm d).$$

Graphically, the sum of two or n complex numbers is a vector whose coordinates is the sum of the coordinates of the complex numbers.

III, IV. Multiplication and division: The product (or quotient) of two complex numbers z_1 and z_2 is a complex number whose argument is the sum (or difference) of the arguments of z_1 and z_2, i.e.,

$$z = z_1 z_2 = r_1 e^{i\theta_1} r_2 e^{i\theta_2} = r_1 r_2 e^{i(\theta_1+\theta_2)} = r_1 r_2 (\cos\overline{\theta_1 + \theta_2} + i\sin\overline{\theta_1 + \theta_2})$$

$$z = \frac{z_1}{z_2} = \frac{r_1 e^{i\theta_1}}{r_2 e^{i\theta_2}} = \frac{r_1}{r_2} e^{i(\theta_1-\theta_2)}.$$

We notice that the multiplication and division of complex numbers are handled easily by the exponential forms. Likewise, the powers of a complex number z can be written in the form of exponential very conveniently; i.e.

$$z^n = (re^{i\theta})^n = r^n e^{i\theta n} = r^n(\cos n\theta + i\sin n\theta),$$

(8.4.15) $$z^{1/n} = (re^{i\theta})^{1/n} = r^{1/n} e^{i\theta/n} = r^{1/n}\left(\cos\frac{\theta}{n} + i\sin\frac{\theta}{n}\right),$$

$$z^n = (re^{\pm i\theta})^n = r^n e^{\pm i\theta n} = r^n(\cos n\theta \pm i\sin n\theta).$$

The expression (8.4.15) is called *De Moivre's Theorem* which is used in finding powers and roots of complex numbers. Thus, the modulus of the nth power of a complex number is equal to the nth power of the modulus of the number and the amplitude of the *n*th power of the complex number is equal to *n* times the amplitude of the number.

Periodicity and Oscillations. Let us take a look at the graphs of $y = \sin x$ and $y = \cos x$. Specifically, $y = \sin x$ demonstrates three characteristics: First, it rises and falls to ± 1 in both directions. This is the highest and the lowest value that $y = \sin x$ takes. This is called the *amplitude* of the function. Second, we notice that the amplitudes are repeated after certain length. In the case of $\sin x$, the same amplitude; *i.e.* ± 1, is reached after 2π. The value after which the same behavior of a function is repeated is called the *period* of the function. Third, we see that $y = 0$ when $x = 0$. That is to say, at the point of origin, the peak is zero. The peak of a function at the point of origin is called the *phase* of the function.

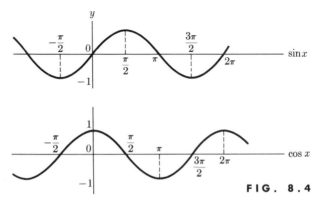

FIG. 8.4

It is to be noticed that an examination of the trigonometric functions shows that the functions repeat themselves after certain "period." These functions and others derived from them are called *Sinusoidal* or *Oscillatory* functions. We observed that a sinusoidal function has three characteristics: *Amplitude, period* and *phase*, which can conveniently be shown by three parameters for sin function by

(8.4.16) $$y = A \sin(\omega x + \epsilon).$$

In (8.4.16), A is the amplitude, ω is the period, and ϵ is the phase since a peak occurs at $x = -\dfrac{\epsilon}{\omega}$. The range of one period is 2π, and its amplitude is $\pm A$. We can also show these parameters for cos function,

(8.4.17) $$y = A \cos(\omega x + \epsilon).$$

Regular, Damped, and Explosive Oscillations. If the amplitude of a trigonometric function is constant over its periods, the function is *regular*. In (8.4.16) and (8.4.17) of the previous paragraph, the amplitudes are $\pm A$ and are fixed over their periods as in Figure 8.5(a). If the function converges as in Figure 8.5(c) so that the amplitude of its successive periods decreases in length, the function is called *damped*. And last, if the function diverges as in Figure 8.5(b) so that the amplitude of its successive periods increases in length, the function is explosive.

We can show the behavior of a sinusoidal function by four parameters: A, α, ω and ϵ. For sin and cos functions we will have

(8.4.18) $$y = Ae^{\alpha\theta}\sin(\omega\theta + \epsilon)$$

(8.4.19) $$y = Ae^{\alpha\theta}\cos(\omega\theta + \epsilon).$$

If $\alpha = 0$, (8.4.18) and (8.4.19) are both regular, *i.e.* the amplitudes are equal over the periods. If $\alpha > 0$, the function will be explosive. And, if $\alpha < 0$ the functions will be damped. The figures exemplify the

$$y = Ae^{\alpha\theta}\cos(\omega\theta + \epsilon).$$

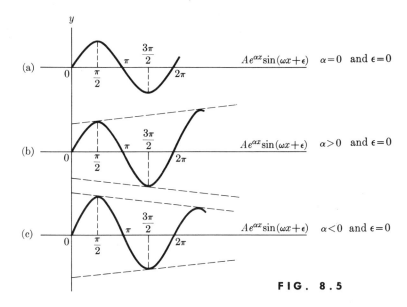

FIG. 8.5

8.5 The Theory of Investment

Under a private enterprise economy, every decision by an entrepreneur with regard to production is, in one sense of the word, an act of investment. But when one speaks of acts of investment as income-generating and capacity-creating processes, one really speaks of investment in fixed capital, of construction of plant and equipment, to exclude expenditures on working capital. In the theory of profit-maximization and profit-expectation, this interpretation is of major importance by reasons of the durability of the results. On the balance of the interpretation, investment is to be defined as an "addition to the existing stock of capital."

Thus, if investment is the dependent variable, the question to be posed is: What should be the independent variable or variables? According to Ricardian economics, a falling or rising rate of profit was the factor which set the pace. On the other hand, recent theories of investment have, by and large, assumed that investment is elastic with respect to the rate of interest rather than the rate of profit. The principal and practical implication of this emphasis has been that investment can be influenced by an appropriate monetary policy which, as investment proceeds, permits the rate of interest to fall *pari passu*.

Recently, Professor Tarshis has remarked: "The inelasticity of the marginal efficiency function is said to be confirmed by empirical observation and explained by theory. This is clearly a powerful team to contest. But the empirical evidence has recently been questioned. And the theoretical arguments which purport to explain why the function is relatively inelastic seem to be less than watertight; at least that will be the contention of this paper."[1]

The literature is replete with debates over the importance or unimportance of the interest rate. We simply cannot quote them here; moreover, they are inconclusive. On the other hand, importance has also been attached to "entrepreneurial behavior" as the determining factor of the level of investment. All in all, our knowledge concerning the determinants of the level of expenditures on investment is still scanty. In sum, the recent theories of investment in vogue, for an institutional framework wherein investment is predominantly undertaken by private individuals and firms, are of two types: One is based fundamentally on the law of preference, while the other follows the Keynesian marginal efficiency of capital theory.

Keynes' Marginal Efficiency of Capital Theory and Microeconomics.
Let us suppose that we have a closed economy where there are two industries producing homogeneous capital and consumption goods under perfect competition and in the short run, as Keynes assumed. Since we are assuming homogeneous outputs for each sector of the economy, we can suppose them as the sum of two "representative firms." Hence, the following analysis, adopted from Keynes macroanalysis, will be applied to a firm's investment decision.

Keynes said that "the inducement to invest depends partly on the investment demand schedule and partly on the rate of interest."[2] That is to say:

(8.5.1) $$I = I(r, i)$$

---

[1] The Elasticity of the Marginal Efficiency Function," *American Economic Review*, Dec. 1961.

[2] *The General Theory*, p. 137.

where r is the marginal efficiency of capital and i is the rate of interest. Let us analyze and explore equation (8.5.1). If I is invested, by an entrepreneur, at the rate of interest i, the total expected returns t-years hence will be

(8.5.2) $$R(t) = Ie^{it}.$$

That is to say, if a man invests I today with the discount rate i, he will receive R t-years hence. Equation (8.5.2) can be rearranged and can be shown in the following form:

(8.5.3) $$I = Re^{-it}$$

where I is called the present or discounted value of R available t-years hence. Since equation (8.5.3) is an exponential function, given t we have $I = I(i)$.

Likewise, if a person expects to earn R_1 at the end of the first period and R_2 at the end of the second period, $\ldots$, and finally R_t at the end of the t-th period, he has to invest

(8.5.4) $$I = \int_1^t Re^{-it} \cdot dt = \frac{R}{i} e^{-i} - \frac{R}{i} e^{-it}$$

where I is the present value of the series of annuities given by the returns expected from an investment outlay for a unit of a particular capital-asset during its lifetime t. Let us suppose that the going rate of interest in the money market is 4 per cent compounded annually. If a firm wishes to receive $100.00 one year from now and $100.00 two years hence and continue to acquire $100.00 every year for 10 years, one should invest $726.25 since

$$\int_1^{10} 100e^{-it} \cdot dt = \frac{100}{.04} e^{-.04} - \frac{100}{.04} e^{-.40} = 726.25$$

corresponding to an interest rate of 4% expected in the future.

It is perceptible that not only the present value is a function of the rate of interest, but the higher the rate of interest the lower the present value of the stream of income and the lower the rate of interest the higher the value of the present value. Now, let us assume a more probable case and suppose that there is a piece of capital equipment which costs only $600.00 and it is guaranteed that it pays $100.00 net a year for 10 years then it will collapse at the end of the 10th year. If the firm is financially prudent and wise, it would purchase the capital asset and would expect to receive $100 a year for 10 years. The difference is, in a sense, an opportunity cost for the firm. Concretely, investment in real capital will continue as long as its supply price lags behind (and in the limit is equal to) the present value of a stream of income corresponding to an expected rate on interest. Thus, the propensity and decision to purchase a piece of income-generating capital asset depends on capital's income stream and on its cost of acquisition as well. The income efficiency of a given asset depends on the discount rate which relates the sum of present value of all its future net income to its supply price. More specifically, if the present value of a particular asset is displayed by (8.5.4) and its supply price by $\int_1^t Ee^{-it} \cdot dt$ and the difference between the two by

$$(8.5.5) \qquad \int_1^t (R - E)e^{-it} \cdot dt$$

that discount rate (i) which would make (8.5.5) equal to zero is Keynes' marginal efficiency of capital.

Or, by setting (8.5.5) equal to zero, we have

$$(8.5.6) \qquad \int_1^t Re^{-it} \cdot dt = \int_1^t Ee^{-it} \cdot dt.$$

The left-hand side member of (8.5.6) is capital-asset's present value of all future income and the right-hand side member represents its supply price. The statement which was advanced before on the earning efficiency of an assumed capital asset is equivalent to stating that the rate of interest or discount rate which equates two sides of (8.5.6) is Keynes' "marginal efficiency of capital."

Assuming the validity of the "maximum-value-criterion," (which is the test of economic performance) the marginal efficiency of capital is a function of the rate of interest. We might conclude that the theory of investment of the firm, based on and derived from Keynes' marginal efficiency diagnosis, makes investment behavior a single function of the rate of interest, at least in the short run during which no exogenous shift factors — technology, population, and other long-run factors — are operative, if the test of performance of economic efficiency is "maximum-value-criterion."

There are many economists who have suggested, on both theoretical and empirical grounds, that there is no *a priori* reason to suppose that the "maximum-value-criterion" is an entrepreneurial test of performance. Recently, Professor Haavelmo has concluded, "What we should reject is the naive reasoning that there is a demand schedule for investment which could be derived from a classical scheme of producers' behavior in maximizing profit."[3] But if the entrepreneur does not use the classical test of performance, what should he use as its substitute? The regrettable fact of the matter is that we do not know the answer yet.

---

[3] *A Study in the Theory of Investment*, Chicago; The University of Chicago Press, 1960, p. 216.

EXERCISES 8

1. Integrate each of the following functions:

$$\int (1 - 2x + \tfrac{1}{3}x^3)\, dx.$$

$$\int \left(\frac{1}{2}\right) \left(\frac{x^3}{3} + 5x^2 - 3x\right) dx.$$

$$\int \frac{3 - x^2}{x^3}\, dx.$$

$$\int \frac{x^2}{x - 2}\, dx.$$

$$\int \frac{x^2 - 3x + 2}{x - 1}\, dx.$$

2. Integrate each of the following expressions by means of a suitable substitution.

$$\int \sqrt{2x - 3}\, dx.$$

$$\int \frac{x}{(x - 3)^{\frac{2}{3}}}\, dx.$$

$$\int \frac{\cos x}{1 + \sin x}\, dx.$$

$$\int \sin x \cos x\, dx.$$

$$\int 4x\sqrt{x^2 + 8}\, dx.$$

3. Find the functions represented by each of the following integrals:

$$\int \sin(3 + 2x) \cdot dx.$$

$$\int \left(e^{3x} + 2x \sin(x^2 + 4)\right) dx.$$

$$\int (2e^{-3x} - 2x) \cdot dx.$$

$$\int 5 \sin x \cos x\, dx.$$

$$\int \frac{1 + 2e^{4x}}{1 - 3e^{2x}}\, dx.$$

$$\int (e^{3x} + x^4 + 3e^{2x})\, dx.$$

$$\int (2x^2 e^{2x^3 - 3} \sin e^{2x^3 - 3})\, dx.$$

4. Integrate each of the following functions by trigonometric substitution.

$$\int \frac{1}{3} \frac{1}{x^2 + 4}\, dx.$$

$$\int \frac{3}{(4x^2 - 5)^{\frac{1}{2}}}\, dx.$$

$$\int \frac{-5}{2(1 - 4x^2)}\, dx.$$

$$\int \frac{2}{3x^2 + 5x + 4}\, dx.$$

5. Integrate by parts, and evaluate each of the following integrals:

$$\int \sin^{-1} 3x\, dx.$$

$$\int 2x \cos^{-1} 2x\, dx.$$

$$\int 3x^2 e^{5x}\, dx.$$

$$\int \log(3x + 1)\, dx.$$

$$\int 3x^2 (\log x)^2\, dx.$$

6. Evaluate each of the following definite integrals:

$$\int_2^6 x^{\frac{2}{3}}\, dx.$$

$$\int_{-2}^5 \frac{2x}{(3-x)^{\frac{2}{3}}}\, dx.$$

$$\int_{-3}^0 \frac{1}{\sqrt{2-4x}}\, dx.$$

$$\int_0^{\pi/2} \cos^2 3x\, dx.$$

$$\int_{-3}^6 \sqrt{2x-x^3}\, dx.$$

$$\int_{-2}^2 x^2/4 - x^2\, dx.$$

$$\int_0^{\pi/4} \sin x \cos x \cdot dx.$$

7. The slope of a cost curve of a firm at any point is $\frac{1}{2}x$ and it passes through $(2, 7)$. Find the equation of the cost curve.

8. The revenue curve of a firm passes through $(2, -3)$ and $(-4, 6)$ and the rate of change of the slope of that with respect to its independent input is $(3 - 4x)$. Find the equation of the revenue curve.

9. The rate of change of the slope of a cost curve of a firm with respect to its independent variable is $4x$. Find the equation of the cost curve if it passes through the points $(3, 4)$, $(5, 7)$.

10. If the population changes at a rate proportional to itself over time, what population will a city of 60,000 have in 30 years hence if 30 years ago it was 20,000?

11. If the national income changes at a rate proportional to itself over time, what will be the level of national income 10 years hence if it increased from $450 billion to $570 billion in the last 5 years?

12. A corporation has estimated that its assets appreciate in value at the rate of 5% per annum. If the original assets had the value of $6,000, when will it be tripled?

13. Find the area divided by the following curves. Draw each figure.

$$2x = y^2 + 3 \quad \text{and} \quad x = y + 3.$$
$$x^2 = 27y - 3 \quad \text{and} \quad x = 3y - 2.$$
$$xy = 3 \quad \text{and} \quad 3x = 2y + 5.$$
$$3x = y - 3 \quad \text{and} \quad x = y^2 - 4.$$

14. Integrate each of the following functions:

$$\int_0^{\pi/2} \int_0^{\pi/2} \sin(2x + 3y)\, dx\, dy.$$

$$\int_1^3 \int_0^{x+1} (x^2 - y^2)\, dy\, dx.$$

$$\int_0^{\pi/4} \int_0^{\pi/4} 2xy \sin(x^2 + y^2)\, dx\, dy.$$

$$\int_{-1}^1 \int_2^y 3xy^2\, dx\, dy.$$

$$\int_0^3 \int_0^{2x} (2x + 3y)\, dy\, dx.$$

$$\int_1^3 \int_2^{\log y} ye^{3x}\, dx\, dy.$$

$$\int_0^1 \int_0^y \int_x^{x+2y} (x^2 + z^2)\, dz\, dx\, dy.$$

$$\int_0^1 \int_0^{y^2} \int_0^{x^2+y^2} \int_0^3 dw\, dz\, dx\, dy.$$

15. Find the domain of convergence of $\displaystyle\sum_{n=1}^{\infty} U_n$ if $U_n(x)$ is:

$$x^n \qquad \frac{x^n}{n} \qquad e^{nx} \qquad \frac{x^n}{(3n)!} \qquad \frac{(-1)^n}{x^n}$$

$$\frac{x^n}{n!} \qquad n!\,x^n \qquad \frac{1}{n}e^{nx} \qquad \frac{x^n}{n(n+1)} \qquad \frac{n}{(x^2-2)^n}.$$

16. Use Taylor's formula to express each of the following as $P_6(x) + R_6(x)$ where

$$P_6(x) = f(0) + Df(0)x + \cdots + \frac{D^6 f(0)}{6!}x^6$$

and $D = \dfrac{d}{dx}$;

$f(x) = (1+x)^{\frac{1}{2}}.$ $\qquad\qquad$ $f(x) = (1+x)^{-\frac{3}{4}}.$

$f(x) = \log(1-x).$ $\qquad\qquad$ $f(x) = e^{-x}.$

$f(x) = \tan x.$

17. Show that

$$\sin x = \frac{e^{ix} - e^{-ix}}{2i}.$$ $\qquad\qquad$ $\cos x = \frac{e^{ix} + e^{-ix}}{2}.$

18. What is arc elasticity and how is it related to point elasticity? (*See* G. Stigler, *op. cit.* pp. 33–36 and 298–299.)

19. The Lorenz curve is a curve which demonstrates the cumulative percentage of aggregate income received by the cumulative percentage of income recipients, cumulating from the lowest incomes. In order to measure the dispersion and inequality of income, one should compare a Lorenz curve with the line of "equality," which is the line of identical incomes. The area between the line of equality and the Lorenz curve of a distribution in comparison with the area under the line of equality is a measure or "index" of inequality. Find a mathematical expression for the "index of inequality." (*See* G. Stigler, *op. cit.* pp. 264–65 and 305–306.)

PART III

Differential and
Difference Equations

9 LINEAR DIFFERENTIAL EQUATIONS IN ECONOMICS

In many economic cases, it is far easier to obtain relations between the rate of change of functions than to obtain those between the actual functions themselves. Any relation, as such, is an equation which involves derivatives and differentials and hence is called a *differential equation*. Thus, a differential equation is a statement of equality between two expressions which run in terms of derivatives or differentials of varying quantities.

The basic task here is to deduce a functional equation from a given differential equation. Suppose that we have an equation involving the rate of change of per capita income, the rate of change of the labor force, and the rate of change of investment over time interval. An expression which explains the relationship among these three rates of change is a differential equation which expresses the relation between aggregate income, employment, and the aggregate volume of investment. A differential equation from which a functional equation can be deduced is said to be solved.

A differential equation, like a functional equation, may have one or many independent variables. A differential equation which has a single independent variable is called an *ordinary differential equation*. In an ordinary differential equation, all the differential coefficients have reference to a single independent variable. Thus

$$dy = \cos x \, dx \qquad y = x \frac{dy}{dx} + \frac{a}{\frac{dy}{dx}}$$

$$\frac{d^2y}{dx^2} = 0$$

are *ordinary differential equations*. If, in a differential equation, several independent variables occur, so that partial derivatives are present, the

209

equation is called *partial differential equation*. Thus

$$y^2 \frac{\partial z}{\partial x} + xy \frac{\partial z}{\partial y} = (n - 1)xz$$

is a partial differential equation.

A differential equation, of any form, has an *order* and a *degree*. The *order* of a differential equation is the order of the highest derivative appearing in that equation. The *degree* of a differential equation is the degree of the highest derivative, when the differential coefficients are free from radicals and fractions. Thus

$$\frac{d^2y}{dx^2} + 2 \frac{dy}{dx} = 5$$

is a differential equation of the *first* degree (linear) and of the *second* order. And

$$\frac{d^3y}{dx^3} + 2 \left(\frac{dy}{dx}\right)^2 = 6$$

is of the *third* order and *first* degree, while

$$\left(\frac{d^3y}{dx^3}\right)^2 + \frac{dy}{dx} = 4$$

is of the *third* order and *second* degree.

9.1 Solutions and Constants of Integration

Mention was made that a *solution* or *integral* of a differential equation is a relation between the variables by means of which and the derivatives obtained therefrom the equation is satisfied. Thus

$$y = A \sin x + B \cos x$$

is the solution of

$$\frac{d^2y}{dx^2} + y = 0,$$

where A and B are called the *arbitrary constants of integration*. The functional equation of a differential equation of order n has n constants. Therefore an nth order differential equation will give rise to a functional equation with n constants. Thus

(9.1.1) $y = A \sin x + B \cos x,$

(9.1.2) $\frac{dy}{dx} = A \cos x - B \sin x,$

(9.1.3) $\frac{d^2y}{dx^2} = -A \sin x - B \cos x.$

Eliminating A and B between (9.1.1), (9.1.2), and (9.1.3), whence

(9.1.4)
$$\frac{d^2y}{dx^2} + y = 0.$$

Then, equation (9.1.1) with two arbitrary constants gives rise to differential equation (9.1.4) of the second order.

If we have an equation in x and y with three arbitrary constants, we need only three additional equations to eliminate the constants. These equations are obtained by repeated differentiation and will introduce derivatives of the third order. Take the equation of the general form

$$f(x, y, c_1, c_2, \ldots, c_n) = 0$$

which contains n arbitrary constants $c_1, c_2, c_3, \ldots, c_n$. Then n times differentiation in succession with respect to x gives:

$$\frac{\partial f}{\partial x} + \frac{\partial f}{\partial y}\frac{dy}{dx} = 0$$

$$\frac{\partial^2 f}{\partial x^2} + 2\frac{\partial^2 f}{\partial x\,\partial y}\frac{dy}{dx} + \left(\frac{dy}{dx}\right)^2 \frac{\partial^2 f}{\partial y^2} + \frac{\partial f}{\partial y}\frac{d^2y}{dx^2} = 0$$

$$\cdots \cdots \cdots \cdots \cdots \cdots \cdots \cdots$$

$$\frac{\partial^n f}{\partial x^n} + \cdots + \frac{\partial f}{\partial y}\frac{d^n y}{dx^n} = 0.$$

There are $n + 1$ equations, the original equation and n differentials from which n constants $c_1, c_2, \ldots, c_n$ should be eliminated and thus will be formed:

$$F\left(x, y, \frac{dy}{dx}, \frac{d^2y}{dx^2}, \frac{d^3y}{dx^3}, \ldots, \frac{d^n y}{dx^n}\right) = 0.$$

Thus, a functional equation with n constants gave rise to an n-order differential equation.

Solutions of the Differential Equations. It was pointed out before that not all algebraic equations are solvable. Likewise, we should know and remember that many differential equations cannot be solved. The equation

$$f\left(x, y, \ldots, \frac{d^{n-1}y}{dx^{n-1}}, \frac{d^n y}{dx^n}\right) = 0$$

is not solvable in any case. As a matter of fact,

$$P\frac{dy}{dx} + Q = 0$$

where $P = f_1(x, y)$ and $Q = f_2(x, y)$ cannot be solved completely.

Generally, one is not confronted with unsolvable differential equations in economics. By and large, the kind of equations which one may see are linear but of different order with constant coefficients. In subsequent sections, an attempt is made to explain the solution of linear differential equations of n-order; *i.e.* when $n \geq 1$.

9.2 Differential Equations of the First Order and Degree

In general these equations appear in the following forms:

1. The equations whose *variables are separable, i.e.*, they are of the form $f_1(x)\, dx + f_2(y)\, dy = 0$. Also in this category there are those differential equations which can easily be reduced to *separable-variables* form.

2. The differential equations which are reduced to *separable-variables* are formed only by special devices. These equations are *homogeneous* in x and y. (We are deliberately omitting the non-homogeneous equations in x and y.)

3. *Exact* differential equations, and those equations which by the use of *integrating factors* can be reduced to *exact* equations.

4. Equations of the first degree called linear, and those which are reducible to this form.

Equations of the form $f_1(x)dx + f_2(y)dy = 0$. In

(9.2.1) $$f_1(x)\, dx + f_2(y)\, dy = 0$$

$f_1(x)$ and $f_2(y)$ are called the coefficients of dx and dy respectively. If the coefficients of the individual differentials are functions of the same variables as their respective differentials, it is said that *variables are separable*. For instance, in

(9.2.2) $$(x^2 + 2x)\, dx + (3y^2 + y)\, dy = 0$$

$(x^2 + 2x)$ is the coefficient of dx and $(3y^2 + y)$ is the coefficient of dy. The former is a function of x and the latter is a function of y. Were these two coefficients constants, such as a, b, etc., then (9.2.2) would be called a linear differential equation with the constant coefficients and first order. Equation (9.2.2), as it stands, is called a linear first-order differential equation with variable coefficients. Moreover, (9.2.2) demonstrates a differential equation whose *variables are separable*.

Judging from (9.2.2), the variables of equation (9.2.1) *are separable* whose solution is

(9.2.3) $$\int f_1(x)\, dx + \int f_2(y)\, dy = C$$

where C is the constant of integration. If we substitute one value of x and y and find the corresponding value for C, the value obtained therefrom is called a *particular solution* of equation (9.2.1).

Let us assume that our differential equation is, for instance, of the form

(9.2.4) $f_2(y) \, dx + f_1(x) \, dy = 0,$

it is easily noticed that equation (9.2.4) can be transformed into (9.2.1) — where the *variables are separable* — by dividing (9.2.4) through by $f_1(x)f_2(y)$; *i.e.,*

(9.2.5) $\dfrac{dx}{f_1(x)} + \dfrac{dy}{f_2(y)} = 0$

the solution of which by inspection is

(9.2.6) $\displaystyle\int \dfrac{dx}{f_1(x)} + \int \dfrac{dy}{f_2(y)} = C.$

Equation (9.2.6) is the complete solution of (9.2.4) and its *particular solution* is attained if the *initial conditions* are given.

Let us find the general solution of

$$\frac{dy}{dx} = \frac{4y + 6}{3 - 2x}$$

which in differential form is $(4y + 6) \, dx + (2x - 3) \, dy = 0$, or

$$\frac{dx}{2x - 3} + \frac{dy}{4y + 6} = 0.$$

The solution of the last expression is

$$\tfrac{1}{2} \log (2x - 3) + \tfrac{1}{4} \log (4y + 6) = \log C.$$

Homogeneous Differential Equations in x and y.   These equations can be put in the form

(9.2.7) $\dfrac{dy}{dx} = \dfrac{f_1(x, y)}{f_2(x, y)} = g(x, y)$

where $g(x, y)$ is such that $g(\lambda x, \lambda y) = g(x, y)$ identically for any value of λ. If this is so, (9.2.7) is said to be homogeneous of order zero, or a homogeneous differential equation.   These equations are solved by putting $y = vx$ which transforms (9.2.7) into a homogeneous equation in which the variables x and v are separable, or

(9.2.8) $v + x \dfrac{dv}{dx} = F(v).$

Separation of the variables in (9.2.8) yields

(9.2.9) $\dfrac{dx}{x} + \dfrac{dv}{v - F(v)} = 0$

which is of the same form mentioned and solved in the previous section and whose solution by integration thereupon is

(9.2.10)
$$\int \frac{dx}{x} + \int \frac{dv}{v - F(v)} = C.$$

As an exercise, let us solve

$$\frac{dy}{dx} = \frac{2x + y}{x} = 2 + \frac{y}{x}.$$

Choosing $y = vx$ and substituting in the equation, we get

$$v + x \frac{dv}{dx} = 2 + v,$$

$$dv = \frac{2}{x} \, dx,$$

whence $v = 2 \log x + C$ or $y = 2x \log x + Cx$.

Exact Differential Equations. The total differential of the implicit function $f(x, y) = 0$ is

(9.2.11)
$$\frac{\partial f}{\partial x} \, dx + \frac{\partial f}{\partial y} \, dy = 0$$

which is exact and formed from $f(x, y) = 0$ (primitive) by direct differentiation without any further operation of reduction or elimination. Should we put any differential equal to zero, we would thereby form an exact differential equation. Therefore,

(9.2.12)
$$M \, dx + N \, dy = 0$$

where

(9.2.13)
$$M = \frac{\partial f}{\partial x}, \quad N = \frac{\partial f}{\partial y}$$

is an exact differential equation in two variables. It can be solved if

$$\frac{\partial M}{\partial y} = \frac{\partial N}{\partial x}$$

which is called the *integrability condition*. Let us suppose that

$$M \, dx + N \, dy = 0 = df$$

then

(9.2.14)
$$f = \int M \, dx + F(y).$$

Differentiating (9.2.14) with respect to y will yield

$$\frac{\partial f}{\partial y} = \frac{\partial}{\partial y} \int M \, dx + \frac{dF(y)}{dy}.$$

By virtue of condition (9.2.13), hence

(9.2.15)
$$\frac{dF(y)}{dy} = N - \frac{\partial}{\partial y} \int M \, dx.$$

If we integrate both members of (9.2.15), we will obtain

(9.2.16)
$$F(y) = \int \left[N - \frac{\partial}{\partial y} \int M \, dx \right] dy + C.$$

Let (9.2.16) be substituted in (9.2.14) so that we can have

$$f(x, y) = \int M \, dx + \int \left[N - \frac{\partial}{\partial y} \int M \, dx \right] dy + C.$$

Thus, the functional equation of (9.2.12) is

$$\int M \, dx + \int \left[N - \frac{\partial}{\partial y} \int M \, dx \right] dy = A.$$

Similarly,

$$\int N \, dy + \int \left[M - \frac{\partial}{\partial x} \int N \, dy \right] dx = A$$

where A is the constant of integration.

Find the solution of

$$(3x + 8y - 3) \, dx + (8x - 5y + 6) \, dy = 0.$$

Here
$$M = \frac{\partial F}{\partial x} = 3x + 8y - 3$$

$$N = \frac{\partial F}{\partial y} = 8x - 5y + 6.$$

Of course, since

$$\frac{\partial M}{\partial y} = \frac{\partial N}{\partial x} = 8$$

the expression is exact. Next, we are to integrate

$$M = \frac{\partial F}{\partial x} = 3x + 8y - 3$$

with respect to x, assuming y constant, to have

$$F(x, y) = \tfrac{3}{2}x^2 + 8xy - 3x + f(y).$$

Now, differentiate this last expression with respect to y to get

$$\frac{\partial F}{\partial y} = 8x + \frac{d}{dy} f(y)$$

which is equal to N, or

$$8x - 5y + 6 = 8x + \frac{d}{dy} f(y)$$

$$\frac{d}{dy} f(y) = -5y + 6,$$

therefore

$$f(y) = -\tfrac{5}{2} y^2 + 6y + C$$

which yields

$$F(x, y) = \tfrac{3}{2} x^2 + 8xy - 3x - \tfrac{5}{2} y^2 + 6y + C.$$

Integrating Factors. There are some differential equations which *prima facie* do not appear to be exact, but if multiplied by a factor they will be transformed into exact ones. A factor which transforms a differential equation into an exact one is called an *integrating factor*. For instance

$$y \, dx - x \, dy = 0$$

is not an exact differential equation but when multiplied by $\dfrac{1}{xy}$ will give

$$\frac{dx}{x} - \frac{dy}{y} = 0$$

which is an exact differential equation whose solution is

$$\log x - \log y = C,$$
$$\frac{x}{y} = A, \quad \text{where } A = e^C.$$

There is no convenient general method for finding integrating factors. Sometimes, by inspection, one can find the proper integrating factor. In the search for integrating factors, however, certain differentials should be kept in mind:

$$d\left(\frac{x}{y}\right) = \frac{y \, dx - x \, dy}{y^2},$$

$$d\left(\log \frac{x}{y}\right) = \frac{y \, dx - x \, dy}{xy},$$

$$d\left(\tan^{-1} \frac{x}{y}\right) = \frac{y \, dx - x \, dy}{x^2 + y^2},$$

$$d\left(\sin^{-1} \frac{x}{y}\right) = \frac{y \, dx - x \, dy}{y\sqrt{y^2 - x^2}}.$$

In the above differentials $1/y^2$, $1/xy$, $1/(x^2 + y^2)$ and $1/y\sqrt{y^2 - x^2}$ are the integrating factors.

Let us solve

$$\frac{dy}{dx} = \frac{y}{x - 2y}$$

which in differential form becomes

$$y \, dx - x \, dy + 2y \, dy = 0.$$

In order to solve the last equation, we must multiply it by $\dfrac{1}{y^2}$, which is an integrating factor, to get

$$\frac{y \, dx - x \, dy}{y^2} + \frac{2 \, dy}{y} = 0$$

which is exact and the solution of which, on integration, is

$$\frac{x}{y} + 2 \log y = C.$$

Let us also solve

$$\frac{dy}{dx} = \frac{y + y^2 x}{x - x^2 y}$$

which in differential form is

$$x \, dy - y \, dx - x^2 y \, dy - y^2 x \, dx = 0.$$

For solving this last expression, it must be multiplied by $\dfrac{1}{xy}$, an integrating factor, to have

$$\frac{x \, dy - y \, dx}{xy} - (x \, dy + y \, dx) = 0$$

or

$$-d \left(\log \frac{x}{y} \right) - d(xy) = 0$$

which is exact and the solution of which, on integration, is

$$- \log \left(\frac{x}{y} \right) - xy = \log C$$
$$y = Cxe^{xy}.$$

By inspecting the example

$$x \, dy - y \, dx + x^2 y \, dy + y^2 x \, dx = 0,$$

it is clear that if we multiply both sides of the equation by $1/xy$, the differential equation will be exact:

$$\frac{dy}{y} - \frac{dx}{x} + y\,dx + x\,dy = 0.$$

Upon integration

$$\log y - \log x + xy = C$$
$$y = Axe^{-xy}, \qquad A = e^{C}.$$

Linear Differential Equations of the First Order. The complete form of the linear differential equation of the first order (when the dependent variable and its derivatives appear only in the first order and degree) is

(9.2.17) $$\frac{dy}{dx} + Py = Q$$

$$dy + Py\,dx = Q\,dx$$

where P and Q are functions of x or are constants. Usually, the solutions of linear differential equations are obtained by substitution. The common practice, from G. W. Leibniz the inventor of the differential calculus up to the present time, is to set up the first member (left-hand side member) equal to zero.

(9.2.18) $$\frac{dy}{dx} + Py = 0.$$

Equation (9.2.18) is called the *auxiliary equation* of the *complete differential equation*. The solution of (9.2.18) is

(9.2.19) $$ye^{\int P\,dx} = C$$

where $e^{\int P\,dx}$ is the integrating factor of (9.2.17). If we multiply (9.2.17) by $e^{\int P\,dx}$ equation

$$e^{\int P\,dx}(dy + Py\,dx) = e^{\int P\,dx} \cdot Q\,dx$$

will be obtained which on integration will yield

(9.2.20) $$y = e^{-\int P\,dx}\left[\int e^{\int P\,dx}Q \cdot dx + C\right].$$

Equation (9.2.20) is the solution of (9.2.17) and since it was given first by Leibnitz, let it be called Leibnitz's equation.

Find the general solution of

$$\frac{dy}{dx} = \frac{4y - 3x^{4}}{x}.$$

Writing it in the Leibnitz form

$$\frac{d\bar{y}}{dx} - \frac{4}{x}y = -3x^{3}$$

we see that $P = -\dfrac{4}{x}$, $Q = -3x^3$. Hence, $\displaystyle\int P\,dx = -\int \dfrac{4}{x}\cdot dx =$

$-4\log x$ and the integrating factor is $e^{\int P\,dx} = e^{\log x^{-4}} = x^{-4}$. Hence

$$y = x^4\left[\int x^{-4}(-3x^3)\cdot dx + C\right]$$

or

$$y = Cx^4 - 3x^4\log x.$$

Bernoulli's Equation or the Equations Reducible to the Linear First Order Form. These equations appear to be of the form

(9.2.21) $$\frac{dy}{dx} + Py = Qy^n$$

where P and Q are functions of x. For solving these equations, we should reduce them to linear form by certain prescribed devices. The procedure is the following: Equation (9.2.21) is to be divided by y^n and multiplied by $(-n + 1)$, then equation (9.2.21) is transformed into

(9.2.22) $$(-n + 1)y^{-n}\frac{dy}{dx} + (-n + 1)Py^{-n+1} = (-n + 1)Q$$

and on assuming $v = y^{-n+1}$, (9.2.21) will be

$$\frac{dv}{dx} + (1 - n)Pv = (1 - n)Q$$

which is linear in v and can be solved by the method explained before.

9.3 The Solution of Higher Order Linear Differential Equations with Constant Coefficients

The equation

(9.3.1) $$\frac{d^n y}{dx^n} + a_1 \frac{d^{n-1}y}{dx^{n-1}} + \cdots + a_{n-1}\frac{dy}{dx} + a_n y = f(x)$$

is a linear equation of order n. Since the coefficients $a_1, \ldots a_n$ are constants, the equation is called a linear equation with constant coefficients. Were the coefficients functions of x, the equation would be called linear with *variable coefficients*. Should $f(x) = 0$, equation (9.3.1) is called *homogeneous*, and if $f(x) \neq 0$, it will be called *complete*.

Since, in economics, the complete n-order linear differential equations with constant coefficients are used rather frequently, the solution of these equations are shown as follows: If the reader looks back on the paragraph concerning linear differential equations of the first order, he will notice that we set the LHS of that equation equal to zero. Having found the solution of the latter, we incorporated that solution with the original equation to give us the complete solution. The procedure for solving (9.3.1) is almost the same. That is to say, we set the LHS of (9.3.1) equal to zero.

$$(9.3.2) \qquad \frac{d^n y}{dx^n} + a_1 \frac{d^{n-1} y}{dx^{n-1}} + \cdots + a_n y = 0.$$

Equation (9.3.2), thus derived, is called the *auxiliary equation*. Our task is to find the solution(s) of the auxiliary equation, then proceed to seek, by the method of *undetermined coefficients*, a *particular integral* of equation (9.3.1). The set of solution(s) of equation (9.3.2) is (are) named the *complementary function*. The sum of the complementary function and the particular integral is the general or *complete solution* of (9.3.1) which is stated, without proof, in the form of the following Lemma:

> **Lemma:** *The complete solution of the complete linear equation with constant coefficients of the form (9.3.1) is given by $y = w + z$ where $y = w$ is the complementary function (the set of solutions of equation (9.3.2)) and $y = z$ is any particular integral of the complete equation.*

It is imperative that we first treat the auxiliary equation and the way that the solutions are derived therefrom.

The Solution of the Auxiliary Equation Having n Unequal Roots. Let us take the equation

$$(9.3.3) \qquad \frac{d^n y}{dx^n} + a_1 \frac{d^{n-1} y}{dx^{n-1}} + \cdots + a_n y = 0$$

where $a_1, a_2, \ldots a_n$ are constants. On setting $y = e^{mx}$, the LHS of (9.3.3) will be

$$(9.3.4) \qquad (m^n + a_1 m^{n-1} + \cdots + a_n) e^{mx} = 0,$$

$$(9.3.5) \qquad (m^n + a_1 m^{n-1} + \cdots + a_n) = 0.$$

Owing to the fact that we assumed (9.3.1) to have n unequal roots, (9.3.5) will have n unequal roots. The complete solution of (9.3.1), therefore, is

$$(9.3.6) \qquad y = C_1 e^{m_1 x} + C_2 e^{m_2 x} + \cdots + C_n e^{m_n x}.$$

Perhaps an example will make the above method clear. Solve

$$(9.3.7) \qquad \frac{d^2 y}{dx^2} + 7 \frac{dy}{dx} + 10y = 0.$$

Set y equal to e^{mx}. (9.3.7) will be

$$m^2 + 7m + 10 = 0.$$

The reduced form of (9.3.7) has two solutions $m_1 = -5$ and $m_2 = -2$. The general solution is

$$y = C_1 e^{-5x} + C_2 e^{-2x}.$$

The Solution of the Auxiliary Equation Having Equal Roots. When r roots of (9.3.3) of the previous paragraph are equal, solution (9.3.6) will be

(9.3.8) $\quad y = (C_1 + C_2 x + C_3 x^2 + \cdots + C_r x^{r-1})e^{m_1 x} + \cdots$

which is complete and general. The following example is given for the elucidation of the solution. Solve

(9.3.9) $\qquad \dfrac{d^4 y}{dx^4} - \dfrac{d^3 y}{dx^3} - 9 \dfrac{d^2 y}{dx^2} - 11 \dfrac{dy}{dx} - 4y = 0.$

On setting y equal to e^{mx}, (9.3.9) will be reduced to

(9.3.10) $\qquad m^4 - m^3 - 9m^2 - 11m - 4 = 0.$

Equation (9.3.10) yields $m_1 = m_2 = m_3 = -1$ and $m_4 = 4$. Therefore, the solution of (9.3.9) is given by

$$y = (C_1 + C_2 x + C_4 x^2)e^{-x} + C_4 e^{4x}.$$

The Solution of the Auxiliary Equation Having Imaginary Roots. When equation

(9.3.11) $\qquad \dfrac{d^n y}{dx^n} + a_1 \dfrac{d^{n-1} y}{dx^{n-1}} + \cdots + a_n y = 0$

has a pair of conjugate complex numbers, $m_1 = \alpha + i\beta$, $m_2 = \alpha - i\beta$ the solution is of the following forms:

$$
\begin{aligned}
y &= C_1 e^{(\alpha + i\beta)x} + C_2 e^{(\alpha - i\beta)x} \\
&= e^{\alpha x}[C_1(\cos \beta x + i \sin \beta x) + C_2(\cos \beta x - i \sin \beta x)].
\end{aligned}
$$

And if $C_1 + C_2 = A$ and $i(C_1 - C_2) = B$, the solution will be

$$y = e^{\alpha x}(A \cos \beta x + B \sin \beta x).$$

What is the solution of the following differential equation?

$$\dfrac{d^2 y}{dx^2} + 8 \dfrac{dy}{dx} + 25y = 0.$$

The roots of the auxiliary equation are $-4 \pm 3i$ and the solution is

$$y = e^{-4x}(A \cos 3x + B \sin 3x).$$

The Operator $\dfrac{1}{f(D)}$. On setting $D^n = \dfrac{d^n}{dx^n}$, $D^{n-1} = \dfrac{d^{n-1}}{dx^{n-1}}, \cdots$.

$D = \dfrac{d}{dx}$, the differential equation

(9.3.12) $\qquad \dfrac{d^n y}{dx^n} + a_1 \dfrac{d^{n-1} y}{dx^{n-1}} + \cdots + a_n y = f(x),$

is reducible to

(9.3.13) $(D^n + a_1 D^{n-1} + \cdots + a_{n-1}D + a_n)y = f(x).$

Equation (9.3.13) can be decomposed into partial fractions

$$(D - m_1)(D - m_2) \ldots (D - m_n)y = f(x)$$

$$y = \frac{1}{(D - m_1)(D - m_2) \ldots (D - m_n)} f(x)$$

(9.3.14) $y = \dfrac{1}{f(D)} f(x).$

$\dfrac{1}{f(D)}$ is the decomposed fractions of the original equation. The

$$\frac{d^2y}{dx^2} - (a + b)\frac{dy}{dx} + aby = f(x),$$

is reducible into

$$y = \frac{1}{D^2 - (a + b)D + ab} f(x),$$

which can be put in the form

$$y = \frac{1}{(D - a)(D - b)} f(x),$$

$$y = \frac{1}{a - b}\left(\frac{1}{D - a} - \frac{1}{D - b}\right)f(x).$$

The Solution of the Complete Linear *n*-Order Equation with Constant Coefficients. The solution of the complete linear *n*-order equation

(9.3.15) $\dfrac{d^n y}{dx^n} + a_1 \dfrac{d^{n-1}y}{dx^{n-1}} + \cdots + a_n y = f(x)$

is composed of two parts: One is the complementary function which is the sum of the individual solutions of the auxiliary equation, and the *particular integral*. This was the gist of the Lemma presented before. The auxiliary equation of (9.3.15) is

(9.3.16) $\dfrac{d^n y}{dx^n} + \cdots + a_n y = 0.$

Let the operator $f(D)$ be applied to equation (9.3.16); *i.e.*

(9.3.17)
$$(D^n + a_1 D^{n-1} + \cdots + a_n)y = 0,$$
$$(D - m_1)(D - m_2) \ldots (D - m_n) = 0.$$

If there are *n* unequal roots, the complementary function is

$$y = C_1 e^{m_1 x} + \cdots + C_n e^{m_n x}.$$

The particular integral is given by

$$y = \frac{1}{f(D)} f(x)$$

$$y = \frac{1}{(D - m_1) \dots (D - m_n)} f(x)$$

$$y = \left(\frac{N_1}{D - m_1} + \frac{N_2}{D - m_2} + \dots + \frac{N_n}{D - m_n} \right) f(x)$$

and the particular has the form

$$N_1 e^{m_1 x} \int e^{-m_1 x} f(x) \, dx + N_2 e^{m_2 x} \int e^{-m_2 x} f(x) \, dx + \dots$$

$$+ N_n e^{m_n x} \int e^{-m_n x} f(x) \, dx.$$

Solve the following function

(9.3.18) $$\frac{d^2 y}{dx^2} - 5 \frac{dy}{dx} + 6y = e^{4x}.$$

Decompose (9.3.18) into component parts

$$(D^2 - 5D + 6)y = e^{4x},$$

from which the following auxiliary equation is deduced

$$(D - 3)(D - 2) = 0.$$

Our complementary function is

$$Y = y_c = C_1 e^{3x} + C_2 e^{2x},$$

and the particular integral is

$$z = y_p = e^{3x} \int e^{-3x} \cdot e^{4x} \cdot dx - e^{2x} \int e^{-2x} \cdot e^{4x} \cdot dx = \tfrac{1}{2} e^{4x}$$

since

$$\frac{1}{D - 3} \frac{1}{D - 2} e^{4x} = \left(\frac{1}{D - 3} - \frac{1}{D - 2} \right) e^{4x}.$$

Now, the complete function of (9.3.18) is given by

$$y = y_c + y_p = C_1 e^{3x} + C_2 e^{2x} + \tfrac{1}{2} e^{4x}.$$

The complete solution is fully defined when, given initial conditions, we can find the values of C_1 and C_2.

The reader may put the following question to himself: How did we reduce $\dfrac{1}{(D - 3)(D - 2)}$ to $\dfrac{1}{(D - 3)} - \dfrac{1}{(D - 2)}$ and in general

$$\frac{1}{(D - m_1)(D - m_2) \dots (D - m_n)}$$

to

(9.3.19) $$\frac{N_1}{(D - m_1)} + \frac{N_2}{(D - m_2)} + \cdots + \frac{N_n}{(D - m_n)}$$

where N_i are known values?

If and only if $f(D) = (D - m_1)(D - m_2) \ldots (D - m_n)$ has n *unequal*, real or complex, roots the numerator of the kth fraction in (9.3.19) is obtained from

(9.3.20) $$N_k = \lim_{D \to m_k} \frac{(D - m_k)}{f(D)}.$$

Whence, in order to have the numerator of, say, the kth fraction, one should simply strike out $(D - m_k)$ from $f(D)$ and set the other D's in $f(D)$ equal to m_k. For instance if

$$\frac{1}{f(D)} = \frac{1}{(D - 3)(D - 4)(D - 2)} = \frac{N_1}{D - 3} + \frac{N_2}{D - 4} + \frac{N_3}{D - 2}$$

then

$$N_1 = \lim_{D \to 3} \frac{1}{(D - 4)(D - 2)} = -1,$$

$$N_2 = \lim_{D \to 4} \frac{1}{(D - 3)(D - 2)} = .5,$$

$$N_3 = \lim_{D \to 2} \frac{1}{(D - 3)(D - 4)} = .5.$$

Finally $$\frac{1}{f(D)} = \frac{-1}{(D - 3)} + \frac{.5}{(D - 4)} + \frac{.5}{(D - 2)}.$$

It is perceptible that (9.3.20) is *not* applicable to the case for which $f(D)$ has equal roots. A simple example, say, $f(D) = D^2 - 4D + 4 = (D - 2)(D - 2)$ can verify the statement. Now, the question may arise as how to determine the particular solution of a differential equation when $f(D)$ has, say, r equal roots. The method *of undetermined coefficients* and the method *of variation of parameters* are two powerful methods which are used for solving particular solutions in all cases whether $f(D)$ has unequal, complex, or equal roots.

The Method of Undetermined Coefficients. Let the differential equation under discussion be denoted by

(9.3.21) $$f(D)y \equiv (D^n + a_1 D^{n-1} + \cdots + a_{n-1}D + a_n)y = f(x)$$

if $a_1, a_2, \ldots, a_n$ are constant coefficients, and if $f(x)$ consists entirely or in part of the terms of the forms

$$Ax^s e^{\alpha x}, \quad Ax^s e^{\alpha x} \sin \beta x, \quad Ax^s e^{\alpha x} \cos \beta x$$

where s is a positive integer or zero, α and β are any real constants, or if $f(x)$ is such that the form of a particular integral may easily be guessed, then the method of undetermined coefficients will be applicable. To use this method and to solve a differential equation with these strictures, one should obey the following rule: When a term in $f(x)$ is a constant write 1. Then add to this the variable parts of $f(x)$. Next, we will classify all terms which can be had from a single term of $f(x)$ in only one class. If no member of an assumed class is a term in the related complementary function, all members of that class remain unchanged. If, however, a member of a class appears as a term of the complementary function, all members of that class are multiplied by the lowest positive integral power of x that makes them all *independent* of any term of the complementary function. At this point, assign a constant coefficient, such as A, B, or, ... C, to each member in all classes and take the obtained sum of the expressions as the particular integral. By repeated differentiation, differentiate this last expression n times and substitute the results in (9.3.21). Finally, set this identically equal to $f(x)$ and match the terms to determine the proper value of the coefficients A, B, ... or C. We illustrate the rule presently with two examples. Find a particular solution of

$$\frac{d^2y}{dx^2} - 5\frac{dy}{dx} + 6y = 4x + 9 + 6e^{-x},$$

or

$$D^2y - 5Dy + 6y = 4x + 9 + 6e^{-x}.$$

Since the auxiliary equation has two roots, 3 and 2, clearly the complementary function will be

$$y_c = C_1e^{3x} + C_2e^{2x}.$$

Since no member of $f(x) = 4x + 9 + 6e^{-x}$ appears in y_c, we take

$$y_p = Ax + B + Ce^{-x}$$

as our particular solution whose constant coefficients A, B, and C are yet to be determined. The first and second derivatives of y_p will be

$$Dy_p = A - Ce^{-x},$$
$$D^2y_p = Ce^{-x}.$$

Substituting D^2y_p, Dy_p and y_p in the differential equation, we find

$$Ce^{-x} - 5A + 5Ce^{-x} + 6Ax + 6B + 6Ce^{-x} \equiv 4x + 9 + 6e^{-x}$$

whence, we must have

$$6Ax = 4x$$
$$-5A + 6B = 9$$
$$12Ce^{-x} = 6e^{-x}$$

or $A = \frac{2}{3}$, $B = \frac{37}{18}$ and $C = \frac{1}{2}$ so that

$$y_p = \frac{2}{3}x + \frac{37}{18} + \frac{1}{2}e^{-x}$$

and the general solution is

$$y = y_c + y_p = C_1 e^{3x} + C_2 e^{2x} + \frac{2}{3}x + \frac{37}{18} + \frac{1}{2}e^{-x}.$$

Find the general solution of

$$D^2 y - 4Dy + 4y = e^{2x}.$$

The complementary function is

$$y_c = (C_1 + C_2 x)e^{2x} = C_1 e^{2x} + C_2 x e^{2x}.$$

According to our previous example, the particular solution must be

$$y_p = A \cdot e^{2x}.$$

But this is the same as the first term of y_c and also Axe^{2x} is similar to the second term of y_c so we should choose

$$y_p = Ax^2 e^{2x}$$

to render the particular solution independent of the terms of the complementary solution. The derivatives of the chosen y_p are

$$Dy_p = 2Ax^2 e^{2x} + 2Axe^{2x},$$
$$D^2 y_p = 4Ax^2 e^{2x} + 8Axe^{2x} + 2Ae^{2x}.$$

Substituting $D^2 y_p$, Dy_p and y_p in the differential equation yields

$$4Ax^2 e^{2x} + 8Axe^{2x} + 2Ae^{2x} - 8Ax^2 e^{2x} - 8Axe^{2x} + 4Ax^2 e^{2x} \equiv e^{2x}$$

or

$$2Ae^{2x} \equiv e^{2x}$$

whence $A = \frac{1}{2}$ and

$$y = y_c + y_p = C_1 e^{2x} + C_2 x e^{2x} + \frac{1}{2}e^{2x}.$$

It has been noticed that the form of the trial particular solution is almost guessed from the form of $f(x)$ of the complete equation. The following table may illustrate the rule for some simple functions.

$f(x)$	y_p
$e^{\alpha x}$	$Ae^{\alpha x}$
$\sin \beta x$, or $\cos \beta x$	$A \sin \beta x + B \cos \beta x$
$e^{\alpha x} \sin \beta x$, or $e^{\alpha x} \cos \beta x$	$e^{\alpha x}(A \sin \beta x + B \cos \beta x)$
x^n	$A_0 x^n + A_1 x^{n-1} + \cdots + A_n$
$x^n e^{\alpha x}$	$e^{\alpha x}(A_0 x^n + A_1 x^{n-1} + \cdots + A_n)$

The Method of Variation of Parameters. So long as the complementary function is known, this method, due to Lagrange, is applicable to all cases, even to linear differential equations with *nonconstant coefficients*. Its only weakness is that it entails cumbersome differentiations and integrations.

Consider the differential equation

(9.3.22) $\qquad a_0(x)D^n y + a_1(x)D^{n-1}y + \cdots + a_n(x)y = f(x)$

with the known complementary function

(9.3.23) $\qquad y_c = c_1 y_1(x) + c_2 y_2(x) + \cdots + c_n y_n(x).$

Replace the arbitrary constants c_i in (9.3.23) by variable parameters to have

(9.3.24) $\qquad Y = c_1(x)y_1(x) + c_2(x)y_2(x) + \cdots + c_n(x)y_n(x).$

Differentiating (9.3.24), we find

$$Y' = c_1(x)y_1'(x) + c_1'(x)y_1(x) + \cdots$$
$$+ c_n(x)y_n'(x) + c_n'(x)y_n(x),$$

or

(9.3.25) $\qquad Y' = [c_1(x)y_1'(x) + \cdots + c_n(x)y_n'(x)] + \cdots$
$$+ [c_1'(x)y_1(x) + \cdots + c_n'(x)y_n(x)].$$

We set the last part of (9.3.25) equal to zero to have

(9.3.25′) $\qquad c_1'(x)y_1(x) + c_2'(x)y_2(x) + \cdots + c_n'(x)y_n(x) = 0$

and

(9.3.26) $\qquad Y' = c_1(x)y_1'(x) + c_2(x)y_2'(x) + \cdots + c_n(x)y_n'(x).$

Again, differentiate (9.3.26) to get

$$Y'' = [c_1(x)y_1''(x) + \cdots + c_n(x)y_n''(x)] + \cdots$$
$$+ [c_1'(x)y_1'(x) + \cdots + c_n'(x)y_n'(x)],$$

or

(9.3.27) $\qquad Y'' = c_1(x)y_1''(x) + c_2(x)y_2''(x) + \cdots + c_n(x)y_n''(x)$

if

(9.3.27′) $\qquad c_1'(x)y_1'(x) + c_1'(x)y_2'(x) + \cdots + c_n'(x)y_n'(x) = 0.$

Finally, following the preceding method, the nth derivative of (9.3.24) will be

(9.3.28) $\qquad Y^{(n)} = [c_1(x)y_1^{(n)}(x) + \cdots + c_n(x)y_n^{(n)}(x)] + \cdots$
$$+ [c_1'(x)y_1^{(n-1)}(x) + \cdots + c_n'(x)y_n^{(n-1)}(x)].$$

Substitute from (9.3.24), (9.3.26), ... (9.3.28) in (9.3.22) to get

(9.3.28′) $c_1'(x)y_1^{(n-1)}(x) + c_2'(x)y_2^{(n-1)}(x) + \cdots$

$$+ c_n'(x)y_n^{(n-1)}(x) = \frac{f(x)}{a_0(x)}.$$

The n linear equations (9.3.25′), (9.3.27′), ... (9.3.28′) may then be solved for $c_1'(x)$, $c_2'(x)$, ... $c_n'(x)$ and the integration of the resulting functions will give $c_1(x)$, $c_2(x)$, ... $c_n(x)$. These values substituted in (9.3.24) will yield the particular solution.

By solving the following example, we can illustrate the preceding rule. Solve

$$D^2 y + D y = \sec x.$$

Since the roots of the auxiliary equation are 0, $\pm i$, the complementary function will be

$$y_c = C_1 + C_2 \sin x + C_3 \cos x.$$

Hence, we set

$$Y = C_1(x) + C_2(x) \sin x + C_3(x) \cos x$$

or

$$Y' = C_2(x) \cos x - C_3(x) \sin x$$

provided that

$$C_1'(x) + C_2'(x) \sin x + C_3'(x) \cos x = 0,$$

consequently

$$Y'' = -C_2(x) \sin x - C_3(x) \cos x$$

again provided that

$$C_2'(x) \cos x - C_3'(x) \sin x = 0$$

and

$$Y''' = -C_2(x) \cos x + C_3(x) \sin x - C_2'(x) \sin x - C_3'(x) \cos x.$$

By substitution in the original differential equation, we have

$$-C_2'(x) \sin x - C_3'(x) \cos x = \sec x.$$

Solving for $C_1'(x)$, $C_2'(x)$ and $C_3'(x)$, we get

$$C_1'(x) = \sec x \qquad C_2'(x) = -\tan x \qquad C_3'(x) = -1,$$

hence

$$C_1(x) = \log (\sec x + \tan x) + C_1, \qquad C_2(x) = \log \cos x + C_2$$
$$C_3(x) = -x + C_3,$$

therefore

$$y = C_1 + C_2 \sin x + C_3 \cos x + \log(\sec x + \tan x)$$
$$+ \sin x \log \cos x - x \cos x.$$

9.4 Some Continuous Dynamic Models

In this section a few familiar dynamic models will be taken up. In all operations the variable t stands for time.

The first simple dynamic model to be taken up is related to the stability of "the first kind *in the small*," of a single market as explained by Samuelson. "Stability of the first kind *in the small* exists if for sufficiently small displacements the equilibrium is stable."[1] Let us suppose that P stands for the price of a single product and that D is the demand for that product:

$$D = D\left(P, \frac{dP}{dt}\right).$$

Also, let S stand for the supply of the product

$$S = S(P)$$

and $\overline{P}$ for equilibrium price, $p = P - \overline{P}$ deviation from the equilibrium price, $\overline{Q}$ the equilibrium quantity, $q = Q - \overline{Q}$ deviation from the equilibrium quantity, and

$$\frac{dp}{dt} = \frac{dP}{dt}.$$

It is also assumed that quantity sold is always determined as a result of equality of demand and supply. If we assume linear functions for the demand and supply to give, say,

$$D = \alpha_1 + \alpha_2 P + \alpha_3 \frac{dP}{dt},$$

and

$$S = \beta_1 + \beta_2 P,$$

we can write

$$Q = \alpha_1 + \alpha_2 P + \alpha_3 \frac{dP}{dt} = \beta_1 + \beta_2 P.$$

For the point of equilibrium, we have

$$\overline{Q} = \alpha_1 + \alpha_2 \overline{P} = \beta_1 + \beta_2 \overline{P}$$

since $\dfrac{dp}{dt} = \dfrac{dP}{dt} = 0$ for the point of equilibrium. Let us subtract the last expression from the preceding one to give

$$q = \alpha_2(P - \overline{P}) + \alpha_3 \frac{dP}{dt} = \beta_2(P - \overline{P}),$$

or

$$q = \alpha_2 p + \alpha_3 \frac{dp}{dt} = \beta_2 p.$$

---

[1] P. A. Samuelson, *Foundations*, pp. 262 and 263–268.

Hence

(9.4.1)
$$\frac{dp}{dt} = \frac{\beta_2 - \alpha_2}{\alpha_3} p$$

which is a homogeneous differential equation of the first order. If we interpret $\frac{dp}{dt}$ as the ratio of differentials, we can write

$$\frac{dp}{p} = \frac{\beta_2 - \alpha_2}{\alpha_3} dt.$$

According to the rule of homogeneous differential equations given in Section 9.2 of this chapter, we can have

$$\int \frac{dp}{p} = \int \frac{\beta_2 - \alpha_2}{\alpha_3} dt$$

which yields

$$\log p = \frac{\beta_2 - \alpha_2}{\alpha_3} t + \log p_0$$

where $\log p_0$ is the constant of integration and p_0 the initial condition. We simplify the expression by

$$\log p - \log p_0 = \log \left(\frac{p}{p_0}\right) = \frac{\beta_2 - \alpha_2}{\alpha_3} t,$$

and

$$\frac{p}{p_0} = e^{[(\beta_2 - \alpha_2)/\alpha_3] t},$$

or

$$p = p_0 e^{[(\beta_2 - \alpha_2)/\alpha_3] t}.$$

If we put $p = P - \bar{P}$ and $p_0 = P_0 - \bar{P}$, we obtain

$$P - \bar{P} = (P_0 - \bar{P}) e^{[(\beta_2 - \alpha_2)/\alpha_3] t},$$

or

(9.4.2)
$$P = \bar{P} + (P_0 - \bar{P}) e^{[(\beta_2 - \alpha_2)/\alpha_3] t}.$$

It is obvious that if the second term of (9.4.2) vanishes, the price will converge to the equilibrium price. It is, however, clear that if

$$\frac{\beta_2 - \alpha_2}{\alpha_3} < 0,$$

then

$$\lim_{t \to \infty} (e^{[(\beta_2 - \alpha_2)/\alpha_3] t}) = 0.$$

Consequently, we may conclude that for a single commodity market, the price converges to the equilibrium value if $\beta_2 > 0$, $\alpha_2 < 0$, $|\beta_2| > |\alpha_2|$ and $\alpha_3 < 0$, which are the conditions of dynamic stability.

This analysis can be explored further by assuming that the amount offered rises if the sellers' price falls short of the buyers' price and with a rate of increase proportional to the excess supply. Suppose that we approximate, again, the demand and supply relations by two linear functions

$$Q = \alpha_1 + \alpha_2 D_p$$

from which we get

$$D_p = \frac{Q - \alpha_1}{\alpha_2},$$

and

$$Q = \beta_1 + \beta_2 S_p$$

from which we have

$$S_p = \frac{Q - \beta_1}{\beta_2},$$

assuming that a certain quantity of Q is sold when the demand and supply are equal or

$$Q = \alpha_1 + \alpha_2 D_p = \beta_1 + \beta_2 S_p$$

and

$$\begin{aligned}
\frac{dQ}{dt} &= -\lambda(S_p - D_p) \\
&= -\lambda \left(\frac{Q - \beta_1}{\beta_2} - \frac{Q - \alpha_1}{\alpha_2} \right) \\
&= -\lambda \left(\frac{1}{\beta_2} - \frac{1}{\alpha_2} \right) Q + \lambda \left(\frac{\beta_1}{\beta_2} - \frac{\alpha_1}{\alpha_2} \right).
\end{aligned}$$

(9.4.3)

(9.4.3) is a linear nonhomogeneous differential equation which can be transformed into a linear homogeneous differential equation if we take its deviation from equilibrium such that

(9.4.4)
$$\frac{dq}{dt} = -\lambda \left(\frac{1}{\beta_2} - \frac{1}{\alpha_2} \right) q$$

provided $q = Q - \bar{Q}$ where $\bar{Q}$ is the equilibrium quantity. Similar to (9.4.1) we can write

$$\frac{dq}{q} = -\lambda \left(\frac{1}{\beta_2} - \frac{1}{\alpha_2} \right) dt,$$

or

$$\int \frac{dq}{q} = \int -\lambda \left(\frac{1}{\beta_2} - \frac{1}{\alpha_2} \right) dt,$$

hence

$$\log q = -\lambda \left(\frac{1}{\beta_2} - \frac{1}{\alpha_2} \right) t + \log q_0,$$

therefore

$$\log q - \log q_0 = \log \left(\frac{q}{q_0} \right) = -\lambda \left(\frac{1}{\beta_2} - \frac{1}{\alpha_2} \right) t,$$

and

$$q = q_0 e^{-\lambda(1/\beta_2 - 1/\alpha_2)t},$$

thus,

$$Q = \bar{Q} + (Q_0 - \bar{Q})e^{-\lambda(1/\beta_2 - 1/\alpha_2)t}.$$

It is clear that $Q \to \bar{Q}$ if

$$\lim_{t \to \infty} \{e^{-\lambda(1/\beta_2 - 1/\alpha_2)t}\} = 0.$$

As t approaches infinity, the limit of the exponential would be zero if and only if

$$\left(\frac{1}{\beta_2} - \frac{1}{\alpha_2}\right) > 0$$

or

$$\beta_2 < \alpha_2$$

which indicates that the numerical value of the slope of the demand should exceed that of the supply if the equilibrium is to be stable *in the small*, that is, if for small displacements the equilibrium could be restored.

The second simple model, which is mathematically consanguineous to the preceding example, is Domar's macro model. Domar proceeds within a Keynesian framework by assuming that savings is a function of income or

(9.4.5) $$S(t) = \gamma Y(t)$$

where S is the savings, Y income, γ the propensity to save, and t the time variable. Also, he takes the simplest expression of the continuous accelerator so as to give

(9.4.6) $$I(t) = I\left\{\frac{d}{dt} Y(t)\right\},$$

or, in particular,

(9.4.7) $$I(t) = \beta \frac{dY}{dt}$$

where I stands for investment while β indicates the power of the accelerator. Further, the savings-investment equilibrium condition is assumed to be satisfied:

(9.4.8) $$S(t) = I(t).$$

The model is dynamic, since the time variable is the important variable of it. Using (9.4.5), (9.4.7), and (9.4.8), we have

$$\gamma Y(t) = \beta \frac{dY}{dt}$$

or

(9.4.9) $$\frac{dY}{Y} = \frac{\gamma}{\beta} dt,$$

which is a linear homogeneous differential equation with the solution being

$$\int \frac{dY}{Y} = \int \frac{\gamma}{\beta} \, dt,$$

or

$$\log Y = \frac{\gamma}{\beta} t + \log Y_0$$

where $\log Y_0$ is the constant of integration and Y_0 the initial condition and

$$\log Y - \log Y_0 = \log \left(\frac{Y}{Y_0}\right) = \frac{\gamma}{\beta} t,$$

hence

$$\frac{Y}{Y_0} = e^{(\gamma/\beta)t}$$

and

$$Y = Y_0 e^{(\gamma/\beta)t}$$

which is the solution of (9.4.9).

Let us suppose that the marginal propensity to save γ is given and positive. According to U.S. data, it is around .05 annually. Whence, our solution, which is an exponential function, will converge to infinity if $\frac{\gamma}{\beta} > 0$ or $\beta > 0$, *i.e.*, if the growth of output accelerates the expansion of capacity and investment. On the other hand, if $\beta < 0$, the solution will converge to zero since

$$\lim_{t \to \infty} \{e^{(\gamma/\beta)t}\} = 0$$

if $\frac{\gamma}{\beta} < 0$ which indicates that if output does not grow enough, with investment falling off and unused capacity appearing (these two latter cases are implied in $\beta < 0$), output will finally decline gradually to zero. It was for these reasons that Domar suggested that "if for some reason output does not grow rapidly enough, unused capacity will develop, investment may fall off, and output will stop expanding and decline. On the other hand, a rapid growth of output presses on existing capacity and encourages investment, which in turn accelerates the growth of output and increases the pressure on capacity. It is quite paradoxical that, with a given propensity to save, to eliminate idle capital, more capital should be built, and to avoid a capital shortage investment should be reduced."[2]

Another interesting example, which uses differential equations, is the Harrod-Domar growth theory which is an interaction between the multiplier analysis and the principle of acceleration. The multiplier analysis gives, in the limit, the ratio of the differential of income to the total

---

[2] E. D. Domar, *Essays in the Theory of Economic Growth*, New York, 1957, p. 31.

amount of investment or expenditure which causes the increase in the income, while the accelerator, in its elementary sense, is the ratio of investment over the instantaneous rate of change of income with respect to time. While the multiplier is related to an autonomous expenditure, the accelerator connects the rate of change of income with induced investment. The multiplier can be either an explosive or a steady relation. Likewise, the accelerator may be either explosive or steady. But the interaction between the multiplier and accelerator results in a steady and progressive growth in income, if the model is exponential and no lags are introduced, as in Domar's or Harrod's model.

Definitionally,

(9.4.10)
$$Y = C + I + \bar{I}$$

where Y stands for national income, C for consumption expenditure, I for investment, and $\bar{I}$ for autonomous investment (often referred to as government expenditures). The consumption and savings functions are

(9.4.11)
$$C(t) = \alpha Y(t)$$
$$S(t) = \gamma Y(t)$$

where

$$\frac{dC}{dY} = \alpha$$

$$\frac{dS}{dY} = \gamma$$

are the marginal propensities to consume and to save respectively, while

$$\gamma = 1 - \alpha$$

and the multiplier, according to Section 7.3, is

$$k = \frac{1}{1 - \alpha} = \frac{1}{\gamma}.$$

The accelerator is

$$I(t) = I\left\{\frac{d}{dt}Y(t)\right\}$$

and, in particular,

(9.4.12)
$$I(t) = \beta\frac{dY(t)}{dt}.$$

Putting (9.4.11) and (9.4.12) in (9.4.10), we get

$$Y(t) = \alpha Y(t) + \beta\frac{dY(t)}{dt} + \bar{I},$$

and by collecting terms, we have

(9.4.13)
$$\frac{dY(t)}{dt} - \frac{\gamma}{\beta} Y(t) = -\frac{I}{\beta}$$

which is a linear nonhomogeneous differential equation.

Let us assume that autonomous investment I is constant. Then, the solution of (9.4.13), according to the rules given in Section 9.2, is

(9.4.14)
$$Y(t) = e^{(\gamma/\beta)t} \left[-\int e^{-(\gamma/\beta)t} \frac{I}{\beta} \, dt + Y_0 \right]$$

where $e^{-(\gamma/\beta)t}$ is the integrating factor of (9.4.13) and is obtained by solving the auxiliary equation

$$\frac{dY(t)}{dt} - \frac{\gamma}{\beta} Y(t) = 0,$$

which is

$$\frac{dY(t)}{Y(t)} = \frac{\gamma}{\beta} \, dt,$$

and

$$\log Y(t) = \frac{\gamma}{\beta} t + \log Y_0,$$

where $\log Y_0$ is the constant of integration and Y_0 the initial condition such that

$$Y(t) = Y_0 e^{(\gamma/\beta)t},$$

hence

$$Y(t)e^{-(\gamma/\beta)t} = Y_0.$$

Solving (9.4.14), we get

$$Y(t) = Y_0 e^{(\gamma/\beta)t} + e^{(\gamma/\beta)t} \left[+ \frac{I}{\gamma} e^{-(\gamma/\beta)t} \right]$$

hence

$$Y(t) = Y_0 e^{(\gamma/\beta)t} + \frac{I}{\gamma}.$$

Since $\frac{I}{\gamma}$ is constant, income grows at a steady exponential rate $\frac{\gamma}{\beta}$ which may be either diverging to infinity or converging to zero, depending on the sign of $\frac{\gamma}{\beta}$. Since, according to U.S. data, savings out of personal income is put around 5 per cent or $\gamma = .05$, and if we suppose $\beta = 3.0$, income would explosively rise at 1.7 per cent annually. If, on the other hand, $\frac{\gamma}{\beta} < 0$, as we have seen before, income would finally reach $\frac{I}{\beta}$.

According to Domar, β is the reciprocal of the *potential social average productivity*, σ, when the economy progresses at a balanced growth rate.[3]

---

[3] *Ibid.*, pp. 74–75.

Since at full employment and full capacity the rate of change of income over time is equal to the rate of change of the productive capacity, we obtain

$$\frac{dP}{dt} = \frac{dY(t)}{dt}$$

where $\frac{dP}{dt}$ is Domar's rate of change of productive capacity.

On the other hand,

$$\sigma = \frac{\dfrac{dP}{dt}}{I(t)},$$

hence

(9.4.15)
$$\frac{dY(t)}{dt} = \frac{1}{\beta} I(t).$$

(9.4.15) should be distinguished from (9.4.12). According to Domar's interpretation reflected in (9.4.15), it is $\frac{dY(t)}{dt}$ that depends on $I(t)$ which is not the accelerator. If, however, income is growing at a steady rate, the sufficient level of investment will be induced according to Domar. Hence the accelerator (9.4.12).

According to Harrod, the accelerator is directly put equal to the difference between savings and autonomous investment. On either Harrod's interpretation or Domar's the interaction of the multiplier and accelerator provides an explosive path for income, whereas the inherent multiplier-accelerator interaction is oscillatory. This may be an objection to the Harrod or Domar simple progressive growth model.

Our last illustrative example of simple dynamic models is a second-order differential equation capital theory developed by P. A. Samuelson.[4] Writing $K(t)$ for the stock of capital for the period t, Samuelson defines net investment, $I(t)$, as the derivative of $K(t)$ with respect to time, or

(9.4.16)
$$I(t) = \frac{dK(t)}{dt}$$

which is proportional to the stock of capital

(9.4.17)
$$mK(t) = \frac{dK(t)}{dt}.$$

(9.4.17) is a homogeneous first-order differential equation the solution of which is

$$K(t) = K_0 e^{mt},$$

[4] P. A. Samuelson, "Dynamic Process Analysis," *Survey of Contemporary Economics*, ed. H. S. Ellis, 1948, pp. 361–63.

or

$$I(t) = mK(t) = mK_0 e^{mt} = I_0 e^{mt}.$$

which shows that the proportion between a stock of capital and a flow of investment can be maintained if there exists a steady exponential growth.

Harrod and Domar growth models pose a more complicated problem. In Samuelson's words, they seek "the conditions of economic expansion which will cause capital, $K(t)$, and income, $Y(t)$, to grow proportionally and at such a rate that investment $I(t)$ or $\dfrac{dK(t)}{dt}$,"[5] would be equal to the savings ratio, $\dfrac{S(t)}{Y(t)} = \gamma$, at full employment. In symbols

(9.4.18) $$K(t) = \beta Y(t),$$

(9.4.19) $$I(t) = \frac{dK(t)}{dt} = \gamma Y(t).$$

Substituting from (9.4.18) into (9.4.19), we have

$$\frac{dK(t)}{dt} = \left(\frac{\gamma}{\beta}\right) K(t)$$

which is a homogeneous linear differential equation whose solution is

(9.4.20) $$K(t) = K_0 e^{(\gamma/\beta)t}$$

where $\log K_0$ is the constant of integration and K_0 the initial stock of capi-tal. Putting (9.4.20) in (9.4.19) and (9.4.18), we have respectively

$$I(t) = I_0 e^{(\gamma/\beta)t}$$

and

$$Y(t) = Y_0 e^{(\gamma/\beta)t}$$

which yield steady exponential growth trends. Stated in words, the smaller is the capital-income ratio, β, and the greater is the savings-income ratio, γ, "the faster must the economic top keep spinning if full employment is to be maintained from growth factors alone."[6]

Next, Samuelson assumes that "a crucial equilibrium" level of capital, $\overline{K}$, depends on income, the interest rate and technology, and that the level of investment, $I(t)$, becomes positive when $K(t) < \overline{K}$ and the investment becomes positive if $K(t) > \overline{K}$. If we allow investment $I(t)$ to be pro-portional to the difference between the "crucial equilibrium" level of capital and $K(t)$, we obtain

$$I(t) = -m[K(t) - \overline{K}] = -mk(t),$$

[5] *Ibid.*, p. 361.
[6] *Ibid.*, p. 362.

and

(9.4.21) $$\frac{dk(t)}{dt} = \frac{d[K(t) - \overline{K}]}{dt} = \frac{dk(t)}{dt} - 0 = I(t),$$

hence

$$\frac{dk(t)}{dt} = -mk(t),$$

therefore,

$$k(t) = k_0 e^{-mt}.$$

Since $m > 0$, $k(t)$ approaches zero as t approaches infinity, while therefore $K(t)$ approaches $\overline{K}$.

On the other hand, "cyclical oscillations will occur if an excess of capital rather than leading to negative investment instead leads to a 'deceleration' of the algebraic rate of investment."[7] In this case,

(9.4.22) $$\frac{dI(t)}{dt} = -mk(t).$$

Differentiating (9.4.21) and putting equal to (9.4.22), we obtain

(9.4.23) $$\frac{d^2k(t)}{dt^2} = -mk(t),$$

which is an incomplete homogeneous second-order differential equation whose solution, according to Section 9.3, is obtained as follows.

We set $k(t) = e^{Pt}$ to have

$$P^2 e^{Pt} = -m e^{Pt},$$

or

$$P^2 = -m$$

and

$$P = \pm\sqrt{-m}.$$

Since m is positive, the roots are complex; and since the roots do not possess the "real part," the solution of (9.4.23) is

$$k(t) = A \cos \sqrt{m}\, t + B \sin \sqrt{m}\, t.$$

Since the solution consists of trigonometric elements, "such a system gives rise to sinusoidal oscillations around the equilibrium — oscillations which are exactly like those of a pendulum. Intuitively, we can glimpse this as follows: Suppose capital is growing, and it pushes through its equilibrium level. Its inertia causes it to overshoot the mark, because the positive level of investment is only gradually tapering off. But after capital

[7] *Ibid.*, p. 363.

has grown to a crucial peak, its decelerating effects finally cause investment to become negative. Capital is now returning toward its equilibrium level at an increasing rate. It passes through the equilibrium level with negative disinvestment at its peak rate. Now there is a downward over-shoot, which lasts until the gradual acceleration of investment, due to capital shortage, causes investment to become positive — at which point capital has reached its trough and has begun to revive. And so on."[8]

9.5 The Stability of Competitive Equilibrium[9]

The Hicksian Conditions. We noticed, in Chapter 3 and the first part of Section 9.4, that the stability of economic equilibrium in a single-product market depends on the assumption that a positive excess demand would increase the price while a positive excess supply causes a fall in price. In other words, if in the neighborhood of the equilibrium position a price below the equilibrium one results in excess demand and a price above the equilibrium one gives rise to excess supply, the equilibrium is said to be stable. But when we translate the stability condition to multiple markets-dimensions, we must be cognizant of, and take into account, the influence of the change in price of a given good on all other goods included in the transactions and related to the given good somehow. This is referred to as static multiple markets stability or the Hicksian conditions due to Professor Hicks.

According to Professor Hicks, a multiple markets equilibrium is *stable perfectly* if an excess demand for a good raises its price even when any subset of other prices of the goods which are related to this good is kept constant; but a system "in which supply does become greater than demand when price rises if all repercussions are allowed for,"[10] is *imperfectly stable.* If the Hicksian conditions are satisfied, the multiple markets equilibrium is restored via the substitution and income effects. In the ensuing pages, we first explain verbally the Hicksian conditions for two markets, and then apply the results to n markets and extend them to dynamic stability.

At the outset, it is fair to state that the Hicksian conditions are tatonnment; that is, the transactions are not allowed at non-equilibrium prices. Let us suppose that there are only two substitutable goods X_1 and X_2 held and produced by A and B in such a manner that in these two markets A consumes part of his own good, X_1, and sells the rest to B. Similarly, the good held by B is partly consumed by B and largely demanded by A. Moreover, we assume that both markets initially are in equilibrium, as in Figure 9.1.

---

[8] *Ibid.*, p. 363.
[9] The reader who is not yet familiar with matrix algebra may omit this section, or he may revert to it after having read Chapters 11–12.
[10] J. R. Hicks, *Value and Capital*, 1961, p. 67.

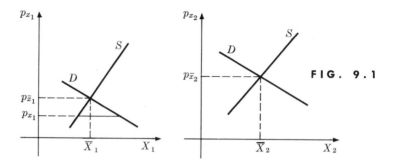

FIG. 9.1

Let us suppose that the price of X_1, due to some exogenous reason, falls to $p_{x_1} < p_{\bar{x}_1}$. Before the price change there was no excess demand in either market; but when the equilibrium price of X_1 fell to a new position, there resulted an excess demand in X_1's market. Assuming that A consumes the same quantity of X_1, his income would fall since the same quantity, with the price being less than what it was before, sold to B will bring A less money income. On the other hand, B's real income, his purchasing power in terms of X_1, will rise, resulting in more demand for X_1 and consequently more X_1 from A's consumption to B's. This brings more income for A which must be earned if A increases his supply. This is the *income effect* which clearly is cancelled on both sides. For this reason alone, the income effect exercises no influence; or its repercussion is negligible in Hicksian analysis. But the *substitution effect* sets a series of effects which may lead to stability if the proper conditions are satisfied.

When the price of X_1 falls, the price ratio shifts in favor of X_1 and against X_2; consequently B would substitute more of X_1 for X_2, since X_1 and X_2 are assumed to be substitutable. On the other hand, since p_{x_1} has fallen, A wishes to sell less and B demands more simply because p_{x_1} has decreased while p_{x_2} has remained unchanged. It is actually the price ratio which has caused the problem. If, for instance, the two prices change in the same direction, nothing of importance will happen. Mathematically, we say that excess demand is homogeneous of zero order. To conclude the discussion, excess demand in X_1's market will raise p_{x_1} back to a point where the equilibrium can be established in that market while allowing for all possible repercussions in X_2's market.

In the preceding paragraph, we gave the following chain of causation: as p_{x_1} fell, there resulted an excess demand in X_1's market and an excess supply in X_2's market which would force p_{x_2} down, or mathematically

$$\frac{dp_{x_2}}{dp_{x_1}} > 0.$$

Also, if p_{x_1} rises, there would result an excess supply in X_1's market and an excess demand in X_2's market, and eventually p_{x_2} will be pushed upward, or mathematically

$$\frac{dp_{x_2}}{dp_{x_1}} > 0.$$

Hicks has shown[11] these conditions in the following figure where the slope of X_1X' is greater than the slope of $X_2X' \cdot X_1X'$ is a curve which indicates that with a given price ratio X_1 is in equilibrium. Likewise, for given price ratios X_2X' shows that X_2 is in equilibrium while X_1 may not be. Only at E are X_1 and X_2 both in equilibrium. Now, the two positive differentials that we gave above may be detected from the diagram.

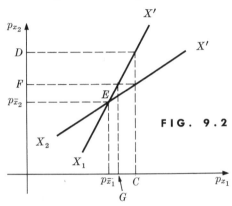

FIG. 9.2

Let us say that $p_{\bar{x}_1}$ rises to C. For X_1 to be in equilibrium $p_{\bar{x}_2}$ must rise to D. But this price puts X_2 in disequilibrium; for X_2 to be in equilibrium p_{x_2} must be consistent with $X_2X'_2$, i.e., F. Although with F and C, X_2 is in equilibrium, X_1 is not in equilibrium. For X_1 to be in equilibrium p_{x_1} must shrink to $G < C$. And so on until E is again reached, for which position X_1 and X_2 are in equilibrium and $p_{\bar{x}_1}/p_{\bar{x}_2}$ is the price ratio.

In symbols, either for normalized or non-normalized prices,[12] we assume

(9.5.1) $$X_1 = \varphi(p_1, p_2),$$

(9.5.2) $$X_2 = \psi(p_1, p_2),$$

where X_1 and X_2 are substitutable. Let us write

$$\frac{\partial X_1}{\partial p_1} = a_{11} < 0, \qquad \frac{\partial X_1}{\partial p_2} = a_{12} > 0,$$

$$\frac{\partial X_2}{\partial p_1} = a_{21} > 0, \qquad \frac{\partial X_2}{\partial p_2} = a_{22} < 0,$$

[11] *Ibid.*, pp. 67–68.
[12] K. J. Arrow and L. Hurwicz, "The Existence of Competitive Equilibrium," *Econometrica*, 1958, pp. 546–550.

owing to substitutability. The total differentials of (9.5.1) and (9.5.2) yield

$$dX_1 = 0 = \frac{\partial X_1}{\partial p_1} dp_1 + \frac{\partial X_1}{\partial p_2} dp_2$$

which implies that

(9.5.3) $$\frac{dp_2}{dp_1} = -\frac{a_{11}}{a_{12}} > 0,$$

and

$$dX_2 = 0 = \frac{\partial X_2}{\partial p_1} dp_1 + \frac{\partial X_2}{\partial p_2} dp_2$$

which gives

(9.5.4) $$\frac{dp_2}{dp_1} = -\frac{a_{21}}{a_{22}} > 0.$$

(9.5.3) and (9.5.4) are the relations which we had before. Now, we are in a position to generalize mathematically the Hicksian conditions[13] and extend them to dynamic stability. Let us assume that there are $n + 1$ goods in the economy and that the $(n + 1)$st good serves as numeraire and money. For the price of the ith good we have

$$p_i(i = 1, 2, \ldots n),$$

and the amount ultimately retained of the ith good by X_i where

(9.5.5) $$X_i = X_i(p_1, p_2, \ldots p_n).$$

The equilibrium is *perfectly stable* if

$$\frac{dX_i}{dp_i} < 0,$$

and

$$\frac{dX_i}{dp_j} = 0 \qquad (i \neq j).$$

The inequality shows that there would be an excess demand when p_i is less than the equilibrium price and an access supply when p_i is more than the equilibrium price. The equations indicate that all other prices are adjusted for possible repercussions to maintain equilibrium in these markets. The total differential of (9.5.5) gives

$$dX_i = \frac{\partial X_i}{\partial p_1} dp_1 + \cdots + \frac{\partial X_i}{\partial p_i} dp_i + \cdots + \frac{\partial X_i}{\partial p_n} dp_n$$

---

[13] J. R. Hicks, *op. cit.* pp. 66ff and 315-316. An excellent mathematical exposition of the Hicksian conditions and dynamic stability conditions is given in O. Lange's Appendix to his *Price Flexibility and Employment*, Bloominton, 1952, pp. 91–97.

which dividing by dp_i entails

$$\frac{dX_i}{dp_i} = \frac{\partial X_i}{\partial p_1}\frac{dp_1}{dp_i} + \cdots + \frac{\partial X_i}{\partial p_i} + \cdots + \frac{\partial X_i}{\partial p_n}\frac{dp_n}{dp_i}.$$

Let us write

$$\frac{\partial X_i}{\partial p_j} = a_{ij},$$

thus,

$$\frac{dX_i}{dp_j} = a_{i1}\frac{dp_1}{dp_j} + \cdots + a_{ij}\frac{dp_i}{dp_j} + \cdots + a_{in}\frac{dp_n}{dp_j}.$$

If we exchange places between $\dfrac{dX_i}{dp_j}$ and $a_{ij}\dfrac{dp_i}{dp_j}$ and find the differentials of (9.5.5) for $i = 1, 2, \ldots n$, we will have a set of n differential equations as follows

$$-a_{1i} = a_{11}\frac{dp_1}{dp_i} + \cdots + 0 + \cdots + a_{1n}\frac{dp_n}{dp_i},$$

$$\cdot \cdot \cdot \cdot \cdot \cdot \cdot \cdot \cdot \cdot \cdot \cdot \cdot,$$

(9.5.6) $$-a_{ii} = a_{i1}\frac{dp_1}{dp_i} + \cdots - \frac{dX_i}{dp_i} + \cdots + a_{in}\frac{dp_n}{dp_i},$$

$$\cdot \cdot \cdot \cdot \cdot \cdot \cdot \cdot \cdot \cdot \cdot \cdot \cdot,$$

$$-a_{ni} = a_{n1}\frac{dp_1}{dp_i} + \cdots + 0 + \cdots + a_{nn}\frac{dp_n}{dp_i}.$$

The solution of (9.5.6) for $\dfrac{dX_i}{dp_i}$ gives

$$\frac{dX_i}{dp_i} = \frac{J}{J_{ii}}$$

where

$$J \equiv \begin{vmatrix} a_{11} & a_{12} & \cdots & a_{1n} \\ a_{21} & a_{22} & \cdots & a_{2n} \\ \cdot & \cdot & \cdot & \cdot \\ a_{n1} & a_{n2} & \cdots & a_{nn} \end{vmatrix}$$

is called a Jacobian determinant and the cofactor of a_{ii} is denoted by J_{ii}. Since any ratio of the form

$$\frac{J}{J_{ii}}$$

is necessarily negative in sign,[14]

$$\frac{dX_i}{dp_i} = \frac{J}{J_{ii}} < 0$$

[14] J. R. Hicks, *op. cit.*, p. 310 and P. A. Samuelson, *Foundations*, p. 272.

which requires that[15]

(9.5.7) $\qquad a_{11} < 0, \begin{vmatrix} a_{11} & a_{12} \\ a_{21} & a_{22} \end{vmatrix} > 0, \ldots \text{sign } J = \text{sign}(-1)^n.$

(9.5.7) are the Hicksian conditions for perfect stability.

Dynamic Stability. According to Samuelson, "the equations of comparative statics are . . . a special case of the general dynamic analysis . . . the problem of stability of equilibrium cannot be discussed except with reference to dynamical considerations, however implicit and rudimentary."[16] In dynamizing stability conditions, Samuelson has made the assumption of the Hicksian conditions explicit — that the excess demand for a good makes its price rise and the excess supply of it makes it fall. It is clear that this assumption is not explicit in the Hicksian conditions. Let the excesss demand for the ith good be X_i. Then, according to dynamic stability,

(9.5.8) $\qquad \text{sign } \dfrac{dp_i}{dt} = \text{sign } X_i.$

In particular, let

$$\frac{dp_i}{dt} = f_i(X_i).$$

The right-hand side of (9.5.8) can be expanded by Maclaurin's theorem to yield

(9.5.9) $\qquad \dfrac{dp_i}{dt} = f'(0)X_i + \cdots$

Since

$$X_i = X_i(p_1, p_2, \ldots p_n)$$

according to Euler's theorem, we have

$$X_i \equiv \frac{\partial X_i}{\partial p_1} p_1 + \cdots + \frac{\partial X_i}{\partial p_j} p_j + \cdots + \frac{\partial X_i}{\partial p_n} p_n,$$

$$\equiv a_{i1}p_1 + \cdots + a_{ij}p_j + \cdots + a_{in}p_n$$

(9.5.10) $\qquad \equiv \displaystyle\sum_{i=1}^{n} a_{ij}p_j \qquad (j = 1, 2, \ldots n).$

Substituting (9.5.10) in (9.5.9), we have

(9.5.11) $\qquad \dfrac{dp_i}{dt} = f'(0) \displaystyle\sum_{i=1}^{n} a_{ij}p_j.$

(9.5.11) is a set of differential equations the solution of which is

$$p_i(t) = \bar{p}_i + \sum_{i=1}^{n} k_{ij}e^{\lambda_j t}$$

---

[15] These are so-called negative definite conditions for a matrix. See Chapter 12, Section 12.8.

[16] P. A. Samuelson, *Foundations*, p. 262.

where $(\lambda_1, \ldots, \lambda_n)$ are the distinct roots of the characteristic equation

(9.5.12)
$$\varphi(\lambda) = \begin{vmatrix} a_{11} - \lambda & a_{12} & \ldots & a_{1n} \\ a_{21} & a_{22} - \lambda & \ldots & a_{2n} \\ \cdot & \cdot & \cdots & \cdot \\ a_{n1} & a_{n2} & \ldots & a_{nn} - \lambda \end{vmatrix}$$

$$= |A - \lambda I| = 0.$$

Of course, k's are polynomials in t and depend on the matrix A and the initial conditions where

$$A = \begin{bmatrix} a_{11} & a_{12} & \ldots & a_{1n} \\ a_{21} & a_{22} & \ldots & a_{2n} \\ \cdot & \cdot & \cdots & \cdot \\ a_{n1} & a_{n2} & \ldots & a_{nn} \end{bmatrix}$$

which is the matrix of the partial derivatives of excess demand of the ith good with respect to the jth price, and $\bar{p}_i$ is the equilibrium price of the ith good. There exists a stable equilibrium; *i.e.*

$$p_i(t) \to \bar{p}_i,$$

if

$$\lim_{t \to \infty} \left\{ \sum_{i=1}^{n} k_{ij} e^{\lambda_j t} \right\} = 0,$$

or $R(\lambda_j) < 0$ as before.[17] [$R(\lambda_j)$ denotes the real part of the root λ_j of (9.5.12).] If, however, $R(\lambda_j) > 0$, we get

$$\lim_{t \to \infty} \left\{ \sum_{i=1}^{n} k_{ij} e^{\lambda_j t} \right\} = \pm \infty$$

and the equilibrium is unstable. When $R(\lambda_j) = 0$, the equilibrium is said to be neutral.[18]

If we assume that the partial derivative of excess demand of the ith good with respect to the jth price — the effect of the price change of the jth commodity on excess demand of the ith good — is the same as the partial derivative of excess demand of the jth good with respect to the ith price,

$$\frac{\partial X_i}{\partial p_j} = \frac{\partial X_j}{\partial p_i},$$

or

$$a_{ij} = a_{ji},$$

---

[17] *Ibid.*, p. 271.
[18] O. Lange, *op. cit.*, p. 96.

which renders matrix A symmetric

$$A = \begin{bmatrix} a_{11} & a_{12} & \cdots & a_{1n} \\ a_{12} & a_{22} & \cdots & a_{2n} \\ \cdot & \cdot & \cdots & \cdot \\ a_{1n} & a_{2n} & \cdots & a_{nn} \end{bmatrix}$$

then, according to a theorem of Hermitian matrices,[19] all the roots of (9.5.12) will be real.

If all the roots of (9.5.12) are to be negative, to make the equilibrium stable dynamically, the principal minors of A should alternate in sign, *i.e.*,

(9.5.13) $a_{11} < 0, \begin{vmatrix} a_{11} & a_{12} \\ a_{21} & a_{22} \end{vmatrix} > 0, \ldots \text{sign } J = \text{sign}(-1)^n;$

that is, it is necessary and sufficient that the Hicksian conditions be satisfied. Or, if a system of competitive equilibrium is to be stable it is necessary and sufficient that the Hicksian conditions are satisfied.

The assumption of symmetrical partial derivatives is a strong one with given implications and restrictions.[20] Many mathematical economists (e.g., Arrow, Hahn, Hurwicz, Morishima, Negishi and Uzawa[21]) have relaxed the symmetrical assumption and only retained the gross substitutability assumption which implies that

$$\frac{\partial X_i}{\partial p_i} < 0, \qquad \frac{\partial X_i}{\partial p_j} > 0,$$

or

(9.5.14) $a_{ii} < 0, \qquad a_{ij} > 0$

for $(i \neq j)$.

Of all contributions, which deal with many other issues as well as stability and the mathematics of which is beyond the scope of this book, we take the most elegant proof given by Negishi. His theorem states that if all goods are gross substitutes; *i.e.*, (9.5.14) are satisfied, matrix $A = (a_{ij})$

---

[19] See Section 12.10 of Chapter 12, Theorems 12.21 and 12.22.

[20] O. Lange, *op. cit.*, pp. 97–99.

[21] K. J. Arrow, H. D. Block and L. Hurwicz, "On the Stability of the Competitive Equilibrium," *Econometrica*, 1959, pp. 82–109. K. J. Arrow and Hurwicz, "On the Stability of the Competitive Equilibrium," *Econometrica*, 1958, pp. 522–552. K. J. Arrow and L. Hurwicz, "Some Remarks on the Equilibrium of Economic System," *Econometrica*, 1960, pp. 640–646. F. H. Hahn, "Gross Substitutes and the Dynamic Stability of General Equilibrium," *Econometrica*, 1958, pp. 169–170. T. Negishi, "A Note on the Stability of an Economy Where All Goods are Gross Substitutes," *Econometrica*, 1958, pp. 445–447. M. Morishima, "On the Law of Change of Price-System in an Economy Which Contains Complementary Commodities," *Osaka Economic Papers*, 1952, pp. 101–113. H. Uzawa, "The Stability of Dynamic Processes," *Econometrica*, 1961, 617–631.

is Hicksian and the system of competitive equilibrium of multiple markets is dynamically stable. Let us approximate the dynamic behavior of prices by

(9.5.15)
$$\frac{dp_i}{dt} = F_i \sum_{i,j=1}^{n-1} a_{ij}(p_i - \overline{p}_i)$$

where F_i are positive constants. If n commodities are assumed to exist within the economy the nth one serving as numeraire and money, then $p_n \equiv 1$ and $\overline{p}_i$ the equilibrium price of the ith good will be taken to be positive.

We pointed out at the beginning of this section that if all prices rise or fall at the same time, excess demand would not be affected; mathematically, excess demand functions are homogeneous of zero order, or

(9.5.16)
$$\sum_{i,j=1}^{n-1} a_{ij}\overline{p}_j = -a_{in}\overline{p}_n = -a_{in}.$$

It is obvious that (9.5.16) is an implication of Walras's Law; *i.e.*, the sum of the value of excess demands of all goods evaluated at their equilibrium prices is equal to negative excess demand for money. Multiplying (9.5.16) on both sides by (-1) and putting

$$-a_{ij} = b_{ij}$$

and

$$a_{in} = b_i$$

we have

(9.5.17)
$$\sum_{i,j=1}^{n-1} b_{ij}\overline{p}_j = b_i$$

where $b_{ij} < 0$, $b_{ii} > 0$, $b_i > 0$ and $\overline{p}_j > 0$.

According to a theorem due to Debreu and Herstein,[22] all the elements of the inverse matrix of (b_{ij}) are to be positive. And, according to the Hawkins-Simon Theorem,[23] if all the elements of the inverse matrix of (b_{ij}) are to be positive, it is necessary and sufficient that the principal minors of (b_{ij}) must be positive. Or all the principal minors of (a_{ij}), which is the negative of (b_{ij}), should oscillate in sign. Thus, if $A = (a_{ij})$ is Hicksian, the system is dynamically stable which completes the proof.

---

[22] G. Debreu and I. N. Herstein, "Non-negative Square Matrices," *Econometrica*, 1953, p. 602.

[23] D. Hawkins and H. A. Simon, "Some Conditions of Macro-economic Stability," *Econometrica*, 1949, p. 247.

EXERCISES 9

1. What is the order of the following functions $\left(\dfrac{d}{dx} = D\right)$?

$x^2 Dy + e^{2y}(D^2 y)^4 = 8.$ $Dy = \cos y + 2x.$

$x Dy + y - 1 = e^{2x}.$ $D^4 y + (Dy)^2 + y = \sin(2x).$

$\sin(Dy) + Dy = y - 2.$

2. Find differential equations for which the following are general solutions (c is the parameter):

$x^2 + (y + c)^2 = 4.$ $y = c_1 x + c_2 x^2.$

$y^2 = x^2 + cx + 1.$ $y = c_1 \cos(3x + c_2).$

3. Which of the following is exact ($d/dx = D$):

$Dy + y \cos x = e^x.$ $(2xy - y^2)\, dx - (2xy - x^2)\, dy = 0.$

$\dfrac{x\, dy}{x^2 + y^2} - \dfrac{y\, dx}{x^2 + y^2} = 0.$

4. Test the following for exactness and, if exact, solve:

$(y + 2x)\, dx + x\, dy = 0.$ $(x^2 - y^2)\, dx = 2xy\, dy.$

$(ax + by)\, dx + (bx + cy)\, dy = 0.$ $(2x^2 + 4xy)\, dx - (2x^2 + y^2)\, dy = 0.$

$(\sin x + x \sin y)\, dy - (\cos y - y \cos x)\, dx = \sin y\, dy.$

5. Find the general solution of each of the following $\left(\dfrac{d}{dx} = D\right)$:

$Dy = \dfrac{3x}{y + 2}.$ $Dy = \dfrac{x - 2xy}{3y}.$

$Dy = \dfrac{\sin y}{x + 3}.$ $Dy = 3xe^{2x+y}.$

$Dy = \dfrac{ye^x}{y - e^x}.$

6. Find the general solution of each of the following $\left(\dfrac{d}{dx} = D\right)$:

$Dy = e^x + 2y.$ $Dy = 4y - xy^2.$

$Dy = 2x - y.$ $Dy = \dfrac{1 - 4xy}{x^2}.$

$Dy = \dfrac{2}{y - x}.$

7. Solve the following by finding an integrating factor:

$x\, dy + y\, dx + x^4 y^2\, dx = 0.$ $x\, dy - y\, dx = (x^2 + 1)\, dx.$

$x\, dy - y\, dx = (x^2 + y^2)\, dx.$ $y^2\, dx + x(x\, dy - y\, dx) = 0.$

$dy + \dfrac{v}{x}\, dx = \sin x\, dx.$

8. Solve each of the following $\left(D = \dfrac{d}{dx} \right)$:

$Dy + \dfrac{y}{x} = 1.$ $\qquad\qquad\qquad$ $y \, dx + x \, dy = \cos x \, dx.$

$(y + y^3) \, dx + 4yx \, dy = 3 \, y \, dy.$ $\qquad$ $x Dy - 4y = x^2.$

$(1 + x^2) \, dy = dx + xy \, dx.$

9. Solve each of the following equations:

$2xy \, dx - (x^2 + y^2) \, dy = 0.$ $\qquad\qquad$ $(x - y) \, dx + (x + y) \, dy = 0.$

$2x^2 \, dy = (x^2 + y^2) \, dx.$ $\qquad\qquad\quad$ $y^2 \, dx + (xy + x^2) \, dy = 0.$

$x^2 y \, dx - (x^3 + y^3) \, dy = 0.$

10. Solve each of the following linear equations:

$$(x - xy) \, dy + (y + xy) \, dx = 0.$$

$$2y^2 \, dx + (4xy - 3y^2) \, dy = 0.$$

$$2xy \, dy = (1 - y^2) \, dx.$$

$$(x^2 + 1) \, dy + 2xy \, dx = 4x^2 \, dx.$$

$$\cos^2 x \, dy + y \, dx = \tan x \, dx.$$

$$dy + \dfrac{xy}{1 - x^2} \, dx = xy^{\frac{1}{2}} \, dx.$$

$$3x(1 - x^2)y^2 \, dy + (2x^2 - 1)y^3 \, dx = ax^3 \, dx.$$

$$(2y \cos 2x + 2 \sin 2x) \, dx + \sin 2x \, dy = 0.$$

$$(y + x^2 - 1) \, dx + x \, dy = 0.$$

$$dy + y \, dx = e^{-x} \, dx.$$

$$(x + 1) \, dy - ny \, dx = e^x(x + 1)^{n+1} \, dx.$$

$$dy + \dfrac{2}{x} y \, dx = 3x^2 y^{\frac{4}{3}} \, dx.$$

11. Find the general solution of each of the following equations $\left(\dfrac{d}{dx} = D \right)$:

$(D^2 - 4)y = 0.$ $\qquad\qquad\qquad\qquad$ $(D^2 - 2D)y = 0.$

$(D^2 - 6D + 9)y = 0.$ $\qquad\qquad\quad$ $(D^2 - 10D + 16)y = 0.$

$(D^2 - 8D + 15)y = 0.$ $\qquad\qquad\quad$ $(D^2 + 6)y = 0.$

12. Find the general solution of each of the following equations $\left(D = \dfrac{d}{dx} \right)$:

$(D^2 - 9)y = x^2 - 3x + 2.$ $\qquad\qquad$ $(D^2 - 4D + 3)y = (x + 3)e^x.$

$(D^2 - 1)y = 3 \sin x.$ $\qquad\qquad\qquad$ $(D^2 - 4D + 4)y = 2e^{-3x} \cos 3x.$

$(D^2 - 5D + 4)y = 4 - e^{-2x}.$ $\qquad\quad$ $(D^2 - 6D + 8)y = 12 - 3e^{-x}.$

10 LINEAR DIFFERENCE EQUATIONS IN ECONOMICS

Every person having had even the slightest acquaintance with modern economic theory has heard or seen the concept of "period analysis." This is a symbolic example of difference equations. That is to say, in difference equations one is concerned with "lagged" or the movement of lagged variables. If we assert that aggregate consumption of one period is related to the level of income of the "previous" period, we are expressing our notion of association of consumption with income in terms of difference equation

$$C_t = \alpha(Y_{t-1})$$

which indicates that the consumption of period t depends on the income of $t - 1$, α being an arbitrary constant.

10.1 Difference Equations and Their Properties

The main task of forming a difference equation is to relate the lagged (or delayed) values of a variable in a way that one can detect from a difference equation the behavior (strictly speaking, *sequence*) of the lagged variable over a specific period. Once upon a time Professor Alvin Hansen, having assumed that

$$C_t = \alpha Y_{t-1}$$
$$I_t = \beta(C_t - C_{t-1})$$
$$G_t = 1$$
$$Y_t = I_t + C_t + G_t,$$

concluded that the sequence (or behavior) of income should be judged from

(10.1.1) $$Y_{t+2} = \alpha(1 + \beta)Y_{t+1} - \alpha\beta Y_t + 1$$

250

where C is consumption, I stands for investment, G for government expenditures, t period under consideration, α and β are the marginal propensity to consume and the accelerator respectively. The multiplier-accelerator process demonstrated by equation (10.1.1) did not, however, prove to be verifiable empirically. There are many other examples that one can find easily in modern economic theory, such as the ones in Sections 10.5 and 10.6.

In difference equations, time is usually the independent variable. That is, a dependent variable is measured against time. For this reason, the number of lags are time intervals. Accordingly, the following definition is in order:

Definition. A difference equation is that which relates a dependent variable to the lags of the independent variable.

A difference equation is *solved* when the values of the dependent variable make the difference equation a true statement for every value of independent variable. Like differential equations, difference equations have *degrees* and *orders*. The *order* of a difference equation depends upon the number of differences or lags of the variable. Thus,

(10.1.2) $a_0 y_{t+n} + a_1 y_{t+n-1} + \cdots + a_n y_t = f(t)$

is a difference equation of order n. The degree of a difference equation is determined by the degree of the term which has the highest order. Accordingly, equation (10.1.2) is of degree one (*linear*). The following examples may make the matter clearer:

$$2y_{t+3} + 3y_{t+2} - 5y_{t+1} - 4y_t = 7 \quad \text{(order 3) (degree 1)},$$
$$y_{t+2}^3 + 3y_t = 4 \quad \text{(order 2) (degree 3)},$$
$$2y_{t+5} + 3y_{t+4} = 2 \quad \text{(order 1) (degree 1)}.$$

The first and third examples are linear and the second one is *nonlinear*. Emphasis should be made that a difference equation which has a few lags should *not* be taken as *nonlinear*.

A linear difference equation with *constant coefficients* (in contradistinction to *variable coefficients*) is called *homogeneous* when the left-hand side member of it is zero. Otherwise, it is called *complete*. Accordingly,

$$y_{t+3} - 2y_{t+2} + 5y_{t+1} + 3y_t = 0$$

is linear third-order homogeneous with constant coefficients.

Solution of a Linear Difference Equation. Like differential equations, the complete solution of a complete difference equation is composed of two parts: One is the complementary function which is the solution of the related homogeneous equation; the second part is the particular solution. Whence, the following theorem is given without proof:

Theorem 10.1.   The complete solution of a linear n-order complete difference equation

(10.1.3) $$y_{t+n} + a_1 y_{t+n-1} + \cdots + a_n y_t = r(t)$$

is

(10.1.4) $$y_t = Y_t + y^*$$

where Y_t, called the complementary function, is the solution of

(10.1.5) $$y_{t+n} + a_1 y_{t+n-1} + \cdots + a_n y_t = 0$$

and y^* is a particular solution of (10.1.3).

The solution of (10.1.5) may not present any major difficulty since it is only a polynomial of degree n.   And the only method for finding the particular solution is the *method of undetermined coefficients* which was described in relation to differential equations.   Like differential equations, this method is only applicable to difference equations with constant coefficients and when the right-hand side member $r(t)$ in (10.1.3) is such that the form of a particular solution may be guessed.   Then, the particular solution may be found by applying the following rule: For all constant parts of $r(t)$, write 1 and assign to each of them a literal constant coefficient. Write the variable parts of $r(t)$ in a way that the similar terms are arranged into groups.   If no member of a given group appears as a term in the complementary function, Y_t, all members of the group are left unchanged. If, however, any member of a group is a term of Y_t, all members of that group must be multiplied by t.   Now, assign a constant coefficient to each member in all groups.   This is the trial particular solution whose literal constant coefficients are yet to be determined.   Determine the needed successive lags for this trial solution and substitute the results in the original difference equation, match corresponding terms with $r(t)$ and produce an identity by determining proper values of the constant coefficients.   The rule will be illustrated by solving examples in the ensuing sections.

10.2 Solution of a Linear First Order Difference Equation

Let us consider

(10.2.1) $$y_{t+1} + a y_t = r_t$$

the homogeneous equation of which is

(10.2.2) $$y_{t+1} + a y_t = 0.$$

Setting $y_t = m^t$, (10.2.2) is reduced to $m + a = 0$ or $m = -a$ whence

(10.2.3) $$Y_t = y_0(-a)^t$$

Moreover, if we add a particular solution y^* which satisfies equations (10.2.1), (10.2.2), and (10.2.3), the general or complete solution will be

$$y_t = y_0(-a)^t + y^*$$

where y_0 is the initial condition and

$$y^* = r_t \frac{1 + a^t}{1 + a}$$

if $a \neq 1$. If, however, $a = 1$, we have

$$y^* = rt.$$

The following theorems relating to the solution of the first order difference equation

$$y_{t+1} = A y_t + B$$

are given without proof.[1]

Theorem 10.2. Let $\{y_k\}$ be the solution of the first order difference equation

(10.2.4) $$y_{t+1} = A y_t + B$$

where

(10.2.5) $$y_k = A^k y_0 + B \frac{1 - A^k}{1 - A}$$

if $A \neq 1$; and

(10.2.6) $$y_k = y_0 + Bk$$

if $A = 1$, where y_0 in both (10.2.5) and (10.2.6) is the initial condition. When the solution of (10.2.4) is (10.2.6), it is obvious that $\{y_k\} = y_0$ — the solution is a constant sequence — if $B = 0$. On the other hand, if $B > 0$, $\{y_k\}$ diverges to $+\infty$ for $k = 1, \ldots$; and if $B < 0$, $\{y_k\}$ diverges to $-\infty$ for $k = 1, 2, \ldots$.

Theorem 10.3. If the solution of (10.2.4) is (10.2.5) or

$$y_k = A^k(y_0 - y^*) + y^*$$

where

$$y^* = \frac{B}{1 - A}$$

the solution $\{y_k\}$ converges to y^* if $-1 < A < 1$. If, however, $|A| > 1$, the solution $\{y_k\}$ diverges unless $y_0 = y^*$.

---

[1] For an excellent treatment of difference equations and a proof of this theorem and other theorems see S. Goldberg's *Introduction to Difference Equations*, New York, 1958, pp. 77–86.

To utilize the results that we just obtained, we will solve two examples. We first consider a simple multiplier-accelerator model for a closed economy without the public sector. Let us assume that

(10.2.7) $$C_t = \beta + \alpha y_t$$

which indicates the consumption function where β is the consumption-intercept and α is the marginal propensity to consume. Also,

(10.2.8) $$\delta I_t = y_t - y_{t-1}$$

represents the investment function where δ is the power of accelerator and I_t for investment in t. We can also add a definition to the equations mentioned above.

(10.2.9) $$y_t = I_t + C_t.$$

By substituting in (10.2.8) from (10.2.7) and (10.2.9), we get

(10.2.10) $$y_{t+1} = \frac{1}{1 + \delta(\alpha - 1)} y_t - \frac{\beta\delta}{1 + \delta(\alpha - 1)}.$$

To simplify the matter, let us suppose that $\delta = 1$, $\beta = 25$ and $\alpha = \frac{1}{2}$ in (10.2.10) to have

(10.2.11) $$y_{t+1} = 2y_t - 50,$$

the complete solution of which is

(10.2.12) $$y_k = y_0 2^k + y^* \qquad (k = 1, 2, \ldots).$$

For seeking y^*, we set y^* equal to A in (10.2.11) thus yielding

$$A = 2A - 50$$

or

(10.2.13) $$A = 50 = y^*.$$

We substitute (10.2.13) into (10.2.12) to have

(10.2.14) $$y_k = y_0 2^k + 50$$

which is the complete solution of (10.2.10). It is obvious from (10.2.14) that for positive y_0 if k increases without bound, y_k will be divergent. To find the behavior of y_k as k increases without bound while y_0 is given is the task of difference equations.

Having in mind the method of undetermined coefficients, let us solve the following examples. Solve

(10.2.15) $$y_{t+1} - 5y_t = 5^t + 4$$

where the right-hand member is a function of time. The corresponding complementary function is

$$Y_k = y_0 5^k \qquad (k = 1, 2, \ldots).$$

Now, our problem is to find y^*. The right-hand member of (10.2.15) is composed of two parts: a constant part, 4, and a variable part 5^t. According to the method of undetermined coefficients, our first trial solution is

$$y_t^* = A5^t + B.$$

Since the first term, $A5^t$, appears in the complementary function, thus not independent of the latter, this term must be multiplied by t and used as the trial solution. Hence

$$y_t^* = At5^t + B$$

is the trial solution. Consequently,

$$y_{t+1}^* = A(t+1)5^{t+1} + B = 5At5^t + 5A5^t + B.$$

Substitution of y_t^* and y_{t+1}^* in (10.2.15) yields

$$5At5^t + 5A5^t + B - 5At5^t - 5B \equiv 5^t + 4.$$

If this identity is to be satisfied, we require that

$$5A5^t = 5^t,$$
$$-4B = 4,$$

therefore $A = \frac{1}{5}$ and $B = -1$, whence $y_k^* = \frac{1}{5}k5^k - 1$.

Therefore, the complete solution of (10.2.15) is

$$y_k = y_0 5^k + \frac{1}{5}k5^k - 1$$

where y_0 is the initial and prescribed condition and obviously if y_0 is positive and k increases without bound, solution y_k will be divergent. Actually, the behavior of y_k (and for that matter the behavior of any solution) depends on the behavior of its *leading term*.

Solve $\qquad y_{t+1} - 3y_t = 3^t + 4t + 5.$

(10.2.16)

The complementary function is $Y_t = y_0 3^k$, thus

$$y_t^* = At3^t + Bt + C,$$

consequently $\quad y_{t+1}^* = A(t+1)3^{t+1} + B(t+1) + C.$

Substitution of y_t^* and y_{t+1}^* in (10.2.16) yields

$$3At3^t + 3A3^t + Bt + B + C - 3At3^t - 3Bt - 3C \equiv 3^t + 4t + 5.$$

If this identity is to hold, we must have

$$3A3^t = 3^t \qquad -2Bt = 4t \qquad B - 2C = 5$$

or

$$A = \tfrac{1}{3} \qquad B = -2 \qquad C = -\tfrac{7}{2}$$

whence

$$y_t^* = \tfrac{1}{3}t3^t - 2t - \tfrac{7}{2}.$$

Thus, the complete solution of (10.2.16) is

$$y_k = y_0 3^k + \tfrac{1}{3}k3^k - 2k - \tfrac{7}{2}$$

which is divergent for y_0 being positive and if k increases without bound.

10.3 Solution of a Linear Second Order Homogeneous Difference Equation

Actually, the method of finding the complete solution of a second order difference equation is the same as the one given for the first order difference equations explained in the preceding section. Accordingly, the following theorem is given without proof:

Theorem 10.4. If the reduced form of

(10.3.1) $y_{t+2} + a_1 y_{t+1} + a_2 y_t = 0$

is

$$m^2 + a_1 m + a_2 = 0$$

where a_1 and a_2 are constants and $a_2 \neq 0$ and m_1 and m_2 are the two roots of the reduced form of (10.3.1), the general solution of (10.3.1) is given by

$$y_k = C_1 m_1^k + C_2 m_2^k \qquad (k = 1, 2, \ldots)$$

if m_1 and m_2 are real and unequal. However, the general solution of (10.3.1) is given by

$$y_k = (C_1 + C_2 k) m_1^k \qquad (k = 1, 2, \ldots)$$

if m_1 and m_2 are real but equal. Finally, the general solution is given by

$$y_k = A r^k \cos(k\theta + \epsilon)$$

if m_1 and m_2 are a pair of complex conjugate $\alpha \pm i\beta$, where

$$m_1 = \alpha + i\beta \qquad m_2 = \alpha - i\beta$$

$$r = \sqrt{\alpha^2 + \beta^2} \qquad \sin\theta = \frac{\beta}{r} \qquad \cos\theta = \frac{\alpha}{r}.$$

We shall presently solve two examples in order to see how the above theorem can be used.

Let us consider the following second order difference equation:

(10.3.2) $y_{t+2} - 3y_{t+1} + 2y_t = 0.$

To solve (10.3.2), we reduce it to a simpler form by setting $y_t = m^t$ so that $y_{t+1} = m^{t+1}$ and $y_{t+2} = m^{t+2}$ to have

$$m^{t+2} - 3m^{t+1} + 2m^t = 0,$$

or

$$m^2 - 3m + 2 = 0$$

the solutions of which are $m_1 = 1$ and $m_2 = 2$.

Since the reduced form has two real and unequal roots, according to Theorem 10.4, we write

$$y_k = C_1 1^k + C_2 2^k \qquad (k = 1, 2, \ldots),$$

where C_1 and C_2 are constant and prescribed.

For the second example, we take

(10.3.3) $$y_{t+2} + 8y_{t+1} + 25y_t = 0$$

the reduced form of it, which is obtained similar to the previous example, is

$$m^2 + 8m + 25 = 0.$$

It is clear that the roots of the reduced form are complex and are

$$m_1 = -4 + 3i \qquad m_2 = -4 - 3i$$

from which

$$r = 5 \qquad \cos\theta = -\tfrac{4}{5} \qquad \sin\theta = \tfrac{3}{5}.$$

Hence, the complete solution of (10.3.3) is

$$y_k = A5^k \cos(k\tfrac{127}{180}\pi + \epsilon) \qquad (k = 1, 2, \ldots).$$

10.4 Complete Solution of the Complete Linear Second Order Difference Equation

The general solution of

$$y_{t+2} + a_1 y_{t+1} + a_2 y_t = r(t)$$

is

$$y_k = H_k + y^*$$

where H_k is the complementary function and the solution of the homogeneous part of the complete equation and y^*, as we defined it in relation to the first order difference equations, is the particular solution.

Solve

(10.4.1) $$y_{t+2} - 5y_{t+1} + 6y_t = 3^t + 5 + 4t$$

the homogeneous part of which is

$$y_{t+2} - 5y_{t+1} + 6y_t = 0.$$

Thus the complementary function of (10.4.1) is

$$H_k = C_1 3^k + C_2 2^k,$$

since the roots of the reduced form of (10.4.1) are 2 and 3. For a particular solution, we should try

$$y_t^* = At3^t + B + Ct;$$

consequently

$$y_{t+1}^* = A(t+1)3^{t+1} + B + C(t+1)$$
$$y_{t+2}^* = A(t+2)3^{t+2} + B + C(t+2).$$

Substitution of y_t^*, y_{t+1}^* and y_{t+2}^* into (10.4.1) yields

$$9At3^t + 18A3^t + B + Ct + 2C - 15At3^t - 15A3^t - 5B$$
$$- 5Ct - 5C + 6At3^t + 6B + 6Ct \equiv 3^t + 5 + 4t.$$

If the identity is to hold, we require that

$$3A3^t = 3^t \qquad -3C + 2B = 5 \qquad 2Ct = 4t$$

hence $A = \frac{1}{3}$, $B = +\frac{11}{2}$ and $C = 2$, or

$$y_t^* = \frac{1}{3}t3^t + \frac{11}{2} + 2t.$$

If we wish to seek the specific values of C_1 and C_2, we will proceed as follows: We take the complementary function

(10.4.2) $$H_k = C_1 3^k + C_2 2^k$$

and solve it for C_1 and C_2. Then, we should have two equations consistent with (10.4.2). For this, we shall try two values of k, say, 1 and 2 and assume two corresponding initial values, say, $H_1 = 3$ and $H_2 = 5$. Whence,

$$3 = 3C_1 + 2C_2$$
$$5 = 9C_1 + 4C_2$$

the simultaneous solution of which gives $C_1 = -\frac{1}{3}$ and $C_2 = 2$, or

$$y_k = -\frac{1}{3}3^k + 2.2^k + \frac{1}{3}k3^k + 2k - \frac{1}{2}.$$

According to the rules of determinants and the solution of the system of linear equations, it is obvious that the unique values of C_1 and C_2 exist if

(10.4.3) $$\begin{vmatrix} m_1(1) & m_2(1) \\ m_1(2) & m_2(2) \end{vmatrix} \neq 0.$$

Solve

(10.4.4) $$y_{t+2} - 4y_{t+1} + 4y_t = t2^t.$$

The complementary function is

$$H_k = C_1 2^k + C_2 k2^k$$

thus, the trial solution is

$$y_t^* = At^2 2^t$$

consequently

$$y_{t+1}^* = A(t+1)^2 2^{t+1} = 2At^2 2^t + 2A2^t + 4At2^t,$$
$$y_{t+2}^* = A(t+2)^2 2^{t+2} = 4At^2 2^t + 16A2^t + 16At2^t.$$

Substituting y_t^*, y_{t+1}^* and y_{t+2}^* in (10.4.4) yields

$$4At^2 2^t + 16A2^t + 16At2^t - 8At^2 2^t - 8A2^t - 16At2^t + 4At^2 2^t \equiv t2^t.$$

If the identity is to hold, we ought to have

$$8A2^t = t2^t$$

or $A = \dfrac{t}{8}$, therefore

$$y_t^* = \tfrac{1}{8}t^3 2^t.$$

Thus, the general solution is

(10.4.5)
$$y_k = C_1 2^k + C_2 k 2^k + \tfrac{1}{8}k^3 2^k$$

which is divergent for $k = 1, 2, \ldots$, if C_1 and C_2 are positive. As soon as the values of C_1 and C_2 are determined in the same manner that they were determined for the previous example, then the leading term of the solution will be defined.

From the results of this section and condition (10.4.3), we are able to deduce the general solution of a complete n-order equation with constant coefficients.

Theorem 10.5. The general solution of

(10.4.6)
$$y_{t+n} + a_1 y_{t+n-1} + \cdots + a_n y_t = r(t)$$

is

$$y_k = H_k + y^* \qquad (k = 1, 2, \ldots),$$

where y^* is the particular solution, as was defined previously, and

$$H_k = C_1 m_1^k + C_2 m_2^k + \cdots + C_n m_n^k$$

is the homogeneous solution if there are n real and unequal roots for the reduced form of (10.4.6). If, however, there are, say, q roots which are equal and the remaining roots are unequal, the solution is given by

$$H_k = (C_1 + C_2 k + \cdots + C_q k^{q-1}) m_1^k + \cdots + y^*.$$

If the roots of the reduced form of (10.4.6) are complex conjugates, the solution is given by

$$Ar^k \cos (k\theta + \epsilon)$$

for each pair of unrepeated complex conjugate roots. If a pair of complex conjugate roots is repeated q times, the solution is

$$r^k \{A_1 \cos(k\theta + \epsilon_1) + A_2 k \cos(k\theta + \epsilon_2) + \cdots + A_q k^{q-1} \cos(k\theta + \epsilon_q)\}.$$

All three cases are subject to the following condition

$$
\begin{vmatrix}
m_1(0) & m_2(0) & \cdots & m_n(0) \\
m_1(1) & m_2(1) & \cdots & m_n(1) \\
\cdot & \cdot & \cdot \cdot \cdot \cdot & \cdot \\
m_1(n) & m_2(n) & \cdots & m_n(n)
\end{vmatrix} \neq 0.
$$

10.5 Some Dynamic Models

In analyzing dynamic market stability and the nature of business cycles, the familiar Cobweb Theorem presents a comprehensive mathematical model using first order difference equations.[2]

Within the static framework of the traditional price theory, where demand is represented by the schedule of the number of units of a good which the households stand willing to purchase within the specific period at different prices and supply represents the number of units of a good which the producers of the product stand willing to sell within the specific period of time at different prices, it has been shown that the price of a commodity, in the short run, is that which equates the planned purchases of consumers to the planned sales of the producers in each period. Moreover, if there is a decrease (increase) in demand, price would rise (fall) to the point at which, again, the above condition is satisfied. In brief, the traditional theory deals with the case where production responds immediately to changes in demand as if the commodity is perishable.

The cobweb theorem deals, on the other hand, with a non-perishable commodity "which fulfills three conditions: (1) where production is completely determined by the producers' response to price, under conditions of pure competition (where the producer bases plans for future production on the assumption that present prices will continue, and that his own production plans will not affect the market); (2) where the time needed for production requires at least one full period before production can be changed, once the plans are made; and (3) where the price is set by the supply available."[3] Hence, we assume that supply of the next succeeding period reacts to the price of this period. If the price of the next period is P_t, then S_t responds to P_{t-1} and S_{t-1} to P_{t-2}; or P_t indicates the pressure on S_{t+1} and P_{t+1} on S_{t+2} and so on ad infinitum. The supply schedule lags one period behind the demand schedule.

Initially, we assume that the price of one period is so that it equates the demand of this period and the supply of the succeeding period so that the

[2] M. Ezekiel, "The Cobweb Theorem," *Quarterly Journal of Economics*, 1938, pp. 255–280; reprinted in *Readings in Business Cycle Theory*, 1944, pp. 422–442. The citations are given from the *Readings*. P. A. Samuelson, "Dynamic Process Analysis," *A Survey of Contemporary Economics*, 1948, pp. 368–374. N. S. Buchanan, "A Reconsideration of the Cobweb Theorem," *Journal of Political Economy*, 1939, pp. 67–81.

[3] M. Ezekiel, *op. cit.*, pp. 437–38.

equilibrium is stable. Next, we suppose that owing to some exogenous causes, there is a permanent increase in demand at the beginning of the first period such that the demand curve in Figure 10.1 shifts from $D_t D_t$ to $D'_t D'_t$.

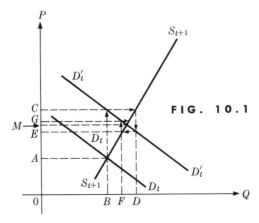

FIG. 10.1

Before the rise in demand, the equilibrium price and its corresponding quantity were $0A$ and $0B$ respectively. However, as a result of a shift in demand, since the quantity is fixed at $0B$, the price would rise to $0C$ where $0C > 0A$ at period one. This rise in price affects producers, who are cognizant of the shift in demand, and make them respond to it. Of course, the path of price in the ensuing periods depends dominantly on how producers implement and revise their production plans.

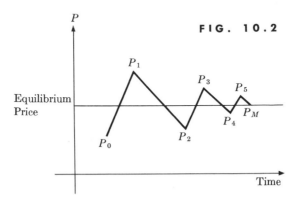

FIG. 10.2

If each producer expects that $0C$ prevails in the first period, then all producers together will plan to supply $0D$ in the next succeeding period $(t + 1)$ where $0D > 0B$. If $0D$ is actually offered in the next succeeding period $(t + 1)$, the corresponding price for that period will be $0E$ which is less than $0C$. Again, if all producers expect the prevalence of $0E$ in $(t + 1)$, they will plan to produce $0F$ in $t + 2$. Now, $0F < 0D$ which increases the price to $0G > 0E$ in $(t + 2)$; and so on *ad infinitum*. The path of price convergence to the new equilibrium price $0M$ is clearly revealed by Figure 10.1 and more clearly by 10.2 where price movement is plotted against time and the actual price. A careful observation of the figure indicates that the given prices oscillate alternatively around the price equilibrium until they converge to it.

The concept of the oscillatory path of price adjustments is the backbone of the "Cobweb Theorem," and is an essential consequence of the assumption concerning the behavior of producers. And, as we demonstrated in Chapter 3, the reason that a new equilibrium could be established is that the numerical slope of the supply curve is greater than the numerical slope of the demand curve at each price.[4] Of course, a cobweb fluctuation will not develop when the commodity is perishable and the producer cannot affect the price of the commodity.

The convergent case results when the numerical slope of the supply curve is greater than that of the demand at each price. If, however, the numerical slope of the demand is greater than that of supply at each price, the equilibrium will not be restored and the cobweb fluctuations will be divergent to minus and plus infinity; if the two curves have had the same numerical slope at each price, the cobweb fluctuations would be continuously oscillatory in their original circle. These two cases are shown in Figures 10.3–10.6.

So far we have measured price along the vertical line and quantity along the horizontal line. We by all means can, in order to obey the rules of geometry, measure price along the horizontal axis and quantity along the vertical axis to show that quantity is a function of price. But in so doing, we must change our stability rules; viz., for a convergent system the numerical slope of the demand must exceed that of the supply curve and for a divergent system, the numerical slope of the supply ought to exceed that of the demand curve. In what follows, we use these conditions.

The most illustrative example of the cobweb theorem is agricultural production where the farmers, in the absence of government control, plan to produce in one period in accordance with the price which prevailed in

---

[4] Ezekiel requires the comparison of the elasticity of demand with that of supply; *op. cit.*, pp. 429–432. He requires more than what is needed. His condition, however, coincides with the one spelled out here only at the equilibrium point, for if we show the demand supply elasticities by

$$\frac{dq_d}{dp} \times \frac{p}{q_d},$$

$$\frac{dq_s}{dp} \times \frac{p}{q_s},$$

it becomes obvious that only at equilibrium point $\frac{p}{q_d} = \frac{p}{q_s}$ and the comparison of the elasticities will be reduced to $\frac{dq_d}{dp} = \frac{dq_s}{dp}$ which is condition demanded here.

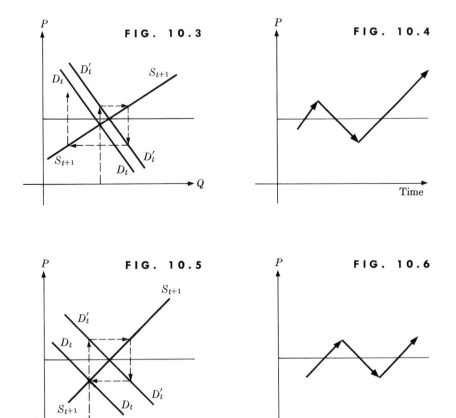

the preceding period, anticipating that the price shall be maintained as though they never learn from their past experience. Of course, when farmers' plans are carried out, the supply may be more than demand which causes the surplus with its repercussion on price for that period and the ensuing periods. Let us denote the periods by $t = 1, 2, \ldots, n$; the supply function at t by S_t denoting the units of farm products at t; the demand function at t by D_t indicating the number of units of output at t and P_t the price of output.

In symbols, we will repeat the basic assumptions of the Cobweb Theorem: (1) if the price of a good in t is P_t, the supply function is given by

$$S_{t+1} = S(P_t);$$

(2) the demand function is shown by

$$D_t = D(P_t),$$

and (3) for market equilibrium, the price should be set to clear the market

$$D_t = S_t.$$

Let us approximate the demand and supply functions by two linear functions

$$D_t = \alpha P_t + a$$

and

$$S_{t+1} = \beta P_t + b,$$

and, of course,

$$D_{t+i} = \alpha P_{t+i} + a$$

for $i = 1, 2, \ldots$, where $\alpha < 0$, which is the slope of the demand curve, and $\beta > 0$, which is the slope of the supply curve, a is the quantity intercept for the demand curve and b is the quantity intercept for the supply curve. We assume that $a > 0$ and $b > 0$.

By virtue of the third assumption for any period, say $t + 1$, we have

$$S_{t+1} = D_{t+1},$$

hence,

$$\beta P_t + b = \alpha P_{t+1} + a,$$

or

$$P_{t+1} = \frac{\beta}{\alpha} P_t + \frac{b - a}{\alpha}.$$

If we put $\dfrac{\beta}{\alpha} = A$ and $\dfrac{b - a}{\alpha} = B$, we get

$$P_{t+1} = A P_t + B$$

which is a complete first order difference equation. According to Theorem 10.3 of this chapter, the complete solution is given by

(10.5.1) $$P_k = P_0 A^k + B \frac{1 - A^k}{1 - A} \qquad (k = 1, 2, \ldots),$$

when $A \neq 1$. If $A = 1$, the solution will be

(10.5.2) $$P_k = P_0 A^k + Bk \qquad (k = 1, 2, \ldots).$$

Since $\dfrac{\beta}{\alpha} = A$ is different from unity, the complete solution given in (10.5.1) is accepted. Further, since $A < 0$, it follows from Theorem 10.3 that the sequence of P over time is oscillatory. The oscillations will be convergent to a unique value if $1 > A > -1$, that is, that the numerical value of the slope of supply must be less than that of the demand. If, however, $A = -1$; *i.e.*, $|\alpha| = |\beta|$, P_t oscillates but constantly in the same position as in Figure 10.5. Finally, if $A < -1$ or $|\alpha| < |\beta|$, P_t diverges from the equilibrium price as t approaches infinity.

Another interesting example that uses a second order difference equation is Samuelson's "Interaction" model.[5] Let the following notations be given:

$$Y_t = \text{income in period } t, \quad (t = 1, 2, \ldots),$$
$$C_t = \text{consumption in period } t,$$
$$I_t = \text{investment in period } t,$$
$$Y_0 = \text{initial income}.$$

According to definition

(10.5.3) $$Y_t = C_t + I_t,$$

where the consumption function is given by

(10.5.4) $$C_t = \alpha Y_{t-1}$$

which relates consumption in t to income of the preceding period. The investment function is given by

(10.5.5) $$I_t = \beta[C_t - C_{t-1}] + \gamma$$

where γ can be either a function of time or constant; investment, *a la* consumption, is related to income of the preceding period.

Substituting (10.5.5) and (10.5.4) in (10.5.3), we get

$$Y_t = \alpha Y_{t-1} + \beta[\alpha Y_{t-1} - \alpha Y_{t-2}] + \gamma,$$
$$= \alpha Y_{t-1} + \alpha\beta Y_{t-1} - \alpha\beta Y_{t-2} + \gamma,$$
$$= \alpha(1 + \beta) Y_{t-1} - \alpha\beta Y_{t-2} + \gamma,$$

or

(10.5.6) $$Y_{t+2} = \alpha(1 + \beta) Y_{t+1} - \alpha\beta Y_t + \gamma$$

which is a complete second order difference equation and the solution of its homogeneous part

(10.5.7) $$Y_{t+2} = \alpha(1 + \beta) Y_{t+1} - \alpha\beta Y_t,$$

according to Theorem 10.4, is

$$Y_k = C_1 m_1^k + C_2 m_2^k \quad (k = 1, 2, \ldots),$$

if m_1 and m_2 are the real and unequal roots of

$$m^2 - \alpha(1 + \beta)m + \alpha\beta = 0$$

---

[5] P. A. Samuelson, "Interaction Between the Multiplier Analysis and the Principle of Accelerator," reprinted in *Readings in Business Cycle Theory*, 1944, pp. 261–269.

where $Y_t = m^t$, $Y_{t+1} = m^{t+1}$ and $Y_{t+2} = m^{t+2}$ and that C_1 and C_2 are constants. If, however, m_1 and m_2 are real but equal, the general solution of (10.5.7) is

$$Y_k = (C_1 + C_2 k) m_1^k.$$

Finally, the general solution of (10.5.7) is given by

$$Y_k = Ar^k \cos(k\theta + \epsilon)$$

if m_1 and m_2 are a pair of complex conjugates $\lambda \pm i\mu$ where $m_1 = \lambda + i\mu$ and $m_2 = \lambda - i\mu$ and $r = \sqrt{\lambda^2 + \mu^2}$ and

$$\sin \theta = \frac{\mu}{r}, \qquad \cos \theta = \frac{\lambda}{r}.$$

For the particular solution, we are to attempt a trial solution, say

$$Y_t = Y^*,$$

in (10.5.6) to have

$$Y^* = \alpha(1 + \beta)Y^* - \alpha\beta Y^* + \gamma$$
$$= \alpha Y^* + \alpha\beta Y^* - \alpha\beta Y^* + \gamma$$

thus

(10.5.8) $$Y^* = \frac{\gamma}{1 - \alpha}.$$

(10.5.8) is the particular solution of (10.5.6). Now, we may have three cases:

(1) When the roots of the homogeneous part of (10.5.6) are real and unequal, the complete solution is given by

$$Y_t = C_1 m_1^k + C_2 m_2^k + \frac{\gamma}{1 - \alpha}.$$

(2) If the roots of the homogeneous part of (10.5.6) are real but equal, the complete solution of (10.5.6) is given by

$$Y_t = (C_1 + C_2 k) m_1^k + \frac{\gamma}{1 - \alpha}.$$

(3) If the roots of (10.5.7) are complex, the complete solution is given by

$$Y_t = Ar^k \cos(k\theta + \epsilon) + \frac{\gamma}{1 - \alpha}$$

where r, θ and γ have already been described.

Now consider the special case[6] of (10.5.6) when $\alpha = .5$, $\beta = 1$ and $\gamma = 1$ to reduce (10.5.6) to

(10.5.9) $$Y_{t+2} - Y_{t+1} + \tfrac{1}{2} Y_t = 1.$$

[6] S. Goldberg, *Introduction to Difference Equations*, New York, 1958, pp. 154–55.

Set $Y_t = m^t$ to have

(10.5.10) $$m^{t+2} - m^{t+1} + \tfrac{1}{2}m^t = 1,$$

the homogeneous part of which is

$$m^{t+2} - m^{t+1} + \tfrac{1}{2}m^t = 0,$$

or

$$m^2 - m + \tfrac{1}{2} = 0$$

from which we get $m_1 = \tfrac{1}{2} + \tfrac{1}{2}i$ and $m_2 = \tfrac{1}{2} - \tfrac{1}{2}i$ which are complex and $r = \dfrac{1}{\sqrt{2}}$, $\cos\theta = \dfrac{\sqrt{2}}{2}$, $\sin\theta = \dfrac{\sqrt{2}}{2}$ and $\theta = \dfrac{\pi}{4}$.

By what was mentioned previously, the solution of the homogeneous part is

(10.5.11) $\quad Y_k = A\left(\dfrac{1}{\sqrt{2}}\right)^k \cos\left(k\,\dfrac{\pi}{4} + \epsilon\right).\qquad (k = 0, 1, \ldots).$

For a particular solution, we set $Y^* = p$ in (10.5.9) to have

$$p - p + \tfrac{1}{2}p = 1,$$

or $p = 2$ which is a constant. To get the complete solution, we must add the particular solution to (10.5.11) to have

(10.5.12) $\qquad Y_k = A\left(\dfrac{1}{\sqrt{2}}\right)^k \cos\left(k\,\dfrac{\pi}{4} + \epsilon\right) + 2.$

If the initial values $Y_0 = 2$ and $Y_1 = 3$ for $k = 0$ and $k = 1$ are assumed, the constants A and ϵ are derived from

$$A\cos\epsilon = 0 \quad\text{and}\quad A\,\frac{1}{\sqrt{2}}\cos\left(\frac{\pi}{4} + \epsilon\right) = 1.$$

According to the first of these, we must have $\epsilon = \dfrac{\pi}{2}$. Putting the latter value in the second expression, we have $A = -2$. Substituting the values of A and ϵ, obtained therefrom, in (10.5.12), we get

$$Y_k = -2\left(\frac{1}{\sqrt{2}}\right)^k \cos\left(k\,\frac{\pi}{4} + \frac{\pi}{2}\right) + 2,$$

or

(10.5.13) $\qquad Y_k = 2\left(\dfrac{1}{\sqrt{2}}\right)^k \sin\dfrac{k\pi}{4} + 2$

since, according to Section 2.3, $\cos\left(\phi + \dfrac{\pi}{2}\right) = -\sin\phi$.

(10.5.13) is a sinusoidal function which renders income an oscillating function of time. Since $r = \dfrac{1}{\sqrt{2}} < 1$, then $\lim\limits_{k=t\to\infty}\left\{\left(\dfrac{1}{\sqrt{2}}\right)^k\right\} = 0$ therefore, $\{Y_k\} \to 2$ which is the constant on the right-hand side of (10.5.13). Thus, "If there is a constant level of governmental expenditure through time, the national income will approach asymptotically a value $\dfrac{1}{1-\alpha}$ times the constant level of governmental expenditure. A single impulse of expenditure or any amount of expenditure followed by a complete cessation will result in a gradual approach to the original zero level of national income."[7] In this analysis, we assumed that the marginal propensity to consume, α, was to be 0.5, and the level of government expenditure, γ, was assumed to be 1. Therefore, the constant that Y_k approaches would be 2. The following model attempts to generalize the results of Samuelson's interaction model.

10.6 Duesenberry's Growth and Cycle Model[8]

The following model, which is a multiplier-accelerator approach to the analysis of income determination, shows how the movement of income can be explained. Duesenberry asserts that an excess of investment over saving generates income; also the rate of investment is a function of the capital-output ratio. Further, according to the modern theories of growth, investment generates income and expands capital capacity. Thus, one of the cardinal characteristic features of a capitalist economy is "a dynamic process in which the income and capital stock of one period determine the investment and consumption for the next period. The investment determines the change in capital stock from one period to the next, while investment and consumption decisions determine the change in income from one period to the next. A multiplier-accelerator process is the simplest dynamic process of that type."[9] Although this is the case, sometimes the multiplier-accelerator model gives a rather deceptive explanation of the interaction. This is due to the use of a rigid capital coefficient and a consumption function which is independent of the returns to scale.

In Duesenberry's model, a large number of variables are taken into account. Let us divide these variables into two sets: (1) A set of variables, each of which is strongly influenced by the current or lagged values of other variables in the set (or by its own lagged values). The variables in this set are called "endogenous," and the set of interrelations among them is called "endogenous system." The present model is an endogenous one. (2) The remaining variables are regarded as having influence on the endogenous variables but not being influenced by them. These variables are called exogenous, which are assumed to be given in this model. Let the

[7] P. A. Samuelson, *op. cit.*, p. 267.

[8] James S. Duesenberry, *Business Cycles and Economic Growth*, New York, 1958, Chapter 9.

[9] *Ibid.*, p. 179.

following notations be given:

I_b = business investment,
I_h = housing investment,
C = consumption expenditure,
Y = gross national product,
R = capital consumption allowances,
K_b = business capital stock (net of depreciation),
K_h = stock of houses (net of depreciation),
P = profits (including those of undistributed business and farms),
d = dividends and entrepreneurial withdrawals,
E = retained earnings of business (corporated and unincorporated),
D = business debt,
Y_d = personal disposable income,
t = time period.

According to certain statistical findings, which Duesenberry cites, we can write

(10.6.1) $I_{bt} = \alpha(Y_{t-1}, K_{bt-1}, E_{t-1}, P_{t-1}, D_{t-1}, R_{t-1})$

which indicates that business investment depends on the income, capital stock of houses, retained earnings of businesses, profits, business debt, and depreciation all of the preceding period. It is obvious that income and capital determine the marginal efficiency of capital; and retained earning, profits, depreciation, and debt determine the cost of raising funds. Also, for the stock of houses, we can have

(10.6.2) $I_{ht} = \beta(Y_{t-1}, K_{ht-1}).$

This is making the demand for investment in housing sector dependent on the age of the capital stock of houses and the lagged level of income. We can also write

(10.6.3) $C_t = \gamma(Y_{dt-1}, C_{t-1})$

which is a sophisticated version of the consumption function and displays consumption as a function of the past disposable income and past consumption. The profit function is represented by

(10.6.4) $P_t = \lambda(Y_t, K_{bt-1})$

which is rendering profits as a function of aggregate demand and capital stock. There is one more functional relation displayed by

(10.6.5) $d_t = \Phi(P_{t-1}, d_{t-1})$

which indicates that the profits and dividends of the previous period determine the dividends of this period.

So far, we have had five functional relations which demonstrate the working of the system. There are also some definitional and functional equations. First, there is the national income definition which is given by

(10.6.6) $$Y_t = I_{bt} + I_{ht} + C_t$$

which gives, according to definition, national income as the sum of business and housing investment plus consumption expenditure. There is another definitional relationship given by

(10.6.7) $$Y_{dt} = Y_t - P_t + d_t - R_{bt} - R_{ht}$$

which makes the current disposable income equal to the sum of current national income and dividends. From this aggregate we should subtract current profits and capital consumption allowances. We have

(10.6.8) $$R_{bt} = \chi K_{bt}.$$

That is, business depreciation is made proportional to business capital stock. Likewise, capital consumption allowance for housing is proportional to the stock of capital in housing sector, or

(10.6.9) $$R_{ht} = \psi K_{ht}.$$

It is obvious that capital stock for each period, in each sector, is composed of the related investment for that period and the depreciation plus the stock of capital in the preceding period, or

(10.6.10) $$K_{bt} = K_{bt-1} + I_{bt} - R_{bt},$$
(10.6.11) $$K_{ht} = K_{ht-1} + I_{ht} - R_{ht}.$$

Also, if we subtract dividends from profits we will have the retained earnings; *i.e.*,

(10.6.12) $$E_t = P_t - d_t.$$

For the business debt, we have

(10.6.13) $$D_t = D_{t-1} + I_{bt} - R_t - E_t$$

which is the algebraic sum of the lagged debt, business investment, depreciation, and retained earnings.

These definitional equations and the preceding functional relationships, if numerically specified, together with the initial conditions determine the path of income and its movement over time, given the exogenous variables of the system. The model composed of these relations is dynamic because it accounts for time lags. Of course, the actual movement of income over time depends on the values of the exogenous variables as well as on the properties of the equations.

Next, in order to solve the system, Duesenberry takes a few simplifying steps such as: (1) eliminating the housing equations from the system so as to let the system of equations deal only with business investment whose influence is stronger than housing investment. (2) He leaves out lagged consumption from the consumption function and lagged dividends from the dividend equation. (3) Finally, he makes investment depend on profits and profits on capital stock at the end of any period rather than at the beginning.

According to what has been assumed and by substituting from one equation into another one, we have the following equations:

(10.6.14) $$I_t = \alpha(Y_{t-1}, K_{t-1}, P_{t-1}, R_t),$$

(10.6.15) $$C_t = \gamma(Y_{t-1} - P_{t-1} - R_{t-1} + d_t),$$

(10.6.16) $$d_t = \varphi(P_{t-1}),$$

(10.6.17) $$P_t = \lambda(Y_t, K_t),$$

(10.6.18) $$R_t = \chi K_{t-1},$$

(10.6.19) $$K_t = K_{t-1} + I_t - R_t,$$

(10.6.20) $$Y_t = I_t + C_t.$$

We can again, by substitution, reduce the above equations to

(10.6.21) $$I_t = \alpha[Y_{t-1}, K_{t-1}, \lambda(Y_{t-1}, K_{t-1}), \chi K_{t-1}],$$

(10.6.22)
$$C_t = \gamma[\{Y_{t-1} - \lambda(Y_{t-1}, K_{t-1}) - \chi K_{t-1}\}, \varphi\{\lambda(Y_{t-1}, K_{t-1})\}]$$

(10.6.23) $$K_t = K_{t-1} + I_t - \chi K_{t-1},$$

(10.6.24) $$Y_t = I_t + C_t.$$

We proceed into another simplifying stage by expressing the last four equations and relations in linear forms:

(10.6.25) $$I_t = \delta Y_{t-1} + \eta K_{t-1},$$

(10.6.26) $$C_t = \rho Y_{t-1} + \mu K_{t-1},$$

(10.6.27) $$K_t = (1 - \chi)K_{t-1} + I_t,$$

(10.6.28) $$Y_t = I_t + C_t.$$

From (10.6.25)–(10.6.28), by substitution, we get two equations: one for income and one for capital:

(10.6.29) $$Y_t = (\delta + \rho)Y_{t-1} + (\eta + \mu)K_{t-1}$$

(10.6.30) $$K_t = \delta Y_{t-1} + [\eta + (1 - \chi)]K_{t-1}.$$

In the last two equations, there are four parameters: δ, η, ρ and μ. Duesenberry describes them as follows: (1) δ "represents the effect of changes in income on investment, which is felt in two ways. A change in income changes the marginal efficiency of investment, and it also changes the marginal cost of funds by changing profits." (2) η "reflects the influence of capital stock on investment working through both marginal efficiency and profits." (3) ρ "is the marginal propensity to consume out of GNP. An increase in the marginal propensity to consume out of disposable income increases [ρ]. But [ρ] also reflects the increase in profits which results (cet. par.) from an increase in income. An increase in the sensitivity of profits to changes in income therefore reduce $[\rho]$. That influence is partly offset by the effect of profits on dividends and the effect of changes in dividends on consumption." (4) μ "reflects the changes in capital stock on profits through the influence of profits in dividends on consumption."[10]

For demonstrating the process of income generation, we multiply (10.6.29) by $(\eta + 1 - \chi)$ and (10.6.30) by $(\eta + \mu)$ to get

(10.6.31) $\quad (\eta + 1 - \chi) Y_t = (\delta + \rho)(\eta + 1 - \chi) Y_{t-1}$
$$+ (\eta + \mu)(\eta + 1 - \chi) K_{t-1},$$

(10.6.32) $\quad (\eta + \mu) K_t = \delta(\eta + \mu) Y_{t-1} + (\eta + \mu)(\eta + 1 - \chi) K_{t-1}.$

On subtracting (10.6.32) from (10.6.31) and rearranging the terms, we get

(10.6.33) $\quad (\eta + \mu) K_t = (\eta + 1 - \chi) Y_t$
$$+ [\delta(\eta + \mu) - (\delta + \rho)(\eta + 1 - \chi)] Y_{t-1},$$

and on substituting in (10.6.29), we get

(10.6.34) $\quad Y_t = [(\delta + \rho) + (\eta + 1 - \chi) Y_{t-1}$
$$+ [\delta(\eta + \mu) - (\delta + \rho)(\eta + 1 - \chi)] Y_{t-2}.$$

This last equation is the generalized multiplier-accelerator model, which in explaining the *modus operandi* of the system, takes into consideration all relevant variables. In the simple multiplier-accelerator, like the one dealt with in the preceding section, depreciation is de-emphasized and investment is taken as net so that $\chi = 0$; and there is no connection between consumption and capital stock so that $\mu = 0$; and the investment equation is written so that $\eta = -1$. If these values are substituted in (10.6.34), we get

$$Y_t = (\delta + \rho) Y_{t-1} + \delta(-1) Y_{t-2}$$

which is similar to (10.5.6) of the previous section.

As a result of comparing the simple version of multiplier-accelerator process with the general one expressed by (10.6.34), "an increase in income will have a much smaller immediate effect on expenditure than would occur in a simple multiplier-accelerator model,"[11] owing to the fact that there are more parameters reckoned in the generalized one and their influences are less than the ones included in the simple multiplier-accelerator one. Further, "The effect of those considerations is to reduce the immediate effect of an increase in income on expenditure but to make the effect persist for some time, since investment will decline slowly (if there is no further increase in income) as capital accumulates. The system will therefore be much more stable than a simple multiplier-accelerator system."[12]

---

[10]*Ibid.*, p. 196.
[11] *Ibid.*, p. 198.
[12] *Ibid.*, p. 198.

Of course, (10.6.34) can be formally solved if we assign numerical values to its parameters and assume two initial conditions. Since the equation is homogeneous, there is no need to search the particular solution. It is obvious that the solution should give an oscillatory sequence of income over time since all dynamic multiplier-accelerator models are displayed by oscillatory fluctuations.

EXERCISES 10

1. Solve the following first order difference equations:

$$y_{t+1} + 4y_t = 7. \qquad\qquad 2y_{t+1} - y_t = 3.$$

$$3y_{t+1} - 5y_t = 0. \qquad\qquad 4y_{t+1} + 3y_t = 2.$$

$$y_{t+1} - 4y_t = 13.$$

2. Find the particular solution of the following difference equations satisfying the initial conditions $y_0 = 1$, $y_1 = 3$.

$$y_{t+2} - 3y_{t+1} + 2y_t = 3. \qquad\qquad 2y_{t+2} - 8y_{t+1} + 8y_t = 6.$$

$$y_{t+2} - 6y_{t+1} + 8y_t = 5. \qquad\qquad y_{t+2} - 8y_{t+1} + 15y_t = 4.$$

3. Find the general solution of each of the following homogeneous difference equations:

$$y_{t+2} - 2y_t = 0. \qquad\qquad 2y_{t+2} - 3y_{t+1} - 4y_t = 0.$$

$$4y_{t+2} + 3y_{t+1} + 2y_t = 0. \qquad\qquad y_{t+2} - y_{t+1} + 3y_t = 0.$$

$$y_{t+2} - 5y_{t+1} + 6y_t = 0. \qquad\qquad 2y_{t+2} - 8y_{t+1} + 9y_t = 0.$$

4. Find the particular solutions of each of the following equations by the method of undetermined coefficients:

$$y_{t+2} - 4y_{t+1} + 2y_t = 3^k + 1.$$

$$y_{t+2} + 3y_{t+1} - 3y_t = e^{k+1}.$$

$$3y_{t+2} + 2y_{t+1} - 4y_t = e^k(k + 2).$$

$$y_{t+2} + y_{t+1} + y_t = k^2.$$

$$y_{t+2} + 2y_{t+1} - y_t = \sin \frac{k\pi}{2}.$$

5. Metzler has advanced an inventory theory based on difference equations in his "The Nature and Stability of Inventory Cycles," *Review of Economics and Statistics*, 1941, pp. 113–129. Accordingly, the volume of production in one period is influenced by the inventories and the lagged production, or

$$y_{t+2} - 2by_{t+1} + by_t = I_0.$$

Let us assume that $1 > b > 0$. Solve this equation and discuss its stability conditions.

6. Let us assume

$$y_{t+1} = by_t + I_0$$

where $I_0 = 50$, $b = .4$, and $y_0 = 100$. Discuss the behavior of the system. Next, let I_0 be increased to 80. Discuss the behavior of the system and its stability.

PART IV

Programming, Games,
and Activity Analysis

11 | MATRIX AND VECTOR ANALYSIS

11.1 Introduction

We have, so far, been concerned with elementary algebra — the domain of the system of "real numbers" and the integral operations upon them for explaining many economic problems, trigonometry — the domain of the system of "complex numbers" for describing the oscillatory movements in variables, a technique especially useful for business cycle analysis, and finally, calculus of infinite and finite differences related to the rates of change of variable(s).

Linear programming, games, and activity analysis have recently been applied to many purely theoretical and concretely practical economic issues. There have been many mathematicians and economists who have devoted much of their attentions to the development of these new branches of mathematical economics. The mathematical nature of these new branches has been found to assert itself. One of the striking facts about the history of these new developments of mathematical economics is that most — one should really say *all* — of these men who have invented and developed linear programming, games, and activity analysis are remarkable mathematicians who have used modern contributions to pure mathematics.

The techniques of our previous chapters, although they bring about perspicuity for exploring economic problems, are not adequate enough to guarantee a full comprehension of the subjects which will be developed henceforward. The topics of the following chapters are rather complicated and complex in a special sense. These topics are complex in the sense that they are not concerned with the properties of a single variable and the behavior of that variable over its domain. They are rather concerned with sets and combinations of elements organized and formed in a certain way. The mathematics of these topics, usually called Advanced or Abstract

Algebra, constitutes elements which can be "real," "complex," "abstract," or indeed anything that a mathematician can imagine.

There are many ways to go about explaining the topics of Advanced Algebra. We choose the following way.

11.2 Vectors in the Plane

In a two-dimensional Cartesian system with coordinates X and Y, a point $P(x, y)$ is called a vector in the space. Then the words "vector" and "point" are interchangeable. Geometrically, the coordinates of the vector P in the fixed rectangular space are x and y. The length of the vector is the distance of it from the origin of the rectangular, as in Figure 11.1.

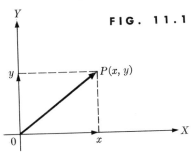

FIG. 11.1

Thus, a vector of length zero is $P(0, 0)$ which is called a zero vector. Also a vector of length 1 is either $P(1, 0)$ or $P(0, 1)$ which are both called unit vectors. In all these examples, x, y, 0, and 1 are called the elements or components of the vectors.

If α is any number or object which is referred to in Advanced Algebra as *scalar(s)*, the product of α-scalar and the vector $P(x, y)$ is the vector $\alpha(x, y)$, or $(\alpha x, \alpha y)$. That is to say, α being any number, every $\alpha(x, y)$ defines a point on the same line through the origin as $P(x, y)$. So far we have been concerned with two-dimensional vectors.

An n-dimensional vector is a sequence

$$A = (a_1, a_2, \ldots, a_n)$$

of variables or objects which are called the *elements* or *components* of A-vector.

Addition and Subtraction of Vectors. Two vectors which have the same number of elements are called *conformable*. We can only add and subtract the vectors which are conformable in addition. The algebraic sum of two conformable vectors

$$A = (a_1, a_2, \ldots, a_n)$$
$$B = (b_1, b_2, \ldots, b_n)$$

is the vector

$$A + B = (a_1 + b_1, a_2 + b_2, \ldots, a_n + b_n)$$

adding by corresponding elements. Then, to every pair A and B, of vectors in a set, there corresponds a vector $A + B$ called the sum of A and B in a way that:

(1) Addition is commutative; *i.e.* the sum of two vectors is the same in whatever order they are added:

$$A + B = B + A,$$

or

$$A + B = (a_1 + b_1, \ldots, a_n + b_n) = B + A$$
$$= (b_1 + a_1, \ldots, b_n + a_n).$$

(2) Addition is associative; *i.e.* the sum of three or more vectors is the same in whatever manner they are grouped in adding

$$A + B + C = A + (B + C) = (A + B) + C,$$

or if

$$A = (a_1, a_2, \ldots, a_n),$$
$$B = (b_1, b_2, \ldots, b_n),$$
$$C = (c_1, c_2, \ldots, c_n),$$
$$A + B + C = a_1 + (b_1 + c_1), \ldots, a_n + (b_n + c_n),$$
$$= (a_1 + b_1) + c_1, \ldots, (a_n + b_n) + c_n.$$

(3) There exists a unique zero vector 0 such that

$$A + 0 = A.$$

(4) The product of any scalar α, by a vector

$$A = (a_1, a_2, \ldots, a_n),$$

is another vector

$$\alpha A = (\alpha a_1, \alpha a_2, \ldots, \alpha a_n).$$

αA is called the *scalar* product.

We have more to say about the vectors in due course.

11.3 Matrices

A rectangular array of objects, numbers, or functions is called a matrix. The objects or numbers are called the elements of the matrix. In a matrix, each element has a location and its location is specified by the *dummy subscripts* i and j where i refers to the row and j to the column of the rectangular array. If a matrix has m rows and n columns, it is called a matrix of m by n or of order "m, n."

A matrix of m by n can be written in different forms:

$$A = \begin{bmatrix} a_{11} & a_{12} & \cdots & a_{1n} \\ a_{21} & a_{22} & \cdots & a_{2n} \\ \cdot & \cdot & & \cdot \\ a_{m1} & a_{m2} & \cdots & a_{mn} \end{bmatrix} = \begin{pmatrix} a_{11} & a_{12} & \cdots & a_{1n} \\ a_{21} & a_{22} & \cdots & a_{2n} \\ \cdot & \cdot & & \cdot \\ a_{m1} & a_{m2} & \cdots & a_{mn} \end{pmatrix}$$

$$= [a_{ij}]_{(m,n)} = (a_{ij})_{(m,n)} = \|a_{ij}\|_{(m,n)}.$$

The array

$$A = \begin{bmatrix} 3 & 1 & -5 & -1 & 7 \\ -1 & 2 & 6 & -2 & 0 \\ 2 & 0 & 1 & 1 & 6 \\ 4 & 3 & 1 & -3 & 2 \end{bmatrix}$$

is called a 4 by 5 *matrix*. The rows of a matrix are vectors which are called its *row-vectors*, and the vertical ones are called its *column-vectors*. In the above example the row

$$(2 \quad 0 \quad 1 \quad 1 \quad 6)$$

is the third row of the matrix and the column vector

$$\begin{pmatrix} -1 \\ -2 \\ 1 \\ -3 \end{pmatrix}$$

its fourth column. If all the elements of a matrix A are zero, we shall call it a zero matrix and shall write

$$A = 0$$

regardless of the number of rows and columns in A. We shall also say that two matrices are equal, and write

$$A = B$$

if they have the same size m by n and are such that corresponding elements are equal.

Needless to say, the position of an element of a matrix is at least as important as its value. It may be described by a statement as to the row and column in which the element appears.

Special Matrices. The elements a_{11}, a_{22}, a_{33}, ..., a_{nn}, or a_{ii} of matrix (a_{ij}) are called the "main diagonal" elements of that matrix. Other elements of the same matrix are called non-diagonal. If all diagonal and non-diagonal elements of the same matrix are zero, the matrix is called *zero-matrix*.

$$0 = A = (a_{ij}) = \begin{bmatrix} 0 & 0 & 0 & \cdots & 0 \\ 0 & 0 & 0 & \cdots & 0 \\ \cdot & \cdot & \cdot & \cdot & \cdot \\ 0 & 0 & 0 & \cdots & 0 \end{bmatrix}.$$

A matrix which has an equal number of rows and columns is called a *square matrix*. If there are n rows and columns, the matrix is called a square matrix of order n. A matrix is in *triangular* form if all the elements below *or* above the main diagonal are zero. The following matrices are in triangular form:

$$\begin{bmatrix} 2 & -1 & 7 \\ 0 & 5 & 3 \\ 0 & 0 & 4 \end{bmatrix} \begin{bmatrix} 1 & 0 & 0 \\ 8 & 4 & 0 \\ 3 & 2 & -3 \end{bmatrix} \begin{bmatrix} 0 & 0 & 0 \\ 2 & 1 & 0 \\ 4 & 3 & -5 \end{bmatrix}$$

A square matrix in triangular form is called a *triangular matrix*. The three matrices which were examined above are *triangular* matrices. If all non-diagonal elements of a square matrix, $A = (a_{ij})$, are zero, the matrix is called diagonal and is written

$$A = \text{diag} (d_1, \ldots, d_n).$$

Or

$$\begin{bmatrix} 1 & 0 & 0 & 0 \\ 0 & 2 & 0 & 0 \\ 0 & 0 & 5 & 0 \\ 0 & 0 & 0 & 12 \end{bmatrix} = \text{diagonal.}$$

A diagonal matrix with equal diagonal elements is called *scalar matrix*. The following matrix is a *scalar* one.

$$\begin{bmatrix} 2 & 0 & 0 \\ 0 & 2 & 0 \\ 0 & 0 & 2 \end{bmatrix} = \text{scalar.}$$

If the diagonal elements of a scalar matrix are all unity, the matrix is called a *unity* or an *identity* matrix. The following matrix is an identity matrix.

$$\begin{bmatrix} 1 & 0 & 0 & 0 \\ 0 & 1 & 0 & 0 \\ 0 & 0 & 1 & 0 \\ 0 & 0 & 0 & 1 \end{bmatrix} = \text{identity.}$$

Transpose of a Matrix. The interchange of rows and columns of a matrix gives the transpose of that matrix. The n by m matrix $A' = (a_{ji})_{(n,m)}$ is the transpose of the m by n matrix $A = (a_{ij})_{(m,n)}$. That is to say, when we rotate $180°$ all the non-diagonal elements of a matrix around its main diagonal, we obtain the transpose. In this case, the rows of a matrix will make up the columns of its transpose and the columns of the same matrix will give the rows of the transpose. For example, if

$$A = \begin{bmatrix} -2 & 4 & 5 \\ 1 & 6 & -4 \\ 3 & 11 & 7 \\ 8 & 3 & -2 \end{bmatrix}$$

its transpose is

$$A' = \begin{bmatrix} -2 & 1 & 3 & 8 \\ 4 & 6 & 11 & 3 \\ 5 & -4 & 7 & -2 \end{bmatrix}.$$

The following theorems are given without proof. If A' and B' are the transposes of A and B, and if α is a scalar

(1) $(A')' = A.$

(2) $(A + B)' = A' + B'.$

(3) $(\alpha A)' = \alpha A'.$

(4) $(AB)' = B'A'.$

Special Vectors. The *inner product* of two vectors:

$$A = (a_1, a_2, \ldots, a_n)$$
$$B = (b_1, b_2, \ldots, b_n),$$

which are conformable, is

$$AB' = (a_1, \ldots, a_n) \begin{bmatrix} b_1 \\ \vdots \\ b_n \end{bmatrix} = a_1 b_1 + \cdots + a_n b_n.$$

But the product of the transpose of A and B produces a matrix where each element of the column vector serves as a scalar for the elements of the row vector, then:

$$A'B = \begin{bmatrix} a_1 \\ \vdots \\ a_n \end{bmatrix} (b_1, \ldots, b_n) = \begin{bmatrix} a_1 b_1 & \cdots & a_1 b_n \\ \vdots & & \vdots \\ a_n b_1 & \cdots & a_n b_n \end{bmatrix}.$$

It is clear that the vectors do not have to be conformable in the sense defined above. The *norm* of A is the inner product

$$AA' = (a_1, \ldots, a_n) \begin{bmatrix} a_1 \\ \vdots \\ a_n \end{bmatrix} = a_1^2 + \cdots + a_n^2.$$

If $AA' = 1$, then A is called a unit vector; i.e., whose length is 1.

Examples for Vector Multiplication. Let us assume that a firm wishes to calculate the unit cost of its homogeneous output (x). Further, let us assume that there are four inputs with specific amounts which make up one unit of output (x) in the following form:

4 (units of land),   2 (hours of labor),   3 (units of capital)

6 (units of raw materials).

Then, our *input-vector* can be shown as

$$A = (4, 2, 3, 6).$$

Let us suppose that the prices of these inputs are the following:

$7 per unit of land, $3 per hour of labor,

$14 per unit of capital, $4 per unit of raw material.

Our *price-vector* can be represented by:

$$B = (7, 3, 14, 4).$$

The total cost per unit of output (x) will be the *inner product* of the two vectors

$$A = (4, 2, 3, 6)$$
$$B = (7, 3, 14, 4).$$

It was noticed before that for the conformable vectors, in multiplication, one row (column) vector is multiplied by the transpose of the other row (column) vector. Vector transposition is exactly the same as matrix transposition. The transpose of a row (column) vector is a column (row) vector with the same dimensions; *i.e.* for a vector $A = (a_i)$, the transpose is $A' = (a_j)$ where $i = j = 1, 2, \ldots, n$.

For our example mentioned above, the *inner product* of *input-vector* and the *price-vector* can be shown by the product of A and the transpose of B, which is B'. Accordingly,

$$AB' = (4, 2, 3, 6) \begin{bmatrix} 7 \\ 3 \\ 14 \\ 4 \end{bmatrix} = (4)7 + (2)3 + (3)14 + (6)4 = \$100.$$

11.4 Addition and Subtraction of Matrices

Two or n matrices which are of the same order are called *conformable for addition or subtraction*. Only can we add up (or subtract) matrices which are conformable for addition (or subtraction). If

$$A = [a_{ij}]_{(m,n)} \qquad B = [b_{ij}]_{(m,n)},$$

we define

$$A + B = [a_{ij}] + [b_{ij}] = [(a_{ij} + b_{ij})]_{(m,n)}.$$

For instance,

$$\begin{bmatrix} 2+a & -3+a \\ 2-a & 1-a \end{bmatrix} + \begin{bmatrix} 3-a & 4 \\ -a & 3 \end{bmatrix} = \begin{bmatrix} 5 & 1+a \\ 2-2a & 4-a \end{bmatrix}$$

Laws of Addition of Matrices. Conformable matrices are commutative and associative in addition (and subtraction). That is to say, the algebraic sum of two or more conformable matrices is the same in whatever order they are added and in whatever manner they are grouped for addition.

If A, B, and C are conformable matrices for addition, we will have

$$A + B = B + A.$$
$$(A + B) + C = A + (B + C).$$
$$A + 0 = A.$$

0 is a zero matrix.

11.5 Matrix Multiplication

If the number of columns of a matrix A is equal to the number of rows of another matrix B, A is said to be *conformable* to B *for multiplication*. We define the product AB, where

$$A = (a_{ij})_{(m,n)} \qquad B = (b_{jk})_{(n,p)}$$

to be the m by p matrix

$$C = (c_{ik})_{(m,p)} = AB$$

in which

$$c_{ik} = a_{i1}b_{1k} + a_{i2}b_{2k} + \cdots + a_{in}b_{nk} = \sum_{k=1}^{n} a_{ij}b_{jk}$$

$$C = \left[\sum_{j=1}^{n} a_{ij}b_{jk} \right]_{(m,p)}.$$

Hence, every element of the inner-product of AB is obtained by adding the products of the row of A by the corresponding element of a column of matrix B. This process is called the row-by-column rule for matrix multiplication.

Multiplication Laws. Multiplication is not in general commutative.

$$AB \neq BA$$

$$(a_{ij})(b_{jk}) \neq (b_{jk})(a_{ij}).$$

(1) The rule $AB = BA$ does not hold true.

(2) $AB = 0$ does not mean that either A or B is zero. For instance

$$\begin{bmatrix} 1 & 2 & 0 \\ 1 & 1 & 0 \\ -1 & 4 & 0 \end{bmatrix} \begin{bmatrix} 0 & 0 & 0 \\ 0 & 0 & 0 \\ 1 & 4 & 9 \end{bmatrix} = \begin{bmatrix} 0 & 0 & 0 \\ 0 & 0 & 0 \\ 0 & 0 & 0 \end{bmatrix}.$$

(3) From $AB = AC$ or $BA = CA$ we cannot say that

$$B = C.$$

(4) Matrix multiplication is associative. If

$$A = (a_{ij})_{(m,n)} \qquad B = (b_{jk})_{(n,p)} \qquad C = (c_{kr})_{(p,q)}$$
$$(AB)C = A(BC).$$

(5) The inner product of any matrix A and zero matrix is another zero matrix.

$$A0 = 0A = 0 = (0_{ij}).$$

(6) The inner product of any matrix and its conformable unit matrix is that matrix itself

$$AI = IA = A = (a_{ij}).$$

(7) Matrix multiplication is distributive. If A, B, and C matrices are conformable, then

$$A(B + C) = AB + AC,$$
$$(D + E)F = DF + EF.$$

Example for Matrix Multiplication. Suppose a baby furniture company engaged in a three-article operation is interested in calculating the total cost and transportation cost of its output from its home plant to New York. The input composition of each product is represented by the following matrix:

	Vinyl	Steel	Machine Time	Labor Time	Misc.
Baby-Bath	3	2	1	1.5	.2
$A =$ Play-pen	2.3	3	2	2.5	.4
Crib	2	2	1.2	2.3	.1

and the total and transportation costs are shown by the following matrix:

$$
\begin{array}{cc}
\text{Cost} & \text{Transportation}
\end{array}
$$

$$
B = \begin{bmatrix}
\$\ .50 & .01 \\
1.42 & .02 \\
.43 & .04 \\
2.50 & .03 \\
.03 & .01
\end{bmatrix}
\begin{array}{l}
\text{Vinyl} \\
\text{Steel} \\
\text{Machine time} \\
\text{Labor time} \\
\text{Misc.}
\end{array}
$$

Then, the inner product of these two matrices is

$$
\begin{bmatrix}
3 & 2 & 1 & 1.5 & .2 \\
2.3 & 3 & 2 & 2.5 & .4 \\
2 & 2 & 1.2 & 2.3 & .1
\end{bmatrix}_{(3,\,5)}
\begin{bmatrix}
.50 & .01 \\
1.42 & .02 \\
.43 & .04 \\
2.50 & .03 \\
.03 & .01
\end{bmatrix}_{(5,\,2)}
=
\begin{array}{cc}
\text{Cost} & \text{Trans.}
\end{array}
\begin{bmatrix}
8.526 & .157 \\
12.532 & .242 \\
10.109 & .178
\end{bmatrix}
\begin{array}{l}
\text{Baby-bath} \\
\text{Play-pen} \\
\text{Crib}
\end{array}
$$

Where

$$
\begin{aligned}
8.526 &= 3(.50) + 2(1.42) + 1(.43) + 1.5(2.50) + .2(.03) \\
.157 &= 3(.01) + 2(.02) + 1(.04) + 1.5(0.03) + .2(.01) \\
12.532 &= 2.3(.50) + 3(1.42) + 2(.43) + 2.5(2.50) + .4(.03) \\
.242 &= 2.3(.01) + 3(.02) + 2(.04) + 2.5(.03) + .4(.01) \\
10.109 &= 2(.50) + 2(1.42) + 1.2(.43) + 2.3(2.50) + .1(.03) \\
.178 &= 2(.01) + 2(.02) + 1.2(.04) + 2.3(.03) + .1(.01).
\end{aligned}
$$

A special case of matrix multiplication is matrix-vector multiplication. Matrix-vector multiplication is a general case of vector multiplication. If the number of elements of a row vector is equal to the number of rows of a matrix, the vector and matrix are conformable for multiplication. The product of a conformable row vector and a matrix is a row vector. Accordingly, if

$$
B = (b_1, b_2, \ldots, b_n)
$$
$$
A = (a_{ij})_{(n,m)}
$$

then, vector B and matrix A, since they are conformable, are multiplicative.

The above rule is applicable when the vector is a column vector and it has the same dimensions as the number of columns of the matrix.

Example for Vector and Matrix Multiplication. Let us take the Baby Furniture Company example once more; with the input-matrix:

$$
A = \begin{bmatrix}
3 & 2 & 1 & 1.5 & .2 \\
2.3 & 3 & 2 & 2.5 & .4 \\
2 & 2 & 1.2 & 2.3 & .1
\end{bmatrix}
$$

Let us assume that the Sales Department receives an order of

$$\begin{matrix} \text{Baby-bath} & \text{Play-pen} & \text{Crib} \\ B = \quad (10 & 20 & 40). \end{matrix}$$

The order has gone to the Production Department for processing. It should first schedule the raw materials which are needed for the production of the articles. We can write:

$$(10 \quad 20 \quad 40) \begin{bmatrix} 3 & 2 & 1 & 1.5 & .2 \\ 2.3 & 3 & 2 & 2.5 & .4 \\ 2 & 2 & 1.2 & 2.3 & .1 \end{bmatrix} = (156 \quad 160 \quad 98 \quad 157 \quad 14)$$

$$\begin{aligned} \text{Vinyl needed} &= 156 = 10(3) + 20(2.3) + 40(2), \\ \text{Steel needed} &= 160 = 10(2) + 20(3) + 40(2), \\ \text{Machine time} &= 98 = 10(1) + 20(2) + 40(1.2), \\ \text{Labor time} &= 157 = 10(1.5) + 20(2.5) + 40(2.3), \\ \text{Misc. needed} &= 14 = 10(.2) + 20(.4) + 40(.1). \end{aligned}$$

The reader is asked to proceed with the inner product of a matrix and a column vector.

11.6 Determinants and Matrices

Students often assimilate matrix with determinant and vice versa. A matrix is used to separate the individual elements of a *set*. A determinant is, on the other hand, a number. However, some matrices do have determinants. All square matrices have determinants. In matrix algebra square matrices are of special importance. And, in programming techniques, square matrices and their determinants occupy the most prominent position. Square matrices and their determinants are important in matrix algebra because they are related to *matrix inversion*, a topic which is cardinal in the theory of matrices. Square matrices, determinants, and their inverses together define the solution of the problems posed in economic programming.

Determinant. Mention was made that all square matrices have determinants. The determinant of a square matrix A is

$$|A| = |a_{ij}|.$$

A matrix is shown by dark capital letters and determinants by light capital letters. The elements of a determinant are formed in the same manner as the elements of its matrix, and the value of the determinant is indicated by a pair of vertical lines placed on the sides of the matrix. Determinants are devices which will lead us to the results of the system of linear equations from which we have gathered the matrix.

Let us examine the system of linear equations below:

(11.6.1)
$$a_1x + b_1y = c_1$$
$$a_2x + b_2y = c_2$$

which is composed of two linear equations in two unknowns. Multiply the left-hand side members of the first equation by b_2 and those of the second equation by $-b_1$. Then, by adding the members of the two resulting equations, we get

(11.6.2)
$$x(a_1b_2 - a_2b_1) = (b_2c_1 - b_1c_2)$$
$$x = \frac{b_2c_1 - b_1c_2}{a_1b_2 - a_2b_1}$$

provided that

$$a_1b_2 - a_2b_1 \neq 0.$$

Likewise, by multiplying the first and second equations by $-a_2$ and a_1, respectively, we obtain

(11.6.3)
$$y = \frac{a_1c_2 - a_2c_1}{a_1b_2 - a_2b_1}$$

provided that

$$a_1b_2 - a_2b_1 \neq 0.$$

A close examination of (11.6.2) and (11.6.3) reveals that their denominators are alike. Moreover, the condition that x and y will have unique values is that their denominators, which are alike, are non-zero.

There is a convenient symbol with which we can represent the numerator and denominator of each fraction. The expression $a_1b_2 - a_2b_1$ can be represented by the symbol

$$\begin{vmatrix} a_1 & b_1 \\ a_2 & b_2 \end{vmatrix}$$

which is called a *determinant*. Since it has two columns and two rows, it is called a second order determinant. The elements of the determinant are $a_1, b_1, b_2,$ and a_2. Using the determinant notation, we may write the solutions of our equations (11.6.1) in the form

$$x = \frac{\begin{vmatrix} c_1 & b_1 \\ c_2 & b_2 \end{vmatrix}}{\begin{vmatrix} a_1 & b_1 \\ a_2 & b_2 \end{vmatrix}} \qquad y = \frac{\begin{vmatrix} a_1 & c_1 \\ a_2 & c_2 \end{vmatrix}}{\begin{vmatrix} a_1 & b_1 \\ a_2 & b_2 \end{vmatrix}}.$$

It is noticed that the numerator of the solution for x is obtained from the denominator by substituting the constant terms c_1 and c_2 in place of a_1

and a_2 which are the coefficients of x in the system of equations (11.6.1). In evaluating the second order determinant, we subtract, from the product of the elements of the main diagonal, the product of the elements of the off-diagonal a_2 and b_1. All determinants of x and y are evaluated similarly.

Let us, now, explore the system of linear equations in three unknowns:

(11.6.4)
$$\begin{cases} a_1x + b_1y + c_1z = d_1 \\ a_2x + b_2y + c_2z = d_2 \\ a_3x + b_3y + c_3z = d_3. \end{cases}$$

Applying the rule given for the system of linear equations with two unknowns to the one with three unknowns, we can solve (11.6.4) for x, y and z:

$$x = \frac{\begin{vmatrix} d_1 & b_1 & c_1 \\ d_2 & b_2 & c_2 \\ d_3 & b_3 & c_3 \end{vmatrix}}{\begin{vmatrix} a_1 & b_1 & c_1 \\ a_2 & b_2 & c_2 \\ a_3 & b_3 & c_3 \end{vmatrix}} \qquad y = \frac{\begin{vmatrix} a_1 & d_1 & c_1 \\ a_2 & d_2 & c_2 \\ a_3 & d_3 & c_3 \end{vmatrix}}{\begin{vmatrix} a_1 & b_1 & c_1 \\ a_2 & b_2 & c_2 \\ a_3 & b_3 & c_3 \end{vmatrix}} \qquad z = \frac{\begin{vmatrix} a_1 & b_1 & d_1 \\ a_2 & b_2 & d_2 \\ a_3 & b_3 & d_3 \end{vmatrix}}{\begin{vmatrix} a_1 & b_1 & c_1 \\ a_2 & b_2 & c_2 \\ a_3 & b_3 & c_3 \end{vmatrix}}.$$

Each determinant of the numerator and the denominator is of third order because each determinant has three rows and three columns. The determinants of order three and more cannot be evaluated unless they are reduced to the second order determinants. The process and technique of reducing a determinant into its lower order determinants is usually called the expansion of determinants.

Expansion of Determinants. A determinant may be expanded in terms of the elements of any row or those of any column. Let us suppose we have the third order square matrix

$$A = \begin{bmatrix} a_1 & b_1 & c_1 \\ a_2 & b_2 & c_2 \\ a_3 & b_3 & c_3 \end{bmatrix},$$

whose determinant is represented by

$$\det A = \begin{vmatrix} a_1 & b_1 & c_1 \\ a_2 & b_2 & c_2 \\ a_3 & b_3 & c_3 \end{vmatrix}.$$

The expansion of det A is done via either its rows or columns. Suppose we decide to expand det A by its first column. If we take any element of that column and delete the elements of the row and column in which that element is located, the undeleted elements of det A form a sub-determinant called the first *minor* of that element. Accordingly, the minor of a_1 is

$$\begin{vmatrix} b_2 & c_2 \\ b_3 & c_3 \end{vmatrix}.$$

Analogously, the minor of a_2 is

$$\begin{vmatrix} b_1 & c_1 \\ b_3 & c_3 \end{vmatrix}.$$

In the same manner, the minors of all other elements are to be found. A minor with a sign (plus or minus) is called the *cofactor*. The cofactor of any element is obtained by

$$(-1)^{i+j} A_{ij}$$

where A_{ij} is the minor of a_{ij}. Accordingly, the sign of a minor is determined by the sum of the number of the row and the number of the column of the element for which the minor is chosen. Thus, in our example, the cofactor of a_1 is

$$(-1)^{1+1} \begin{vmatrix} b_2 & c_2 \\ b_3 & c_3 \end{vmatrix}$$

and the cofactor of a_3 is

$$(-1)^{3+1} \begin{vmatrix} b_1 & c_1 \\ b_2 & c_2 \end{vmatrix}$$

because a_3 is in the third row and the first column.

Having known the rules concerning the minors and cofactors of a determinant, we can expand any determinant of any size and order. Therefore, on the balance of what has been said, we can write

$$\det A = \begin{vmatrix} a_1 & b_1 & c_1 \\ a_2 & b_2 & c_2 \\ a_3 & b_3 & c_3 \end{vmatrix} = a_1 \begin{vmatrix} b_2 & c_2 \\ b_3 & c_3 \end{vmatrix} - a_2 \begin{vmatrix} b_1 & c_1 \\ b_3 & c_3 \end{vmatrix} + a_3 \begin{vmatrix} b_1 & c_1 \\ b_2 & c_2 \end{vmatrix}.$$

Similarly, any determinant can be expanded. We should remember one mathematical *trick*. It is obvious that the expansion of a determinant of order, let us say for the sake of discussion, 15 or 20 by the method described above is "rather" cumbersome. Then, in order to get around this difficulty, we should resort to a simpler method. The simpler device is that we change to zero all elements except one of a row or column while not changing the value of the determinant. Then, expand the determinant in terms of that row or column which has all the elements equal to zero except one. Perhaps, an example may illustrate the trick. Suppose we want to expand the following determinant:

$$A = \begin{vmatrix} 1 & 2 & 3 & 4 \\ 4 & 5 & 6 & 4 \\ 7 & 8 & 9 & 7 \\ 1 & 2 & 3 & 1 \end{vmatrix}.$$

According to certain rules which we will explain in the next section, the above determinant is equal to

$$A = \begin{vmatrix} -3 & 2 & 3 & 4 \\ 0 & 5 & 6 & 4 \\ 0 & 8 & 9 & 7 \\ 0 & 2 & 3 & 1 \end{vmatrix}.$$

We can now expand the determinant in terms of the first column:

$$A = -3 \begin{vmatrix} 5 & 6 & 4 \\ 8 & 9 & 7 \\ 2 & 3 & 1 \end{vmatrix}$$

and the rest of minors will be equal to zero because they should be multiplied by zero elements. This rule makes the job of computation easier than before.

Properties of Determinants. The following properties, which are given without proof, are very useful in evaluating determinants and serve as the basis of the rule for numerical evaluation of any order determinant.

(1) If we interchange the corresponding rows and columns of a determinant, the value of that determinant does not change.

(2) If every element of a row (or a column) is zero, the value of that determinant is zero.

(3) If we multiply every element of a column (or a row) by the same constant, the determinant is multiplied by that constant.

(4) If we interchange two rows (or two columns) of a determinant, the sign of the determinant does not change.

(5) If two rows (or two columns) of a determinant are identical, the value of that determinant is zero.

(6) The value of any determinant does not change if each element of any row (or any column), or each element multiplied by any given number, is added to (or subtracted from) the corresponding element of any other row (or column).

(7) If the determinant of a square matrix is zero, the matrix is called *singular*.

(8) On the other hand, if the determinant of a square matrix is non-zero, the matrix is called *non-singular*.

Although determinants have many uses, we are here interested in their application to the inversion of matrices and the solution of the system of linear equations.

11.7 The Adjoint Matrix

The transpose of the matrix of cofactors of a matrix is called its *adjoint matrix*. And the matrix of cofactors of a matrix, say $A = (a_{ij})_{(n,n)}$ is given by

$$(-1)^{i+j}(A_{ij}) = (b_{ij})$$

where A_{ij} is the minor of a_{ij} of A. According to the definition, the transpose of the above expression will be the Adjoint matrix of A displayed by

$$\text{Adj. } A = (-1)^{j+i}(A_{ji}) = (b_{ij})' = (b_{ji}).$$

As an illustrative example, the Adjoint matrix of the following square matrix

$$A = \begin{bmatrix} 2 & 1 & 1 \\ 3 & 1 & 2 \\ 2 & 3 & 1 \end{bmatrix}$$

will be given. For defining the Adjoint matrix of A, one should replace each element of A by its cofactor to get the matrix of cofactors:

$$\text{Matrix of Cofactor} = \begin{bmatrix} -5 & 1 & 7 \\ 2 & 0 & -4 \\ 1 & -1 & -1 \end{bmatrix}$$

If we transpose the matrix of the cofactors of A, the Adjoint matrix will be obtained:

$$\text{Adj. } A = \begin{bmatrix} -5 & 2 & 1 \\ 1 & 0 & -1 \\ 7 & -4 & -1 \end{bmatrix}.$$

11.8 The Inverse of a Square Matrix

A square matrix A has an inverse shown by A^{-1} if and only if

$$AA^{-1} = A^{-1}A = I.$$

If the product of a matrix and its inverse is an identity matrix, the inverse matrix can be found by

$$A^{-1} = \frac{1}{|A|} \text{ Adj. } A$$

provided that $|A| \neq 0$.

Since the value of the determinant of the preceding section is $|A| = -2$, the inverse of that example is:

$$A^{-1} = \frac{1}{|A|} \text{ Adj. } A = \begin{bmatrix} \frac{-5}{-2} & \frac{2}{-2} & \frac{1}{-2} \\ \frac{1}{-2} & 0 & \frac{-1}{-2} \\ \frac{7}{-2} & \frac{-4}{-2} & \frac{-1}{-2} \end{bmatrix}.$$

It is quite clear that if $|A| = 0$, then the inverse would not exist. Then, A has an inverse if and only if $|A| \neq 0$ which is tantamount to stating that matrix A has to be nonsingular.

A few useful results concerning inverse matrices can now be established. The first one is that the inverse of a product is the product of inverses in reverse order, *e.g.*

$$(ABCD)^{-1} = D^{-1}C^{-1}B^{-1}A^{-1}.$$

To demonstrate this result, we premultiply both sides of it by $(ABCD)$ to have

$$(ABCD)(ABCD)^{-1} = ABCDD^{-1}C^{-1}B^{-1}A^{-1}.$$

By setting $ABCD = E$, the left hand side will be reduced to an identity and

$$\begin{aligned} I &= ABC(DD^{-1})C^{-1}B^{-1}A^{-1}, \\ &= AB(CC^{-1})B^{-1}A^{-1}, \\ &= A(BB^{-1})A^{-1}, \\ &= AA^{-1} = I. \end{aligned} \qquad \text{Q.E.D.}$$

The second result is that the transpose of the inverse is the inverse of the transpose:

$$(A^{-1})' = (A')^{-1},$$

and immediately related to this rule, we can state that if A is nonsingular and symmetric, its inverse, A^{-1}, will also be symmetric.

The task of computing the inverse matrices is not nowadays very immense and difficult for some robust electronic computers can compute matrix inversions.

11.9 The Rank of a Matrix

A matrix is said to be of rank r if and only if it has at least one determinant of order r which is not zero, but has no determinant of order more than r which is non-zero. For example, if

$$A = \begin{bmatrix} -2 & 3 & 1 \\ 1 & 4 & 5 \\ -1 & 3 & 2 \end{bmatrix}$$

its determinant is equal to zero, *i.e.*

$$\text{det. } A = \begin{vmatrix} -2 & 3 & 1 \\ 1 & 4 & 5 \\ -1 & 3 & 2 \end{vmatrix} = 0.$$

But a sub-determinant of the determinant of A is non-zero, *i.e.*

$$\begin{vmatrix} -2 & 3 \\ 1 & 4 \end{vmatrix} \neq 0.$$

According to our definition, the rank of our matrix is 2. To find the rank of a matrix in this fashion is often awkward and laborious, especially if the order of the matrix is relatively high. An easier method with the help of *elementary transpositions* is adopted in many books on Abstract Algebra. We give the following theorems without proof.

Theorem 11.1. Elementary transformations do not change the rank and order of a matrix.

Theorem 11.1. Two or n matrices, whose elements are given explicit numbers, are equivalent if and only if they have the same rank and order. By equivalence is meant "of the same rank and order." *Do not* read anything else into the definition.

Theorem 11.3. The rank of the product of two matrices cannot exceed the rank of either matrix.

11.10 Elementary Transformations

The following operations are called the elementary transformations of a matrix.

1. If any two parallel lines of a matrix are interchanged.

2. If all elements of any line are multiplied by the same non-zero constant.

3. If we add to any line an arbitrary multiple of any other line.

When the elementary transformations are applied to a matrix, the rank of the resultant matrix does not change. Therefore, in order to find the rank of a matrix with the elementary transformations, one should apply the rules of transformations so that the given matrix would be transformed into an equivalent one with zero elements for off-diagonal and distinct and non-zero numbers for the main-diagonal elements. The number of non-zero elements of the main diagonal is the rank of the given matrix.

EXERCISES 11

1. Perform the matrix multiplication:

$$\begin{bmatrix} 2 & 3 & 0 & 1 \\ 5 & 6 & 7 & 2 \\ 0 & 4 & 2 & 1 \\ 1 & -1 & 2 & 3 \end{bmatrix} \begin{bmatrix} -1 & 2 & 1 & 2 & 2 \\ 2 & -4 & 2 & 1 & 3 \\ 3 & 1 & 1 & 2 & 3 \\ 1 & 2 & 1 & 3 & -2 \end{bmatrix}.$$

$$(a_1 \quad a_2 \quad a_3 \quad a_4) \begin{bmatrix} a_1 \\ a_2 \\ a_3 \\ a_4 \end{bmatrix}.$$

$$\begin{bmatrix} 3 \\ 2 \\ 1 \\ -2 \end{bmatrix} (3 \quad 2 \quad 1 \quad 4).$$

$$\begin{bmatrix} 2 & 0 & 0 \\ 0 & 2 & 0 \\ 0 & 0 & 2 \end{bmatrix} \begin{bmatrix} a_{11} & a_{12} & a_{13} & a_{14} \\ a_{21} & a_{22} & a_{23} & a_{24} \\ a_{31} & a_{32} & a_{33} & a_{34} \end{bmatrix}.$$

$$(2 \quad -1 \quad 3) \begin{bmatrix} 2 & -1 \\ 3 & 2 \\ 1 & -4 \end{bmatrix} \begin{bmatrix} 3 \\ 2 \end{bmatrix}.$$

2. Prove that $aA \cdot bB \cdot cC = abc(ABC)$ and in particular

$$(-A)(-B)(-C) = -ABC.$$

3. A determinant $|a_{ij}|$ is said to be dominated by its diagonal elements if

$$|a_{rr}| > \sum_{\substack{s=1 \\ s \neq r}}^{n} |a_{rs}|.$$

Prove that the value of a determinant with real and positive diagonal elements which is dominated by its diagonal elements is positive. (See L. Mirsky, *Linear Algebra*, 1961, pp. 32–3.)

4. Show that

$$\begin{vmatrix} 1 + a_1 & a_2 & \cdots & a_n \\ a_1 & 1 + a_2 & \cdots & a_n \\ \cdot & \cdot & \cdots & \cdot \\ a_1 & a_2 & \cdots & 1 + a_n \end{vmatrix} = 1 + a_1 + a_2 + \cdots + a_n.$$

5. Show that

$$
\begin{vmatrix}
a_{11} & a_{12} & \cdots & a_{1n} \\
0 & a_{22} & \cdots & a_{2n} \\
\cdot & \cdot & \cdots & \cdot \\
0 & 0 & \cdots & a_{nn}
\end{vmatrix} = \prod_{i=1}^{n} a_{ii}.
$$

6. Prove that if the corresponding elements of two columns or rows of a square matrix are proportional, its determinant vanishes.

7. Show that

$$
\begin{vmatrix}
1 - n & 1 & \cdots & 1 \\
1 & 1 - n & \cdots & 1 \\
\cdot & \cdot & \cdots & \cdot \\
1 & 1 & \cdots & 1 - n
\end{vmatrix} = 0.
$$

8. Determine the inverse and rank of each of the following:

$$
\begin{bmatrix}
0 & 2 & 1 & 3 \\
4 & 5 & 6 & 3 \\
2 & 1 & 0 & 2 \\
-1 & 3 & 2 & 0
\end{bmatrix}
\begin{bmatrix}
1 & 0 & 0 & k \\
0 & 0 & 1 & 2 \\
0 & 0 & 3 & 4 \\
4 & -1 & 3 & 0
\end{bmatrix}
\begin{bmatrix}
0 & -1 & 3 & 2 & -5 \\
0 & 0 & 2 & 0 & 1 \\
1 & 3 & -1 & -2 & 0 \\
0 & 2 & 3 & 1 & 0
\end{bmatrix}
$$

9. Show that if $\det A \neq 0$, then from $AB = AC$ we can deduce $B = C$.

12 MATHEMATICAL ANALYSIS FOR PROGRAMMING

12.1 Linear Equations in Matrix Notation

A system of m linear non-homogeneous equations in n unknowns is represented by

(12.1.1)
$$\sum_{i=1}^{m} a_{ij}x_j = b_i \qquad j = 1, \ldots, n.$$

The expanded form of (12.1.1) is shown by

(12.1.2)
$$\begin{aligned}
a_{11}x_1 + a_{12}x_2 + \cdots + a_{1n}x_n &= b_1 \\
a_{21}x_1 + a_{22}x_2 + \cdots + a_{2n}x_n &= b_2 \\
\cdot \quad \cdot \quad \cdot \quad \cdot \quad \cdot \quad \cdot \quad \cdot \quad \cdot \quad \cdot \quad \cdot \quad \cdot \quad \cdot \\
a_{m1}x_1 + a_{m2}x_2 + \cdots + a_{mn}x_n &= b_m.
\end{aligned}$$

Gathering from our knowledge of matrix and vector manipulation, the system of (12.1.2) may in matrix form be represented by

(12.1.3)
$$\begin{bmatrix}
a_{11} & a_{21} & \cdots & a_{1n} \\
a_{21} & a_{22} & \cdots & a_{2n} \\
\cdot & \cdot & \cdot & \cdot \\
a_{m1} & a_{m2} & \cdots & a_{mn}
\end{bmatrix}
\begin{bmatrix}
x_1 \\ x_2 \\ \vdots \\ x_n
\end{bmatrix}
=
\begin{bmatrix}
b_1 \\ b_2 \\ \vdots \\ b_m
\end{bmatrix}.$$

If

$$A = \begin{bmatrix}
a_{11} & a_{12} & \cdots & a_{1n} \\
a_{21} & a_{22} & \cdots & a_{2n} \\
\cdot & \cdot & \cdot & \cdot \\
a_{m1} & a_{m2} & \cdots & a_{mn}
\end{bmatrix}
\qquad
X = \begin{bmatrix}
x_1 \\ x_2 \\ \vdots \\ x_n
\end{bmatrix}
\qquad
B = \begin{bmatrix}
b_1 \\ b_2 \\ \vdots \\ b_m
\end{bmatrix}$$

the system of (12.1.3) will be reduced to the much simpler form of

(12.1.4) $AX = B.$

If we bring (b_i) from the right-hand side of (12.1.3) to the left-hand side and include it in the (a_{ij}), we will have

$$\begin{bmatrix} a_{\bar{1}1} & a_{12} & \cdots & a_{1n}, b_1 \\ a_{21} & a_{22} & \cdots & a_{2n}, b_2 \\ \cdot & \cdot & \cdot & \cdot & \cdot & \cdot & \cdot \\ a_{m1} & a_{m2} & \cdots & a_{mn}, b_m \end{bmatrix} = A, B$$

which is the same as $A = (a_{ij})$ except that a column consisting of the constant terms has been attached. The matrix $A = (a_{ij})$ is called the *coefficient matrix*, and $A, B = (a_{ij}, b_i)$ is named the *augmented matrix* of the system of equations of (12.1.1) or (12.1.2). Any set of values of $x_1, x_2, \ldots, x_n$ from a field $\mathfrak{F}$ which simultaneously satisfy (12.1.2) is called the *solution* over $\mathfrak{F}$ of the system.

12.2 Linear Transformation

Let $AX = B$ which takes the linear vector X into B. If $B = f(X)$, we can write $AX = f(X)$. This last expression is called a *linear transformation* since it transforms the vector X into the vector B. Also, $B = f(X)$ is called a *linear vector function* which relates the unique vector B to each vector X of the same domain.

If distinct vectors $x_1, x_2, \ldots,$ of the domain of x, give rise to distinct vectors $B_1 = AX_1, B_2 = AX_2, \ldots,$ the linear transformation $AX = B$ is called *non-singular*. It is non-singular because the *coefficient matrix* is to be non-singular in order to have distinct vectors. It is evident that it is the coefficient matrix which is fundamental in linear transformation.

12.3 Consistent and Inconsistent Systems of Equations

A system of non-homogeneous linear equations is often expressed in two forms:

(12.3.1) $AX = B$

(12.3.2) $AX + B = 0$

where A is the coefficient matrix and A, B is the augmented matrix of (12.3.1) or (12.3.2).

A system of non-homogeneous linear equations in n unknowns is called *consistent* if the given system has one or more solutions. If, on the other hand, it has no solutions, not even zero, the said system is named *inconsistent*.

Use of Determinants in Solving Equations. Mention was made before that the determinants may be used for the solution of the system of linear equations. In Chapter 11, we already expressed the solution of n linear equations in n unknowns in terms of determinants. Again, let us take a system of linear equations containing the same number of equations as unknowns:

(12.3.3)
$$a_{11}x_1 + a_{12}x_2 + \cdots + a_{1n}x_n = b_1$$
$$a_{21}x_1 + a_{22}x_2 + \cdots + a_{2n}x_n = b_2$$
$$\cdot \quad \cdot \quad \cdot \quad \cdot \quad \cdot \quad \cdot \quad \cdot \quad \cdot \quad \cdot \quad \cdot \quad \cdot \quad \cdot \quad \cdot$$
$$a_{m1}x_1 + a_{m2}x_2 + \cdots + a_{mn}x_n = b_m.$$

We have already shown that the unique solution of any variable is obtained by the determinants of those variables. It is desirable to name

(12.3.4)
$$\begin{vmatrix} a_{11} & a_{12} & \cdots & a_{1n} \\ a_{21} & a_{22} & \cdots & a_{2n} \\ \cdot & \cdot & \cdot & \cdot \\ a_{m1} & a_{m2} & \cdots & a_{mn} \end{vmatrix},$$

which is the determinant of the coefficient of the variables, the *determinant of the system* of equations of (12.3.3). We have noted that (12.3.3) can have a set of unique solutions for $x_1, \ldots, x_n$ if and only if (12.3.4) is non-zero. This exemplifies what is known as Cramer's Rule. It follows that if (12.3.4) is zero (12.3.3) may produce infinite solutions for its variables. A system of linear equations with exactly the same number of equations as unknowns has a set of unique solutions for the variables if and only if the rank of the coefficient matrix is n. If, however, the rank of the coefficient matrix is less than n, the number of unknowns, the system may produce infinite solutions though this may not be the sufficient condition as will be explicated in the ensuing section.

First, in linear programming one may not be really interested in the existence of a set of unique solutions. Rather, emphasis may have to be placed on other solutions. Secondly, our aim is to illustrate that if the rank of the coefficient matrix is less than n, the number of unknowns, this by itself does not guarantee the existence of other solutions for the system (12.3.3). The line of demarcation which we have just established between the set of *unique* and *other* solutions leads us to a remark which deserves being mentioned in passing. Let us imagine a straight line which according to definition is the locus of infinite solutions or points. Any one point has exactly the same property as any other point of the assumed line; there is nothing *unique* about any point of it. Now, suppose that this line is crossed by another line in one point. It is obvious that the point of the first line which is also the intersection point has the property of being a unique intersection point. Analogously, a set of unique solutions is that which has a unique property not shared by other sets of solutions of a system of equations.

12.4 The Condition Which Renders a System of Linear Equations Consistent

Let the following system of three equations in three unknowns be given:

(12.4.1)
$$-2x_1 + 3x_2 + x_3 = 5$$
$$x_1 + 4x_2 + 5x_3 = 3$$
$$-x_1 + 3x_2 + 2x_3 = 4.$$

By the use of the techniques of the elementary transformations, we shall see presently that the rank of the coefficient matrix

(12.4.2)
$$\begin{bmatrix} -2 & 3 & 1 \\ 1 & 4 & 5 \\ -1 & 3 & 2 \end{bmatrix}$$

is $r = 2$. From the definition given for the rank of a matrix, it follows that the determinant of the coefficient matrix is zero:

$$\begin{vmatrix} -2 & 3 & 1 \\ 1 & 4 & 5 \\ -1 & 3 & 2 \end{vmatrix} = 0.$$

(We found this result in the preceding chapter in a round-about way.)

According to Cramer's Rule, (12.4.1) does not possess the set of unique solutions for x_1, x_2 and x_3. Nevertheless, (12.4.1) can, by elimination, be reduced to

(12.4.3)
$$\begin{cases} x_1 = -x_3 - 1 \\ x_2 = -x_3 + 1 \end{cases}$$

from which we may obtain infinite solutions by substituting arbitrary values for x_3 and get values for x_1 and x_2. Also, the system (12.4.3) satisfies (12.4.1). Therefore, (12.4.1) has many solutions and *quo ad hoc* consistent. (12.4.3) is called the complete solution of (12.4.1) and *particular* solutions are those values which are consistent and obtained by assigning particular and arbitrary values to x_3.

Remember! We contended that not all systems of linear equations for which the rank of the coefficient matrix is less than the number of unknowns has infinite solutions. The reason that (12.4.1) is consistent is not that the rank of its coefficient matrix is less than the number of its unknowns, 3. Rather, it possesses a unique property which has made it consistent. Let us explore this unique property.

The coefficient and augmented matrices of (12.4.1) are (12.4.2) and

(12.4.4)
$$\begin{bmatrix} -2 & 3 & 1 & -5 \\ 1 & 4 & 5 & -3 \\ -1 & 3 & 2 & -4 \end{bmatrix}$$

respectively. It is immediately noticed that the ranks of (12.4.2) and (12.4.4) are $r = 2$, respectively. This is the condition which has rendered (12.4.1) consistent; *viz.*, it has infinite solutions. Accordingly, on the balance of whatever we have stressed and asserted so far, the following theorem is given without proof:

Theorem 12.1. A system of n-linear equations in n unknowns is consistent if and only if the rank of the coefficient matrix is equal to the rank of the augmented matrix.

With this theorem in mind, let us examine the following example:

(12.4.5)
$$\begin{aligned} -2x_1 + 3x_2 + x_3 &= 5 \\ x_1 + 4x_2 + 5x_3 &= 3 \\ -x_1 + 3x_2 + 2x_3 &= 8. \end{aligned}$$

The coefficient and augmented matrices of (12.4.5) are

$$\begin{bmatrix} -2 & 3 & 1 \\ 1 & 4 & 5 \\ -1 & 3 & 2 \end{bmatrix}, \quad \begin{bmatrix} -2 & 3 & 1 & -5 \\ 1 & 4 & 5 & -3 \\ -1 & 3 & 2 & -8 \end{bmatrix}$$

respectively. The rank of the coefficient matrix is $r = 2$ and the rank of the augmented matrix is $r = 3$. From our theorem, it is deduced that (12.4.5) is *inconsistent;* namely, we cannot have any solution not even a zero one for (12.4.5). The reader is asked to examine the inconsistency of (12.4.5).

From Theorem (12.1) we can set up the following rather important corollary:

Corollary 12.2. A system of homogeneous linear equations is always consistent, since the coefficient and augmented matrices differ only by a column zero vector which cannot change the rank of the matrix.

It is obvious that the system of linear homogeneous equations

$$\sum_{j=1}^{n} a_{ij}x_j = 0 \qquad (i = 1, \ldots, m)$$
$$AX = 0$$

has always the trivial, zero, solution

$$x_1 = x_2 = \cdots = x_n = 0.$$

One may wish to be concerned with the idea that whether or not a system of homogeneous linear equations has non-trivial, non-zero solutions, in addition to its trivial solutions. This is a perfectly legitimate question, and the answer is given by the following theorem without proof.

Theorem 12.3. A system of m homogeneous linear equations in n unknowns

$$\sum_{j=1}^{n} a_{ij}x_j = 0 \qquad (i = 1, \ldots m)$$

has non-trivial solutions if and only if the rank of the coefficient matrix is less than the number of unknowns. This is a necessary and sufficient condition.

The above theorem is rather general. There are two special cases which are commonly used and useful. We state these two cases as the corollaries of the previous theorem:

Corollary 12.4. When the number of equations (n) is equal to the number of unknowns (n), the necessary and sufficient condition for having non-trivial solutions, in a system of homogeneous linear equations, is that the coefficient matrix is singular.

Corollary 12.5. If the number of homogeneous linear equations (m) is less than the number of unknowns (n), the system has always non-trivial solutions.

It should be remembered, and this is cardinal, that if a system of homogeneous linear equations in n unknowns is found to have non-trivial solutions and the rank of the coefficient matrix is found to be r, then it can be proved easily that r unknowns of the system can be grouped in terms of the remaining $(n - r)$ unknowns of the system to make up the *complete solution*. This result is extremely important and of practical use.

We give the following examples to illustrate the contents of our theorems and corollaries and the result deduced from the last theorem. Let the following system be given:

$$\begin{aligned} x_1 + 3x_2 - x_3 &= 0 \\ 4x_1 - 2x_2 + x_3 &= 0 \\ 2x_1 + x_2 + 3x_3 &= 0. \end{aligned}$$

The rank of the coefficient matrix

$$\begin{bmatrix} 1 & 3 & -1 \\ 4 & -2 & 1 \\ 2 & 1 & 3 \end{bmatrix}$$

is $r = 3$; from which one deduces that the coefficient matrix is not singular. According to our theorem, the given system does not possess non-trivial, non-zero solutions. The only set of solutions that it has is the trivial set

$$x_1 = x_2 = x_3 = 0.$$

We solve another example in passing. Let the following system be given

(12.4.6)
$$2x_1 + 3x_2 - x_3 = 0$$
$$-x_1 - 2x_2 + x_3 = 0$$
$$4x_1 + x_2 + 3x_3 = 0.$$

The rank of the coefficient matrix

$$\begin{bmatrix} 2 & 3 & -1 \\ -1 & -2 & 1 \\ 4 & 1 & 3 \end{bmatrix}$$

is $r = 2$. According to our theorem, the system has non-trivial solutions. And, in conformity with the purpose of that important result previously stressed, if the rank of the coefficient matrix is 2, then two unknowns of the system can be found in terms of the remaining $(3 - 2 = 1)$ unknowns:

(12.4.7)
$$\begin{cases} x_1 = -x_2 \\ x_3 = x_2 \\ x_2 = 0. \end{cases}$$

It has been a fashion, and perhaps it is desirable, to call x_1 and x_3 (and any unknown found and arranged likewise) dependent variables and x_2 (and any unknown of this nature) independent variable of the system (12.4.6). This latter definition is misleading but as long as it serves a good purpose it can be retained.

We shall revert to the discussion of the solution of the homogeneous and non-homogeneous linear equations after explaining a few necessary and essential topics pertaining to the linear dependency of vectors and matrices.

12.5 The Linear Dependency of Vectors and Matrices

The Linear Dependency of Vectors. If there are k unknowns $x_1, x_2, \ldots x_k$ related to each other in

(12.5.1)
$$P_1 x_1 + P_2 x_2 + \cdots + P_k x_k$$

where P_j are constants, (12.5.1) is called a linear combination of the unknowns x_j. If for some set of P's, not all zero, the linear combination (12.5.1) is identically equal to zero

(12.5.2)
$$P_1 x_1 + P_2 x_2 + \cdots + P_k x_k = 0$$

the unknowns x_j are defined to be *linearly dependent*. If, however, (12.5.2) holds when P's are all zero, then the unknowns x_j are said to be *linearly independent*. If the reader ponders (12.5.2) momentarily, he will find out intuitively that linear dependency is analogous to the idea of proportionality in *college algebra*.

Therefore, two vectors are linearly dependent if they are proportional. The notion of linear dependency and independency can be applied to vectors. We say that if there are k n-dimensional vectors

(12.5.3)
$$A_1 = (a_{11}\ a_{21} \ldots a_{n1})$$
$$A_2 = (a_{12}\ a_{22} \ldots a_{n2})$$
$$\cdot \quad \cdot \quad \cdot \quad \cdot \quad \cdot \quad \cdot \quad \cdot$$
$$A_k = (a_{1k}\ a_{2k} \ldots a_{nk})$$

the linear combination of them is

(12.5.4)
$$P_1 A_1 + P_2 A_2 + \cdots + P_k A_k,$$

where P's are constants. These vectors are *linearly dependent* if for some set of constants P's, not all of which are zero, we have

(12.5.5)
$$P_1 A_1 + P_2 A_2 + \cdots + P_k A_k = 0.$$

On the other hand, when (12.5.5) holds true if and only if P's are all zero, the set of k vectors is *linearly independent*.

Since (12.5.5) is the sum of k conformable vectors, according to the vector summation rule (*i.e.* corresponding elements ought to be added up), it can be expressed as

(12.5.6) $(P_1 a_{11}\ \ P_1 a_{21} \ldots P_1 a_{n1}) + (P_2 a_{12}\ \ P_2 a_{22} \ldots P_2 a_{n2})$
$$+ \cdots + (P_k a_{1k}\ \ P_k a_{2k} \ldots P_k a_{nk}) = 0$$

or

$$(P_1 a_{11} + P_2 a_{12} + \cdots + P_k a_{1k},\ \ P_1 a_{12} + P_2 a_{22}$$
$$+ \cdots + P_k a_{2k}, \ldots,\ \ P_1 a_{n1} + P_2 a_{n2} + \cdots + P_k a_{nk}) = 0.$$

This last expression is a vector which is equal to another zero vector (sometimes called null vector) and can therefore be represented by the following system of homogeneous linear equations:

(12.5.7)
$$\begin{cases} a_{11}P_1 + a_{12}P_2 + \cdots + a_{1k}P_k = 0 \\ a_{21}P_1 + a_{22}P_2 + \cdots + a_{2k}P_k = 0 \\ \cdot \quad \cdot \quad \cdot \quad \cdot \quad \cdot \quad \cdot \quad \cdot \quad \cdot \quad \cdot \\ a_{n1}P_1 + a_{n2}P_2 + \cdots + a_{nk}P_k = 0. \end{cases}$$

(12.5.7) is a system of n linear homogeneous equations in k unknowns P's with the coefficient matrix

$$\begin{bmatrix} a_{11} & a_{12} & \cdots & a_{1k} \\ a_{21} & a_{22} & \cdots & a_{2k} \\ \cdot & \cdot & & \cdot \\ a_{n1} & a_{n2} & \cdots & a_{nk} \end{bmatrix}.$$

We pointed out definitionally that if all P's in (12.5.5) are zero, trivial, the given vectors are linearly independent; while if some or all of P's are non-zero, non-trivial, the k n-dimensional vectors are linearly dependent. The linear dependency or independency of k n-dimensional vectors, which are conformable in addition, is another way of stating whether or not the system of homogeneous linear equations in k unknowns has trivial or non-trivial solutions in P's.   If (12.5.7) has non-trivial solutions the given vectors, which are the columns of the system, are linearly dependent; contrariwise, if the only set of possible solutions for $P_1, P_2, \ldots P_k$ in (12.5.7) is trivial the vectors are linearly independent.

From the results of the previous paragraph, we write the following procedure for finding whether or not the k n-dimensional vectors are linearly dependent (or independent). Given a set of vectors which are conformable in addition, we write out a system of homogeneous linear equations whose coefficient matrix is constituted of the given vectors as its columns and with P's composing its unknowns. The question of dependency of the given vectors is reduced to the responsibility of finding non-trivial solutions for the given system. We venture to illustrate the procedure via an example:

Given the following vectors:

(12.5.8)
$$\begin{cases} A_1 = (1 & -1 & 4 & 2) \\ A_2 = (4 & 1 & 1 & 1) \\ A_3 = (2 & -1 & 0 & 1) \\ A_4 = (3 & 2 & 2 & 3) \\ A_5 = (1 & 1 & 1 & 1) \end{cases}$$

it is desired to know whether or not the given vectors are linearly dependent. We can write

(12.5.9) $$P_1 A_1 + P_2 A_2 + P_3 A_3 + P_4 A_4 + P_5 A_5 = 0$$

or according to the procedure

(12.5.10)
$$\begin{cases} P_1 + 4P_2 + 2P_3 + 3P_4 + P_5 = 0 \\ -P_1 + P_2 - P_3 + 2P_4 + P_5 = 0 \\ 4P_1 + P_2 + 0 + 2P_4 + P_5 = 0 \\ 2P_1 + P_2 + P_3 + 3P_4 + P_5 = 0 \end{cases}$$

Accordingly, the question of the linear dependency of vectors (12.5.8) becomes one of finding the necessary and sufficient condition for having non-trivial solutions for (12.5.10), the system of linear equations. Remember the theorem which asserted the necessary and sufficient conditions that a system of homogeneous linear equations has non-trivial solutions. We said that if the rank of the coefficient matrix of the system of linear equations is less than the number of the unknowns, the system has non-trivial solutions.

In our example, the coefficient matrix

$$\begin{bmatrix} 1 & 4 & 2 & 3 & 1 \\ -1 & 1 & -1 & 2 & 1 \\ 4 & 1 & 0 & 2 & 1 \\ 2 & 1 & 1 & 3 & 1 \end{bmatrix}$$

has rank $r = 4$ which is less than 5, the number of unknowns of the system (12.5.10). Therefore, the system (12.5.10) has non-trivial solutions; namely, the vectors (12.5.8) are linearly dependent.

From the preceding discussion and explanation, the ensuing theorems are in order:

Theorem 12.6. If the rank of the matrix $(A_1, A_2, \ldots A_k)$, with the k n-dimensional vectors $A_1, A_2, \ldots A_k$ as its columns, is less than k, the given k vectors are linearly dependent.

Theorem 12.7. The necessary condition that the k n-dimensional vectors $A_1, A_2, \ldots A_k$ are linearly dependent is that $k > n$.

Theorem 12.8. If there are k n-dimensional vectors $A_1, A_2, \ldots, A_k$ which are linearly dependent, then at least one of them, which has non-zero coefficient, can be expressed as a linear combination of the rest:

$$A_1 = -P_2/P_1(A_2) \cdots -P_k/P_1(A_k).$$

Theorem 12.9. This is the converse of Theorem 12.8. Suppose there are k n-dimensional vectors and one, say A_1, of them can be expressed as a linear combination of $A_2, A_3, \ldots A_k$, then the k vectors $A_1, A_2, \ldots A_k$ are necessarily linearly dependent.

Theorem 12.10. If the k n-dimensional vectors of the previous theorems are linearly independent; suppose further that the $k + 1$ n-dimensional vectors

$$A_1, A_2, \ldots A_k, W$$

are linearly dependent, then W can be expressed as a linear combination of

$$A_1, A_2, \ldots A_k.$$

Linear Dependence of Matrices. This is the general case of linear dependence of vectors and is exactly similar to the foregoing explanation.

12.6 Bilinear Forms

If the coefficients a_{ij} belong to the field $\mathfrak{F}$, and if there are $m + n$ variables $x_1, x_2, \ldots x_m$ and $y_1, y_2, \ldots y_n$ such that

(12.6.1) $$b(x_i, y_j) = X'AY = \sum_{j=1}^{n} \sum_{i=1}^{m} a_{ij}x_iy_j,$$

$b(x_i, y_j)$ is called a *bilinear form over* $\mathfrak{F}$. For instance,

(12.6.2) $$(x_1\ x_2\ x_3\ x_4) \begin{bmatrix} 1 & 2 \\ 0 & 1 \\ 2 & 1 \\ 0 & -1 \end{bmatrix} \begin{bmatrix} y_1 \\ y_2 \end{bmatrix}$$

$$= x_1y_1 + 2x_3y_1 + 2x_1y_2 + x_2y_2 - x_4y_2 + x_3y_2$$

is a *real bilinear form* (*i.e.*, a bilinear form over the real number field).

If the variables x and y are independent, the rank of the coefficient matrix A is the rank of the *bilinear form*. The coefficient matrix A is usually called *the matrix of the bilinear form*. In the above example, the rank of the form is 2 because the rank of the coefficient matrix is 2.

Let us suppose that we have the bilinear form $X'AY$ and that the variables x and y are especially related to w and z via two non-singular coefficient matrices B and C such that $X = BW$ and $Y = CZ$. The bilinear form $X'AY$ may be transformed into another bilinear form with w and z variables, *i.e.*

(12.6.3) $X'AY = (BW)'A(CZ) = W'(B'AC)Z.$

Let the following bilinear form be given:

$$X'AY = X'\begin{bmatrix} 1 & 2 & 1 \\ 1 & 0 & 1 \\ 2 & -1 & 0 \end{bmatrix} Y = x_1y_1 + x_2y_1 + 2x_3y_1 + 2x_1y_2 - x_3y_2$$

(12.6.4)

where $\begin{bmatrix} 1 & 2 & 1 \\ 1 & 0 & 1 \\ 2 & -1 & 0 \end{bmatrix}$ is the coefficient matrix of the form with its rank

being 3. Let us suppose that the variables x and y are, via two non-singular matrices, related to w and z:

(12.6.5) $$X = \begin{bmatrix} 1 & 0 & 0 \\ 1 & 0 & -1 \\ 0 & 1 & 1 \end{bmatrix} W,$$

and

(12.6.6) $$Y = \begin{bmatrix} 1 & 1 & 1 \\ -1 & 0 & 1 \\ 0 & 1 & 0 \end{bmatrix} Z.$$

On substituting (12.6.5) into (12.6.3), we can obtain

$$X'AY = W'\begin{bmatrix} 1 & 1 & 0 \\ 0 & 0 & 1 \\ 0 & -1 & 1 \end{bmatrix}\begin{bmatrix} 1 & 2 & 1 \\ 1 & 0 & 1 \\ 2 & -1 & 0 \end{bmatrix}\begin{bmatrix} 1 & 1 & 1 \\ -1 & 0 & 1 \\ 0 & 1 & 0 \end{bmatrix} Z$$

(12.6.7) $X'AY = W'\begin{bmatrix} 0 & 4 & 4 \\ 3 & 2 & 1 \\ 2 & 0 & 0 \end{bmatrix} Z$

$$= 3w_2z_1 + 2w_3z_1 + 4w_1z_2 + 2w_2z_2 + 4w_1z_3 + w_2z_3.$$

The rank of the coefficient matrix of (12.6.7) is 3, whereby it is non-singular. As we notice, (12.6.4) and (12.6.7) are equivalent since their coefficient matrices have the same rank and order, and the variables x and y are related to variables w and z via two non-singular matrices

$$\begin{bmatrix} 1 & 0 & 0 \\ 1 & 0 & -1 \\ 0 & 1 & 1 \end{bmatrix} \quad \text{and} \quad \begin{bmatrix} 1 & 1 & 1 \\ -1 & 0 & 1 \\ 0 & 1 & 0 \end{bmatrix}.$$

From the above example we may deduce the following theorem:

Theorem 12.11. Two bilinear forms over the field $\mathfrak{F}$, are equivalent if and only if their coefficient matrices have the same rank and order.

12.7 Quadratic Forms

ax^2, where a is a constant and x a variable, is the most general *unary quadratic form*. The identity

$$
\textbf{(12.7.1)} \qquad
\begin{aligned}
q(x_1, x_2) &\equiv ax_1^2 + 2bx_1x_1 + cx_2^2 \\
&\equiv ax_1^2 + cx_2^2 + bx_1x_2 + bx_1x_2,
\end{aligned}
$$

expressible in matrix notation:

$$
\textbf{(12.7.2)} \qquad
q(x_1, x_2) = (x_1\ x_2) \begin{bmatrix} a & b \\ b & c \end{bmatrix} \begin{bmatrix} x_1 \\ x_2 \end{bmatrix}
$$

where a, b and c are constants and x_1 and x_2 are variables, may represent the general *binary quadratic form*. The identity

$$
\textbf{(12.7.3)} \qquad
\begin{aligned}
q(x_1, x_2, x_3) &\equiv ax_1^2 + bx_2^2 + cx_3^2 + 2rx_1x_2 + 2sx_1x_3 + 2tx_2x_3 \\
&\equiv ax_1^2 + bx_2^2 + cx_3^2 + rx_1x_2 + rx_1x_2 + sx_1x_3 \\
&\quad + sx_1x_3 + tx_2x_3 + tx_2x_3,
\end{aligned}
$$

expressible in matrix notation

$$
\textbf{(12.7.4)} \qquad
\equiv (x_1\ x_2\ x_3) \begin{bmatrix} a & r & s \\ r & b & t \\ s & t & c \end{bmatrix} \begin{bmatrix} x_1 \\ x_2 \\ x_3 \end{bmatrix}
$$

where a, b, c, r, s, and t are constants and x_1, x_2, x_3 are variables, may represent the general *ternary quadratic form*. One observation is to be made. The coefficient matrices of (12.7.2) and (12.7.4) are symmetric because $a_{ij} = a_{ji}$.* That is to say, for illustrating our quadratic forms by

---

* One should remember that A in $X'AX$ may not be symmetric for

$$
X'AX = 2x_1^2 + 3x_2^2 + 4x_1x_2 \equiv X' \begin{bmatrix} 2 & 2 \\ 2 & 3 \end{bmatrix} X \equiv X' \begin{bmatrix} 2 & 3 \\ 1 & 3 \end{bmatrix} X
$$

where $\begin{bmatrix} 2 & 3 \\ 1 & 3 \end{bmatrix}$ in the second formulation of $X'AX$ is not symmetric. In that case A is called *quasi-symmetric*.

matrix notations, we have divided the coefficients of each term, which is not to the power of 2, by 2 to obtain their means. The rule can be applied to all quadratic forms if they are to be represented by matrix notations.

A polynomial in $x_1, x_2, \ldots x_n$ which is a sum of terms $a_{ij}x_ix_j$ for $i = 1, \ldots n$ and $j = 1, \ldots n$ of the type

$$\text{(12.7.5)} \qquad X'AX = \sum_{i,j=1}^{n} a_{ij}x_ix_j$$

is called a quadratic form over a field $\mathfrak{F}$ if the coefficient $A = (a_{ij})$ n by n dimensions, is over a field $\mathfrak{F}$. The coefficients of x_i^2 are the constants a_{ii} and the total coefficient of $x_{ij} = x_{ji}$ is $a_{ij} + a_{ji}$. As we pointed out before, it is customary and convenient to write the total coefficients of x_{ij} as twice a number which was designated as a_{ij} and so have $a_{ij} = a_{ji}$, to have and make (a_{ij}) symmetric. Then, (12.7.5) may be expressed in matrix notations

$$\text{(12.7.6)} \qquad q(x_i, x_j) = X'AX = X' \begin{bmatrix} a_{11} & a_{12} & \cdots & a_{1n} \\ a_{21} & a_{22} & \cdots & a_{2n} \\ \cdot & \cdot & \cdot & \cdot \\ a_{n1} & a_{n2} & \cdots & a_{nn} \end{bmatrix} X$$

where X' is the transpose of X.

The symmetric matrix A is called the matrix of the quadratic form and its rank is the rank of the quadratic form. We wish to illustrate the following quadratic form:

$$\text{(12.7.7)} \quad q(x_1, x_2, x_3, x_4) = 3x_1^2 + 6x_3^2 + 4x_2^2 + 4x_1x_2 + 3x_1x_3$$
$$+ \tfrac{1}{2}x_2x_4 + x_1x_3 + 2x_3x_4,$$

in matrix notation. We just arrange the quadratic form subscriptwise; and then, complete it; *i.e.*,

(12.7.8)

$$q(x_1, x_2, x_3, x_4) = 3x_1^2 + 4x_2^2 + 6x_3^2 + 0x_4^2 + 4x_1x_2$$
$$+ 4x_1x_3 + 0x_1x_4 + 0x_2x_3 + \tfrac{1}{2}x_2x_4 + 2x_3x_4.$$

Then, we divide the coefficients of all x_{ij} by two to have:

$$q(x_1, x_2, x_3, x_4) = 3x_1^2 + 4x_2^2 + 6x_3^2 + 0x_4^2 + 2(2x_1x_2)$$
$$+ 2(2x_1x_3) + 2(0x_1x_4) + 2(0x_2x_3)$$
$$+ 2(\tfrac{1}{4}x_2x_4) + 2(x_3x_4),$$

$$q(x_1, x_2, x_3, x_4) \equiv (x_1 \quad x_2 \quad x_3 \quad x_4) \begin{bmatrix} 3 & 2 & 2 & 0 \\ 2 & 4 & 0 & \tfrac{1}{4} \\ 2 & 0 & 6 & 1 \\ 0 & \tfrac{1}{4} & 1 & 0 \end{bmatrix} \begin{bmatrix} x_1 \\ x_2 \\ x_3 \\ x_4 \end{bmatrix}.$$

(12.7.9)

Equivalence of Quadratic Forms. Let

$$(12.7.10) \qquad q(x_1, x_2, \ldots x_n) \equiv X'AX$$

be a quadratic form where A is a symmetric matrix ($a_{ij} = a_{ji}$) and X is a column vector of n dimensions. Let there be an n-dimensional column vector Y related to X by

$$(12.7.11) \qquad X = CY$$

where $C = (c_{ij})$ is a non-singular matrix. Then, according to (12.6.3) we can write

$$(12.7.12) \qquad X'AX = (CY)'A(CY) = Y'(C'AC)Y = Y'BY$$

where

$$(12.7.13) \qquad B = C'AC.$$

The two matrices A and B, both over $\mathfrak{F}$, which are related to each other by an n non-singular matrix C are called congruent. (If we find a sequence of elementary transformations on the rows of A such that it, followed by the sequence of the corresponding column transformations, will carry A into B, then it can be easily shown that A and B are congruent.)

Now, in (12.7.12), there are two quadratic forms which are equivalent, thus:

Theorem 12.12. Two quadratic forms are equivalent if and only if their coefficient matrices, both over the same field $\mathfrak{F}$, are congruent.

Lagrange's Reduction. The method of Lagrange's reduction, simply a repeated completing of the square, is a method whereby one can reduce a quadratic form to a simple form with which the rank of the matrix will be readily noticed.

Let us notice and consider the quadratic form:

$$q(x_1, x_2, x_3) = (x_1 \quad x_2 \quad x_3) \begin{bmatrix} 2 & 1 & 1 \\ 1 & 2 & -1 \\ 1 & -1 & 1 \end{bmatrix} \begin{bmatrix} x_1 \\ x_2 \\ x_3 \end{bmatrix}$$

$$= 2x_1^2 + 2x_1x_2 + 2x_1x_3 + 2x_2^2 + x_3^2 - 2x_2x_3$$

$(12.7.14)$

the rank of which is 3, since

$$\begin{vmatrix} 2 & 1 & 1 \\ 1 & 2 & -1 \\ 1 & -1 & 1 \end{vmatrix} = 3 \neq 0$$

is non-singular. We can rearrange (12.7.14) to have

(12.7.15) $q(x_1, x_2, x_3) = 2[x_1^2 + x_1(x_2 + x_3)] + 2x_2^2 + x_3^2 - 2x_2x_3$

which is (12.7.14) with all the terms containing x_1 being grouped and the coefficient of x_1^2 being factored. Next, we add to and subtract from, the quadratic form, the square of one-half of the coefficient of x_1. (This is, incidentally, called "completing the square" on x_1.) Thus, we have

$$q(x_1, x_2, x_3) = 2[x_1^2 + x_1(x_2 + x_3) + (\tfrac{1}{2}x_2 + \tfrac{1}{2}x_3)^2] - \tfrac{1}{2}x_2^2$$

(12.7.16)
$$- \tfrac{1}{2}x_3^2 - x_2x_3 + 2x_2^2 + x_3^2 - 2x_2x_3,$$
$$= 2(x_1 + \tfrac{1}{2}x_2 + \tfrac{1}{2}x_3)^2 + \tfrac{3}{2}x_2^2 - 3x_2x_3 + \tfrac{1}{2}x_3^2,$$
$$= 2(x_1 + \tfrac{1}{2}x_2 + \tfrac{1}{2}x_3)^2 + \tfrac{3}{2}(x_2^2 - 2x_2x_3) + \tfrac{1}{2}x_3^2.$$

Now we complete the square on x_2 to obtain:

$$q(x_1, x_2, x_3) = 2(x_1 + \tfrac{1}{2}x_2 + \tfrac{1}{2}x_3)^2 + \tfrac{3}{2}(x_2^2 - 2x_2x_3 + x_3^2)$$

(12.7.17)
$$- \tfrac{3}{2}x_3^2 + \tfrac{1}{2}x_3^2$$
$$= 2(x_1 + \tfrac{1}{2}x_2 + \tfrac{1}{2}x_3)^2 + \tfrac{3}{2}(x_2 - x_3)^2 - x_3^2.$$

Let us substitute

(12.7.18)
$$\begin{cases} y_1 = x_1 + \tfrac{1}{2}x_2 + \tfrac{1}{2}x_3 \\ y_2 = x_2 - x_3 \\ y_3 = x_3 \end{cases}$$

to have

(12.7.19) $q(x_1, x_2, x_3) = 2y_1^2 + \tfrac{3}{2}y_2^2 - y_3^2.$

It can be checked that the determinant of the substitution matrix *i.e.*:

$$\begin{vmatrix} 1 & \tfrac{1}{2} & \tfrac{1}{2} \\ 0 & 1 & -1 \\ 0 & 0 & 1 \end{vmatrix} = 1 \neq 0$$

is non-singular, so that the rank of the substitution matrix is 3. We already noticed that the rank of our quadratic form (12.7.14) is 3, too. Thus, according to our theorem (12.12) the quadratic forms (12.7.14) and (12.7.18) are equivalent. In matrix notation, we can rewrite (12.7.18):

$$Y = \begin{bmatrix} 1 & \tfrac{1}{2} & \tfrac{1}{2} \\ 0 & 1 & -1 \\ 0 & 0 & 1 \end{bmatrix} X,$$

or

(12.7.20) $$X = \begin{bmatrix} 1 & -\tfrac{1}{2} & -1 \\ 0 & 1 & 1 \\ 0 & 0 & 1 \end{bmatrix} Y$$

so that

$$X' \begin{bmatrix} 2 & 1 & 1 \\ 1 & 2 & -1 \\ 1 & -1 & 1 \end{bmatrix} X = Y' \begin{bmatrix} 1 & 0 & 0 \\ -\frac{1}{2} & 1 & 0 \\ -1 & 1 & 1 \end{bmatrix} \begin{bmatrix} 2 & 1 & 1 \\ 1 & 2 & 1 \\ 1 & -1 & 1 \end{bmatrix} \begin{bmatrix} 1 & -\frac{1}{2} & -1 \\ 0 & 1 & 1 \\ 0 & 0 & 1 \end{bmatrix} Y$$

$$= Y' \begin{bmatrix} 2 & 0 & 0 \\ 0 & \frac{3}{2} & 0 \\ 0 & 0 & -1 \end{bmatrix} Y$$

which shows that the reduction of (12.7.14) to (12.7.18) resulted in the equivalence of the two forms. The following theorem is deduced from the above example. (The reader should not assume that the preceding example is a proof of our theorem. The theorem is actually given without the proof.)

Theorem 12.13. Every quadratic form, which is not identically zero, over a real number field $\mathfrak{F}$ can be reduced to the form

$$p_1 t_1^2 + p_2 y_2^2 + \cdots + p_r y_r^2$$

where the coefficients are over a number field $\mathfrak{F}$ and r is the rank of the coefficient matrix of the given quadratic form.

The Sign of the Quadratic Forms. The *value* of every quadratic form $q(x_1, \ldots x_n)$ over a real number field $\mathfrak{F}$ is a real number $q(a_1, \ldots a_n)$. The quadratic form $q(x_1, \ldots x_n)$ is called a *positive*, over a real number field $\mathfrak{F}$, if every value of $q(a_1, \ldots a_n)$ is ≥ 0. It can be demonstrated that $q(x_1, \ldots x_n)$ is *positive* if and only if its rank and index are equal. Also, when all the values of $q(x_1, \ldots x_n)$ except $q(0, \ldots 0)$ are negative, $q(x_1, \ldots x_n)$ is called *negative definite* and this happens when $-q(x_1, \ldots x_n)$ is *positive definite*, since the negative forms are simply the negatives of the positive forms. From the definition given for positive definite, it follows that if $X'AX$ is positive then det $A > 0$, and that every principal minor determinant of A is positive.

If the matrix of a form is, by elementary transformations, carried to a diagonal one, the number of positive elements of the diagonal matrix will be the index and all the non-zero elements of the diagonal will be the rank of the matrix. In view of the definition given above, let us find out if the following matrix is positive definite:

(12.7.21) $$q(x_1, x_2, x_3) = (x_1 \quad x_2 \quad x_3) \begin{bmatrix} 2 & -1 & 3 \\ -1 & 1 & -2 \\ 3 & -2 & 1 \end{bmatrix} \begin{bmatrix} x_1 \\ x_2 \\ x_3 \end{bmatrix}$$

$$= 2x_1 + x_2 + x_3 - 2x_1 x_2 + 6x_1 x_3 - 4x_2 x_3.$$

Since, by elementary transformation, we can carry the matrix of the form into a diagonal one, we obtain:

$$
\begin{bmatrix} 2 & -1 & 3 \\ -1 & 1 & -2 \\ 3 & -2 & 1 \end{bmatrix} \sim \begin{bmatrix} 1 & 0 & 0 \\ 0 & -7 & 0 \\ 0 & 0 & 8 \end{bmatrix}
$$

where the index is 2 because there are two positive diagonal elements, and the rank is 3 because there are three non-zero diagonal elements. Thus (12.8.21) is not positive definite according to our definition.

12.8 A Necessary and Sufficient Condition for Positive Definiteness

Let us assume, for the moment, that

(12.8.1) $$q(x_1, \ldots, x_n) = (x_1 \ldots x_n) \begin{bmatrix} a_{11} & \cdots & a_{1n} \\ a_{21} & \cdots & a_{2n} \\ \cdot & \cdot & \cdot \\ a_{n1} & \cdots & a_{nn} \end{bmatrix} \begin{bmatrix} x_1 \\ x_2 \\ \vdots \\ x_n \end{bmatrix},$$

is complete in the sense that the process of completing the square on x_i is not stopped. Thus, we carry (12.8.1) to a linear combination of squares

(12.8.2)
$$
\begin{aligned}
q(x_1, \ldots, x_n) \equiv{} & p_1(x_1 + c_{12}x_2 + \cdots + c_{1n}x_n)^2 \\
& + p_2(x_2 + c_{23}x_3 + \cdots + c_{2n}x_n)^2 \\
& + \ldots \ldots \ldots \ldots \ldots \ldots \ldots \\
& + p_r(x_r + c_{r,\,r+1}x_{r+1} + \cdots + c_{rn}x_n)^2
\end{aligned}
$$

where as in (12.7.18) the coefficient of $x_j = 1$ and the rank of the matrix $r \leq n$. If, we put

(12.8.3)
$$
\begin{aligned}
y_1 &= x_1 + c_{12}x_2 + \cdots + c_{1n}x_n \\
y_2 &= \phantom{x_1 + c_{12}} x_2 + \cdots + x_{2n}x_n \\
&\ \cdot \ \cdot \ \cdot \ \cdot \ \cdot \ \cdot \ \cdot \ \cdot \ \cdot \\
y_r &= \phantom{x_1 + c_{12}} x_r + \cdots + c_{rn}x_n
\end{aligned}
$$

we obtain

(12.8.4) $$q(x_1, \ldots, x_n) \equiv p_1 y_1^2 + p_2 y_2^2 + \cdots + p_r y_r^2$$

where

(12.8.5) $$p_1 = a_{11}$$

and

(12.8.6) $$P_2 = a_{22} - p_1 c_{12}^2 = \frac{a_{11}a_{22} - a_{12}^2}{a_{11}}.$$

Since the matrix is symmetrical, we can write

(12.8.7) $$p_2 = \frac{a_{11}a_{22} - a_{12}a_{21}}{a_{11}} = \frac{\begin{vmatrix} a_{11} & a_{12} \\ a_{21} & a_{22} \end{vmatrix}}{a_{11}}.$$

Let us specify the leading principal minor determinants of our matrix as follows:

$$D_0 = 1, D_1 = a_{11}: D_2 = \begin{vmatrix} a_{11} & a_{12} \\ a_{21} & a_{22} \end{vmatrix}, \ldots,$$

$$D_n = \begin{vmatrix} a_{11} & a_{12} & \cdots & a_{1n} \\ a_{21} & a_{22} & \cdots & a_{2n} \\ \cdot & \cdot & & \cdot \\ a_{n1} & a_{n2} & \cdots & a_{nn} \end{vmatrix} = \det A.$$

Now, we can rewrite (12.8.5) and (12.8.6) as follows:

$$p_1 = \frac{D_1}{D_0} \neq 0$$

$$p_2 = \frac{D_2}{D_1} \neq 0$$

$$\cdot \quad \cdot \quad \cdot \quad \cdot \quad \cdot$$

$$p_r = \frac{D_r}{D_{r-1}} \neq 0.$$

Substituting the proper values in (12.8.4), we will have the identity:

(12.8.8) $$q(x_1, \ldots, x_n) \equiv \frac{D_1}{D_r} y_1^2 + \frac{D_2}{D_1} y_2^2 + \cdots + \frac{D_r}{D_{r-1}} y_r^2.$$

We noticed that the condition that (12.8.8) exists and for the form to have rank r is that D_i be different from zero. This condition will make the form positive. Furthermore, we concluded that the necessary condition for two forms, such as (12.8.8), to be equivalent is that their rank and order should be equal $r = n$. Then, the necessary and sufficient condition for a quadratic form to be positive definite is that $r = n$ and that the *leading principal minor determinants* of its matrix are all positive:

$$D_0 > 0, \qquad D_1 > 0, \qquad D_2 > 0, \qquad \ldots \qquad D_n > 0.$$

We pointed out before, since the negative forms are simply the negatives of the positive forms, we do not subsequently explain them.

In the sequel, a non-linear model of investment programming is submitted. This model is based on the results obtained in the preceding pages of this chapter. Basically, the Lagrange Reduction and the conditions for the positivity of a form are utilized in the model. As a matter of fact, t model is the continuation of the investment theory presented at the end of Chapter 8. It is suggested that the reader might reread that section in Chapter 8.

A Non-Linear Model of Micro-Investment Programming. Investment planning always constitutes an important source of difficulty for the economic theorist. This difficulty lies in the determination of the variates which govern investment programming. We noticed in Chapter 8 that according to Keynes' theory of investment and assuming the "maximum-value-criterion" and perfect certainty concerning future streams of *income*, investment is geared to the rate of interest only down to the critical point of the "liquidity trap." On the other hand, we pointed out with classical economists one finds himself with the rate of interest as the single determinant of investment and the system of general equilibrium. This is the reason why classical economists supposed that the monetary policy through the impersonal *laissez faire* mechanism of interest rate change can "regulate and control" the economy toward the automatic equilibrium of full employment. And Keynes considered the monetary policy influential only down to the critical point where the interest rate is asymptotic to the liquidity trap. Thereafter the interest rate policy is ineffective, and the fiscal policy will come to the forefront of action.

It is becoming apparent, in the field of investment programming, that the "maximum-value-criterion" is losing its universal application, as many economists have suggested. Today, a representative firm pursues a good many objectives in attaining its wealth. The introduction of other objectives has, indeed, made investment programming complex, and the astonishing fact is that firms try to maximize the combination of objectives.

There have been a few studies which identify the determinants of an investment project.[1] These variables include net profit, net total sales, changes in sales, depreciation reserves, depreciation expenses, and capacity variables. Let these variables be called $X_1, \ldots X_6$. Then, we can have

(12.8.9) $$I = I(X_1, X_2, X_3, X_4, X_5, X_6).$$

The value of an investment project is a maximum when all these values are maximal. If (12.8.9) contains continuous partial derivatives, the differential of investment is given by

(12.8.10) $$dI = \sum_{j=1}^{6} dX_j \frac{\partial I}{\partial X_j}$$

(12.8.11) $$\frac{dI}{I} = \sum_{j=1}^{6} \frac{\partial(\log I)}{\partial(\log X_j)} \frac{dX_j}{X_j}.$$

Taking the partial elasticities of investment with respect to six variables, the rate of change of investment depends on the rate of change of those variables. The combination of these variables makes the investment maximum at:

$$X_1 = a_1, X_2 = a_2, \ldots X_6 = a_6,$$

---

[1] J. Meyer and E. Kuh, *The Investment Decision, An Empirical Study*, 1959.

if

$$\phi(a_1 + X_1, a_2 + X_2, \ldots a_6 + X_6) - \phi(a_1, a_2, \ldots a_6) < 0.$$

Since the function has been assumed to have continuous partial derivatives up to any desired order at the points $(a_1, a_2, \ldots, a_6)$, Taylor's series gives for any integral of (n)

$$\phi(a_1 + x_1, a_2 + X_2, \ldots a_6 + X_6) - \phi(a_1, a_2, \ldots a_6)$$

(12.8.12)
$$= dI + \frac{1}{2!} d^2 I + \cdots + \frac{1}{n!} d^n I + R_n(X_1, \ldots X_6)$$

where the last term is the Lagrange's Remainder which should approach zero if investment is to be maximal. When $dI = 0$, the function $I = I(X_1, X_2, X_3, X_4, X_5, X_6)$ is a maximum at $a_1 = X_1, \ldots a_6 = X_6$ for all values and variations of the independent variables. The necessary condition for having an extreme value of investment is

$$\frac{\partial I}{\partial X_1} = \frac{\partial I}{\partial X_2} = \frac{\partial I}{\partial X_3} = \frac{\partial I}{\partial X_4} = \frac{\partial I}{\partial X_5} = \frac{\partial I}{\partial X_6} = 0.$$

The sufficient condition for having a maximum value for investment is satisfied when $d^2 I < 0$. On the other hand

(12.8.13)
$$d^2 I = \sum_{j=1}^{6} \sum_{i=1}^{6} \left(\frac{\partial^2 I}{\partial X_i \partial X_j} \right) dX_i \, dX_j < 0.$$

If the coefficients $\dfrac{\partial^2 I}{\partial X_i \partial X_j}$ belong to a field $\mathfrak{F}$, then (12.8.13) is a quadratic form over $\mathfrak{F}$, which, by Lagrange reduction, is reduced to:

(12.8.14)
$$d^2 I = \sum_{i=1}^{6} \sum_{j=1}^{6} \frac{p_j}{p_{j-1}} y_j^2 < 0$$

where

$$p_0 = 1, p_1 = \frac{\partial^2 I}{\partial X_1^2}, \ldots, p_6 = \begin{vmatrix} \dfrac{\partial^2 I}{\partial X_1^2} & \cdots & \dfrac{\partial^2 I}{\partial X_1 \partial X_6} \\ \vdots & & \vdots \\ \dfrac{\partial^2 I}{\partial X_1 \partial X_6} & \cdots & \dfrac{\partial^2 I}{\partial X_6^2} \end{vmatrix}$$

$$\begin{aligned} y_1 &= dX_1 + \alpha_{12} \, dX_2 + \cdots + \alpha_{16} \, dX_6 \\ y_2 &= \qquad\qquad\quad dX_2 + \cdots + \alpha_{26} \, dX_6 \\ &\;\cdot \quad \cdot \quad \cdot \quad \cdot \quad \cdot \quad \cdot \quad \cdot \quad \cdot \quad \cdot \quad \cdot \\ y_6 &= \qquad\qquad\qquad\qquad\qquad\quad dX_6 \end{aligned}$$

and $\alpha_{ij} = \dfrac{\dfrac{\partial^2 I}{\partial X_i \partial X_j}}{\dfrac{\partial^2 I}{\partial X_i^2}}$ can be called the marginal rate of substitution between

X_i and X_j. Here, all the partial derivatives are evaluated at the point $(a_1, \ldots a_6)$.

The sufficient condition for the maximum value of investment will be satisfied if the quadratic form is negative; *i.e.*, the leading principal minor determinants are alternately negative and positive; namely,

$$p_1 = \frac{\partial^2 I}{\partial X_1^2} < 0, \; p_2 = \begin{vmatrix} \dfrac{\partial^2 I}{\partial X_1^2} & \dfrac{\partial^2 I}{\partial X_1 \partial X_2} \\[2ex] \dfrac{\partial^2 I}{\partial X_1 \partial X_2} & \dfrac{\partial^2 I}{\partial X_2^2} \end{vmatrix} > 0, \ldots,$$

$$p_6 = \begin{vmatrix} \dfrac{\partial^2 I}{\partial X_1^2} & \cdots & \dfrac{\partial^2 I}{\partial X_1 \partial X_6} \\ \vdots & & \vdots \\ \dfrac{\partial^2 I}{\partial X_1 \partial X_6} & \cdots & \dfrac{\partial^2 I}{\partial X_6^2} \end{vmatrix} > 0.$$

The above inequalities are the *stability conditions* for the demand for investment; these conditions are given as limitations on the form of investment programming. If all inequalities are satisfied, the position of investment equilibrium will be *stable*. If there is only one variate; *e.g.*, the interest rate, it can be readily shown that the satisfaction of the stability condition implies a schedule of the marginal efficiency of capital which is sloped downward and concave to the origin at all points, at least within a certain range. Further, in Keynesian methodology, the equilibrium of output and employment will be stable if investment is completely interest-elastic.

Under more general conditions where investment is dependent upon the cluster of such complex variables, as we examined, the influence of the interest rate policy on the behavior of entrepreneur concerning investment expenditures will become rather questionable. It is in this context and for this reason that investment should be planned and programmed rather than left to the vagaries of an "impersonal corrective mechanism" which may be otiose to begin with.

In what follows we wish to give the necessary and sufficient conditions for investment programming if there are n variables on which an investment project shows dependability. Let us assume that the "investment project of our representative firm" is influenced by n variables x_j for $j = 1, \ldots n$. Then the investment function can be written as

(12.8.15) $I = I(x_1, \ldots x_j, \ldots x_n).$

Our objective function is to maximize (12.8.15) subject to certain constraints which will be found later. If I is to be a maximum, all x_j are to be maximal. If (12.8.15) contains continuous partial derivatives, the differential of investment is given by:

(12.8.16) $$dI = \sum_{j=1}^{n} dx_j \frac{\partial I}{\partial x_j}$$

or

(12.8.17)
$$\frac{dI}{I} = \sum_{j=1}^{n} \frac{\partial(\log I)}{\partial(\log x_j)} \frac{dx_j}{x_j}.$$

The combination of the variables makes the investment a maximum at $x_1 = a_1, \ldots x_n = a_n$ if $\phi(a_1 + x_1, \ldots a_n + x_n) - \phi(a_1, \ldots, a_n) < 0$. By Taylor's series we will have:

(12.8.18) $\quad \phi(a_1 + x_1, \ldots a_n + x_n) - \phi(a_1, \ldots a_n)$
$$= dI + \frac{1}{2!} d^2 I + \cdots + \frac{1}{n!} d^n I + R_n(x_j).$$

Of course, the remainder $R_n(x_j)$ should approach zero if there is to be a maximum value for investment. When $dI = 0$, then (12.8.15) is a maximum at the point $x_1 = a_1, \ldots, x_n = a_n$. Again the necessary and sufficient conditions are:

$$\frac{\partial I}{\partial x_j} = 0 \text{ and } d^2 I < 0. \text{ On the other hand}$$

(12.8.19)
$$d^2 I = \sum_{i=1}^{n} \sum_{j=1}^{n} \left(\frac{\partial^2 I}{\partial x_i \, \partial x_j}\right) dx_i \, dx_j < 0$$

respectively.

If $\dfrac{\partial^2 I}{\partial x_i \, \partial x_j}$ belongs to a field $\mathfrak{F}$, (12.8.19) will be a *quadratic form* over $\mathfrak{F}$.

Investment Optimization Theorem. Let the coefficient matrix $\left(\dfrac{\partial^2 I}{\partial x_i \, \partial x_j}\right)$ of the investment quadratic form (12.8.19), over a number field $\mathfrak{F}$, be symmetric and of rank $r = n$; i.e.

$$\frac{\partial^2 I}{\partial x_i \, \partial x_j} = \frac{\partial^2 I}{\partial x_j \, \partial x_i}.$$

Then, the quadratic form (12.8.19) can be reduced by a nonsingular transformation with coefficients into the form

(12.8.20)
$$d^2 I = \frac{p_1}{p_0} y_1^2 + \frac{p_j}{p_1} y_2^2 + \cdots + \frac{p_n}{p_{n-1}} y_n^2,$$

where

$$p_0 = 1, \ p_1 = \frac{\partial^2 I}{\partial x_1^2}, \ \ldots, \ p_n = \begin{vmatrix} \dfrac{\partial^2 I}{\partial x_1^2} & & \dfrac{\partial^2 I}{\partial x_1 \, \partial x_n} \\ \vdots & & \vdots \\ \dfrac{\partial^2 I}{\partial x_1 \, \partial x_n} & \cdots & \dfrac{\partial^2 I}{\partial x_n^2} \end{vmatrix}$$

and

$$y_j = x_j + \alpha_{j,j+1} x_{j+1} + \cdots + \alpha_{jn} x_n$$

and if and only if $p_j \neq 0$, $j = 1, 2, \ldots, n$.

Proof: If we write $\dfrac{p_1}{p_0} = c_1 \neq 0, \ldots \dfrac{p_n}{p_{n-1}} = c_n \neq 0$, equation (12.8.20)

will be

$$d^2 I = c_1 y_1^2 + c_2 y_2^2 + \cdots c_n y_n^2.$$

It is obvious, on inspection, that the necessary condition for the equality to hold is that $p_1, p_2, \ldots p_n$ should be different from zero. If $p_j \neq 0$, then the rank of the matrix will be $r = n$.

The sufficient condition will be proved by induction. The expression (12.8.19) can be written as a linear combination of squares of linear forms

$$\begin{aligned} d^2 I = \; & c_1(dx_1 + \alpha_{12}\, dx_2 + \cdots + \alpha_{1n}\, dx_n)^2 \\ & + c_2(dx_2 + \alpha_{23}\, dx_3 + \cdots + \alpha_{2n}\, dx_n)^2 \\ & \cdot \quad \cdot \quad \cdot \quad \cdot \quad \cdot \quad \cdot \quad \cdot \quad \cdot \quad \cdot \quad \cdot \quad \cdot \\ & + c_n\, dx_n. \end{aligned}$$

From the transformation

$$\begin{aligned} y_1 &= dx_1 + \alpha_{12}\, dx_2 + \cdots + \alpha_{1n}\, dx_n \\ y_2 &= \phantom{dx_1 + {}} dx_2 + \cdots + \alpha_{2n}\, dx_n \\ & \cdot \quad \cdot \quad \cdot \quad \cdot \quad \cdot \quad \cdot \quad \cdot \quad \cdot \quad \cdot \quad \cdot \\ y_n &= \phantom{dx_1 + \alpha_{12}\, dx_2 + \cdots + \alpha_{2n}\,} dx_n \end{aligned}$$

we obtain

(12.8.21)
$$d^2 I = c_1 y_1^2 + c_2 y_2^2 + \cdots + c_n y_n^2$$

where, of course

$$c_1 = \frac{\partial^2 I}{\partial x_1^2} = \frac{p_1}{p_0} \neq 0 \qquad p_1 = 1$$

and the coefficient of dx_2^2 in $d^2 I$ is $\dfrac{\partial^2 I}{\partial x^2}$ and

$$\alpha_{12} = \frac{\dfrac{\partial^2 I}{\partial x_1\, \partial x_2}}{\dfrac{\partial^2 I}{\partial x_1^2}}$$

$$c_2 = \frac{\partial^2 I}{\partial x_2^2} - \frac{\partial^2 I}{\partial x_1^2}\left(\frac{\dfrac{\partial^2 I}{\partial x_1\, \partial x_2}}{\dfrac{\partial^2 I}{\partial x_1^2}}\right)^2 = \frac{p_2}{p_1}$$

$$\cdot \quad \cdot \quad \cdot \quad \cdot \quad \cdot \quad \cdot \quad \cdot \quad \cdot$$

$$c_n = \frac{p_n}{p_{n-1}}.$$

In substituting for the coefficients of (12.8.21), we will obtain

(12.8.22)
$$d^2 I = \frac{p_1}{p_0} y_1^2 + \frac{p_2}{p_1} y_2^2 + \cdots + \frac{p_n}{p_{n-1}} y_n^2$$

which completes the proof.

Now the necessary and sufficient conditions for (12.8.20) to be negative definite (so that equation (12.8.15) be a maximum) are that the leading principal minor determinants would be alternately negative and positive, viz.,

$$p_0 = 1, \ p_1 = \frac{\partial^2 I}{\partial x_1^2} < 0, \ p_2 = \begin{vmatrix} \dfrac{\partial^2 I}{\partial x_1^2} & \dfrac{\partial^2 I}{\partial x_1 \partial x_2} \\[2ex] \dfrac{\partial^2 I}{\partial x_1 \partial x_2} & \dfrac{\partial^2 I}{\partial x_2^2} \end{vmatrix} > 0, \ldots,$$

and

$$p_n = \begin{vmatrix} \dfrac{\partial^2 I}{\partial x_1^2} & \cdots & \dfrac{\partial^2 I}{\partial x_1 \partial x_n} \\ \vdots & & \vdots \\ \dfrac{\partial^2 I}{\partial x_1 \partial x_n} & \cdots & \dfrac{\partial^2 I}{\partial x_n^2} \end{vmatrix}$$

will be positive if n is even, and negative if n is odd. Thus, we have given the conditions for extreme values of investment.

If an entrepreneur can assume the supply of and the demand for factors and the market conditions as given, needless to say, he should be able to afford setting a performance test, "maximum-value-criterion," and program its production accordingly. But if he must abandon the assumption of perfect availability of factors perforce, it will be unlikely that he would use or be tempted to use any test *a posteriori*. That is not to say that he should not have any guide or principle whereby he could undertake the investment activity. As we pointed out above, "profit-maximization" is not an objective in a classical or Keynesian model: it is only a guide or principle which directs the activity of the firm or of the economy. Nowadays, when a firm contemplates an investment project, it finds itself confronted with certain limitations or complex of objectives, the managerial problem of such a firm apparently is a philosophical one of coping with the sum of objectives, let alone the perfect test of performance. In this situation, that rule or method of production which provides for the "best" (optimum) possible solution, in contrast to the *absolute* solution is the one which is aimed at by the modern entrepreneur.[2] Undoubtedly, the optimum

---

[2] With respect to the responsibilities and tasks before modern corporations, Lord Keynes many years ago (1926) remarked cognizantly and cogently: "But more interesting . . . is the trend of Joint Stock Institutions, when they have reached a certain age and size, to approximate to the status of public corporations rather than that of individualistic private enterprise. One of the most interesting and unnoticed developments of recent decades has been the tendency of big enterprise to socialize itself. A point

solution should satisfy the *stability* condition of the system. That is, the specific conditions set by the Theorem of optimum investment should be satisfied, if the project is to be at once optimum and stable.

In conclusion, as far as micro-investment programming is concerned, our adaptation of Keynes' original diagnosis seems to be a better first approximation to the real world than his own. Our adaptation may have more cogently demonstrated that the power of monetary policy diminishes as the number of variables and constraints accumulates, that the reliance on that "impersonal corrective mechanism" of which classical economists were so proud becomes questionable, and that planning for a given investment project becomes essential rather than detrimental.

12.9 Orthogonal Matrices

If there is a matrix A such that

(12.9.1) $$A A' = I,$$

or

$$A' = A^{-1},$$

that is, the transpose of A is equal to its inverse, A is called an *orthogonal matrix*. It follows that the columns and rows of an orthogonal matrix $A A' = I$ are unit vectors, that is to say, they are pair-wise orthogonal, $aa' = 1$ and $a_i a_j = 0$ for any $i \neq j$.

12.10 The Characteristic Roots of a Characteristic Equation

Let us suppose that we desire to determine the scalars λ which, with a given matrix A of order n and the given n-dimensional non-zero vector X simultaneously, satisfy

(12.10.1) $$AX = \lambda X,$$

which is the same as

(12.10.2) $$(A - \lambda I)X = 0,$$

which is a system of n linear homogeneous equations in n unknowns. (12.10.2), according to Section 12.3, has a set of non-trivial solutions if

(12.10.3) $$\det(A - \lambda I) = \begin{vmatrix} a_{11} - \lambda & a_{12} & \cdots & a_{1n} \\ a_{21} & a_{22} - \lambda & \cdots & a_{2n} \\ \cdot & \cdot & & \cdot \\ a_{n1} & a_{n2} & \cdots & a_{nn} - \lambda \end{vmatrix} = 0$$

---

arrives in the growth of a big institution — $\cdots$ — at which the owners of the capital, *i.e.*, the stockholders, are almost entirely dissociated from the management, with the result that the direct personal interest of the latter in the making of great profit becomes quite secondary. When this stage is reached, the general stability and reputation of the institution are more considered by the management than the maximum profit for the stockholder." *Essays in Persuasion*, London: Rupert Hart-Davis, 1952, pp. 314–315.

where

(12.10.4)
$$\begin{vmatrix} a_{11} - \lambda & a_{12} & \cdots & a_{1n} \\ a_{21} & a_{22} - \lambda & \cdots & a_{2n} \\ \cdot & \cdot & \cdot & \cdot \\ a_{n1} & a_{n2} & \cdots & a_{nn} - \lambda \end{vmatrix}$$

is the *characteristic determinant* of the square matrix A and

$$\det(A - \lambda I) = \varphi(\lambda) = 0$$

is its *characteristic equation* with $\lambda_1, \lambda_2, \ldots, \lambda_n$ as its *characteristic roots*.
Consider the square matrix A

$$A = \begin{bmatrix} 1 & 0 \\ 4 & 3 \end{bmatrix}$$

whose characteristic determinant is

$$\det(A - \lambda I) = \begin{vmatrix} 1 - \lambda & 0 \\ 4 & 3 - \lambda \end{vmatrix}$$

with

$$\varphi(\lambda) = \lambda^2 - 4\lambda + 3 = 0$$

as its characteristic equation and $\lambda_1 = 1, \lambda_2 = 3$ as its characteristic roots.

Definition 12.14. A square matrix B is said to be *similar* to A if there exists a nonsingular matrix P such that

$$B = P^{-1}AP.$$

Theorem 12.15. Similar matrices have the same characteristic determinants and therefore the same characteristic equations and roots.

Proof. Let there be a square matrix B that is similar to A such that

(12.10.5)
$$B = P^{-1}AP.$$

It is obvious that the determinants of both sides of (12.10.5) hold, or

$$\det B = \det(P^{-1}AP).$$

Also

$$\det(P^{-1}AP) = \det P^{-1} \det A \det P.$$

Since $P^{-1}P = I$, then

$$\det P^{-1} \det P = \det I = 1,$$

hence,

(12.10.6)
$$\det B = \det A. \qquad\qquad \text{Q.E.D.}$$

Moreover, it is obvious that for two similar matrices A and B we have

$$\det B - \det \lambda I = \det A - \det \lambda I,$$

and

$$|B - \lambda I| = |A - \lambda I|, \qquad \text{Q.E.D.}$$

or

$$\varphi(\lambda) = (-1)^n |B - \lambda I| = (-1)^n |A - \lambda I| = 0. \qquad \text{Q.E.D.}$$

Theorem 12.16.   The characteristic roots of a diagonal matrix $D = [d_1, d_2, \ldots, d_n]$ are the diagonal elements of D.

Proof. Let us consider the diagonal matrix D

$$\begin{bmatrix} d_{11} & 0 & \cdots & 0 \\ 0 & d_{22} & \cdots & 0 \\ \cdot & \cdot & \cdot \cdot \cdot & \cdot \\ 0 & 0 & \cdots & d_{nn} \end{bmatrix}$$

whose characteristic determinant is

$$\begin{vmatrix} d_{11} - \lambda & 0 & \cdots & 0 \\ 0 & d_{22} - \lambda & \cdots & 0 \\ \cdot & \cdot & \cdot \cdot \cdot & \cdot \\ 0 & 0 & \cdots & d_{nn} - \lambda \end{vmatrix}$$

and its characteristic equation is

(12.10.7) $\varphi(\lambda) = (d_{11} - \lambda_1)(d_{22} - \lambda) \ldots (d_{nn} - \lambda_n) = 0.$

If the polynomial (12.10.7) is to hold, we must have

$$d_{11} = \lambda_i, \qquad d_{22} = \lambda_2, \qquad \ldots, \qquad d_{nn} = \lambda_n. \qquad \text{Q.E.D.}$$

Definition 12.17. *The characteristic equation of*

$$det(A - \lambda I)$$

is the polynomial

(12.10.8)
$$\begin{aligned} |A - \lambda I| = \{n\} + (-1)\{n - 1\}\lambda \\ + (-1)^2 \{n - 2\}\lambda^2 + \cdots + (-1)^k \{n - k\}\lambda^k \\ + \cdots + (-1)^{n-1}\{1\}\lambda^{n-1} + (-1)^n \lambda^n = 0 \end{aligned}$$

where the coefficients of λ_i are the sum of all principal minors of the determinant having an order indicated by the symbol $\{ \ \}$. The value of $\{n\}$ is the value of det A. Thus, (12.10.8) can be rewritten as

$$\begin{aligned} |A - \lambda I| = \det A + (-1)\sum A_{ij}^{n-1}\lambda + (-1)^2 \sum A_{ij}^{n-2}\lambda^2 \\ + \cdots + (-1)^{n-1}\sum A_{ij}^1 \lambda^{n-1} + (-1)^n \lambda^n = 0, \end{aligned}$$

where $\sum A_{ij}^p$ is the sum of all principal minors of p-order of a_{ij} element of A.

To clarify the definition, we solve the following example. Let A be

$$\begin{bmatrix} 2 & 3 & 1 \\ 1 & 2 & 3 \\ 0 & 1 & 4 \end{bmatrix}$$

the characteristic determinant of which is

$$\begin{vmatrix} 2 - \lambda & 3 & 1 \\ 1 & 2 - \lambda & 3 \\ 0 & 1 & 4 - \lambda \end{vmatrix}$$

whose expansion, according to Definition 12.17, gives

$$\begin{vmatrix} 2 & 3 & 1 \\ 1 & 2 & 3 \\ 0 & 1 & 4 \end{vmatrix} - \left(\begin{vmatrix} 2 & 3 \\ 1 & 2 \end{vmatrix} + \begin{vmatrix} 2 & 3 \\ 1 & 4 \end{vmatrix} + \begin{vmatrix} 2 & 1 \\ 0 & 4 \end{vmatrix} \right)$$

$$\lambda + (2 + 2 + 4)\lambda^2 - \lambda^3 = 0,$$

or

$$\varphi(\lambda) = -\lambda^3 + 8\lambda^2 - 14\lambda - 1 = 0.$$

Theorem 12.18. $\lambda = 0$ is a characteristic root of a square matrix A if A is singular.

Proof. The characteristic determinant and equation of A are

(12.10.9) $|A - \lambda I| = \det A + (-1)\sum A_{ij}^{n-1}\lambda + \cdots + (-1)^n\lambda^n = 0$
$$= \det A + \lambda_1(A_{ij} - \lambda_2) \ldots (A_{ij} - \lambda_n) = 0.$$

If (12.10.9) is to hold and it is assumed that $\det A = 0$; *i.e.*, A is singular, we require $\lambda_1 = 0$; if, however $\lambda_1 = 0$, it is required that

$$\det A = 0. \hspace{4cm} \text{Q.E.D.}$$

Theorem 12.19. A square matrix and its transpose have the same characteristic roots.

Proof. Let A be a square matrix whose transpose is displayed by A'. It is obvious that

$$\det A = \det A',$$

or

$$\det(A - \lambda I) = \det(A' - \lambda I) = 0. \hspace{3cm} \text{Q.E.D.}$$

Theorem 12.20. If U is a unitary matrix and

(12.10.10) $$U^*AU = D[d_1, d_2, \ldots d_n]$$

where D is a diagonal matrix the diagonal elements of which are $d_1, d_2, \ldots$ d_n; the diagonal elements of D are the characteristic roots of A.

Proof: A matrix with imaginary elements is called *complex*. When the elements of a complex matrix are replaced by their conjugates, a *conjugate matrix* is formed. The transposed conjugate matrix is called *tranjugate*. A *unitary* matrix is the one whose tranjugate is equal to its inverse, or

(12.10.11) $$U^* = U^{-1}.$$

Putting (12.10.11) in (12.10.10), we get $U^{-1}AU = D$, which renders A and D similar. Since A and D are similar, according to Theorem 12.15, they have the same characteristic roots. And since according to Theorem 12.16, the diagonal elements of D are its elements, therefore $d_1, d_2, \ldots d_n$ are the characteristic roots of A. This completes the proof.

Theorem 12.21. The characteristic roots of a Hermitian matrix are all real.

Proof. A Hermitian matrix is a matrix whose tranjugate is equal to itself. Now, let A be Hermitian and assume that λ is any characteristic root of A and there is a vector X such that

(12.10.12) $$AX = \lambda X.$$

Multiply (12.10.12) by X^* on the left to get

$$X^*AX = X^*\lambda X$$
$$= \lambda X^*X = \lambda.$$

But according to the definition of a Hermitian matrix, we have $A = A^*$ and since X^*AX is a scalar, hence

$$X^*AX = X^*A^*X = (X^*AX)^* = \overline{X^*AX},$$

which indicates that X^*AX, a scalar, is equal to its own conjugate and is, therefore, real. If X^*AX is real and also

$$X^*AX = \lambda$$

hence λ must be real which completes the proof. A special case of Theorem 12.21 is the following theorem which has been used in the discussion of stability of competitive equilibrium. See Section 9.5 of Chapter 9.

Theorem 12.22. The characteristic roots of a real symmetric matrix are all real.

12.11 Matrices, Differential Equations and Application

If $y = (y_1, \ldots y_n)$ is an n by 1 vector and its elements are functions of the scalar x and $y = y(x)$, then $\dfrac{dy}{dx}$ is an n by 1 vector of simple derivatives, or

(12.11.1)
$$\frac{dy}{dx} = \begin{bmatrix} \dfrac{dy_1}{dx} \\ \vdots \\ \dfrac{dy_n}{dx} \end{bmatrix}.$$

Now, if y is a scalar and also a function of the elements of $x = (x_1, \ldots x_n)$, then we can define $\dfrac{\partial y}{\partial x}$ as

(12.11.2)
$$\frac{\partial y}{\partial x} = \begin{bmatrix} \dfrac{\partial y}{\partial x_1} \\ \vdots \\ \dfrac{\partial y}{\partial x_n} \end{bmatrix}.$$

Furthermore, the integral of the vector $y(x)$ is defined to be

$$\int^x y(x)\, dx = \begin{bmatrix} \displaystyle\int^x y_1(x)\, dx \\ \vdots \\ \displaystyle\int^x y_n(x)\, dx \end{bmatrix}.$$

Next, we shall consider $y = y(x_{11}, \ldots x_{1n}, \ldots x_{m1}, \ldots x_{mn})$ or $y = y(X)$ where X is an m by n matrix $(x_{ij})_{(m,n)}$, then $\dfrac{\partial y}{\partial X}$ is shown to be the m by n matrix of partials:

(12.11.3)
$$\frac{\partial y}{\partial X} = \begin{bmatrix} \dfrac{\partial y}{\partial x_{11}} & \cdots & \dfrac{\partial y}{\partial x_{1n}} \\ \vdots & & \vdots \\ \dfrac{\partial y}{\partial x_{m1}} & \cdots & \dfrac{\partial y}{\partial x_{mn}} \end{bmatrix}.$$

Let us suppose that there are two vectors $y = (y_1, \ldots y_n)$ and $x = (x_1, \ldots x_n)$ such that $y = y(x)$, then the partial $\dfrac{\partial y}{\partial x}$ is defined to be:

(12.11.4)
$$\frac{\partial y}{\partial x} = \begin{bmatrix} \dfrac{\partial y_1}{\partial x_1} & \cdots & \dfrac{\partial y_n}{\partial x_1} \\ \vdots & & \vdots \\ \dfrac{\partial y_1}{\partial x_m} & \cdots & \dfrac{\partial y_n}{\partial x_m} \end{bmatrix}.$$

Finally, let us suppose that there exists matrix $Y = (y_{ij})_{(m,n)}$ and that its elements are all functions of the scalar x, then the partial $\dfrac{\partial Y}{\partial x}$ is defined to be

(12.11.5)
$$\frac{\partial Y}{\partial x} = \begin{bmatrix} \dfrac{\partial y_{11}}{\partial x} & \cdots & \dfrac{\partial y_{1n}}{\partial x} \\ \vdots & & \vdots \\ \dfrac{\partial y_{m1}}{\partial x} & \cdots & \dfrac{\partial y_{mn}}{\partial x} \end{bmatrix}.$$

Of course, the second and/or the nth derivative of all preceding cases are treated likewise.

Now, let us consider two column vectors x and a the inner product of which is

$$y = x'a = x_1 a_1 + \cdots + x_n a_n$$
$$= \sum_{1}^{n} x_i a_i.$$

The partial derivative of y with respect to any element x_i, via scalar operations, is defined to be

$$\frac{\partial y}{\partial x_i} = \frac{\partial \sum\limits_{1}^{n} x_i a_i}{\partial x_i} = a_i.$$

Then,

(12.11.6)
$$\frac{\partial y}{\partial x} = \frac{\partial x'a}{\partial x} = a.$$

Similarly, if $y = A'x$, then

$$\frac{\partial A'x}{\partial x} = A,$$

and if $y = Ax$, then

(12.11.7)
$$\frac{\partial Ax}{\partial x} = A'.$$

It is quite clear, then, that the derivative of a quadratic form $Q \equiv x'Ax$, by virtue of (12.11.2) is

(12.11.8)
$$\frac{\partial Q}{\partial x} = \frac{x'Ax}{x} = 2Ax.$$

For instance, the derivative of

$$Q \equiv 2x_1^2 + 3x_2^2 + 4x_1 x_2 \equiv (x_1 \quad x_2) \begin{bmatrix} 2 & 2 \\ 2 & 3 \end{bmatrix} \begin{bmatrix} x_1 \\ x_2 \end{bmatrix}$$

is

$$\frac{\partial Q}{\partial x} = \begin{bmatrix} \dfrac{\partial Q}{\partial x_1} \\ \dfrac{\partial Q}{\partial x_2} \end{bmatrix} = \begin{bmatrix} 4x_1 + 4x_2 \\ 4x_1 + 6x_2 \end{bmatrix} = 2 \begin{bmatrix} 2 & 2 \\ 2 & 3 \end{bmatrix} \begin{bmatrix} x_1 \\ x_2 \end{bmatrix}.$$

Next, we take the case where the elements of matrices A and B and vector x are functions of another variable, say, t. By (12.11.5), we can show that

(12.11.9)
$$\frac{d}{dt}(x, y) = \frac{dx}{dt}y + x\frac{dy}{dt},$$

and for $y = Ax$

(12.11.10)
$$\frac{dy}{dt} = \frac{d(Ax)}{dt} = \frac{dA}{dt}x + A\frac{dx}{dt},$$

and for $AB = C$

(12.11.11)
$$\frac{dC}{dt} = \frac{d(AB)}{dt} = \left(\frac{dA}{dt}\right)B + A\frac{dB}{dt}.$$

In addition, let there be a matrix D whose inverse, D^{-1}, exists and is a function of t, then:

(12.11.12)
$$\frac{dD^{-1}}{dt} = -D^{-1}\frac{dD}{dt}D^{-1}.$$

This last expression can be proved quite easily. Since D has an inverse, then $DD^{-1} = I$ and by virtue of (12.11.11) we can write

$$\frac{d(DD^{-1})}{dt} = \frac{dD}{dt}D^{-1} + D\frac{dD^{-1}}{dt} = \frac{dI}{dt} = 0.$$

On premultiplying the last expression by D^{-1} and transposing

$$DD^{-1}\frac{d(D^{-1})}{dt},$$

which is equal to $\dfrac{d(D^{-1})}{dt}$, to the right (12.11.12) will be obtained.

Differential Equations and Matrix Exponential. We studied differential equations in Chapter IX without matrix notations. There, the existence and uniqueness of the solution of an assumed differential equation was taken for granted. In addition, we made no reference to the fundamentals of the concept of *stability* of a differential equation. Here, the task before us is to discuss these cardinal issues. But our discussion will be confined to *ordinary* differential equations in the real domain. That is, we consider those equations whose terms are derivatives with respect to a real variable t. Conventionally, t has been used as a time-variable.

Let the following vector differential equation

(12.11.13)
$$\frac{dx}{dt} = A(t)x$$

be given for the initial condition $x(0) = C$ where $A(t)$ is a continuous n by n matrix of a complex function on a real interval t. Like the scalar case of Chapter IX, (12.11.13) is called a *linear homogeneous* system of the nth order. For a long time, even such eminent mathematicians as Lagrange and Laplace seem to have taken the solution of (12.11.13) for granted. The great French mathematician Cauchy for the first time proved the existence of appropriate solutions for a broad class of systems of differential equations. Mention should be made that since Cauchy, other sharper and more elegant existence proofs have been given. In what follows we give, without proof, a simple version of the classical existence theorem of Cauchy-Lipschitz.

Existence and Uniqueness Theorem. If $A(t)$ in (12.11.13) is continuous for $t \geq 0$, then its solution which may be written as

$$x = X(t)C,$$

exists and is unique for $t \geq 0$ where $X(t)$ is the unique matrix which satisfies the matrix differential equation

$$\frac{dX}{dt} = A(t)X \qquad X(0) = I.$$

Now, consider the particular case for which $A(t)$ is a constant matrix, or

(12.11.14)
$$\frac{dX}{dt} = AX.$$

Analogous to the scalar case $\dfrac{dy}{dt} = ay$ the solution of which for $y(0) = c$

is $y = e^{at}c$, one can write

(12.11.15)
$$X = e^{At} \cdot C$$

for the solution of (12.11.14) where e^{At} is an exponential matrix and

$$e^{At} = I + \sum_{n=1}^{\infty} \frac{A^n t^n}{n!}$$

where A^n is the nth power of A. The series defining the exponential matrix e^{At} is convergent for all A since for any positive integers p, q,

$$\left| \sum_{n=p+1}^{p+q} \frac{A^n}{n!} \right| \leq \sum_{n=p+1}^{p+q} \frac{|A|^n}{n!}$$

is convergent since it displays the Cauchy difference.[3] Thus the sign of e^{At} depends on the sign of A, or

$$e^{At} = I + At + \cdots .$$

---

[3] E. Coddington and N. Levinson, *The Theory of Differential Equations*, New York, 1955, pp. 64–65.

Intuitively, for the elements of e^{At} to be non-negative it is necessary and sufficient that matrix A must be non-negative for $t > 0$, or $a_{ij} \geq 0$ for $i \neq j$.

Then, the following important result: If C is non-negative and $t \geq 0$, then the necessary and sufficient condition that

$$\frac{dX}{dt} = AX$$

has non-negative solutions is that

$$a_{ij} \geq 0 \qquad \text{for} \qquad i \neq j.$$

Further, if A happens to be symmetric and its characteristic roots are distinct, then there is a matrix T which is constant and diagonalizes $X = e^{At}$ such that

$$e^{At} = T \begin{vmatrix} e^{\lambda_n t} & 0 & \cdots & 0 \\ 0 & e^{\lambda_2 t} & \cdots & 0 \\ \vdots & & & \vdots \\ 0 & 0 & \cdots & e^{\lambda_1 t} \end{vmatrix} T^{-1}.$$

The results obtained in the preceding paragraph can be readily applied to the input-output analysis. Leontief's input-output model has assumed two forms. One is the *open* system which assumes that the final demand sector is exogenous whereas the *closed* system, the second form, treats the final demand sector as endogenous. Each system can be either static or dynamic. In short

(12.11.16) $\quad X = AX + Y \qquad \text{or} \qquad (I - A)X = Y$
$$\text{Leontief's static open-system}$$

(12.11.17) $\quad X = AX \qquad \text{or} \qquad (I - A)X = 0$
$$\text{Leontief's static closed-system}$$

(12.11.18) $\quad X = AX + B\dfrac{dX}{dt} \qquad \text{or} \qquad (I - A)X = B\dfrac{dX}{dt}$
$$\text{Leontief's dynamic closed system}$$

where A is the flow matrix of input coefficients and $B = (b_{ij})$ is the stock matrix of capital coefficients where

$$\frac{dK_{ij}}{dt} = b_{ij}\frac{dX_j}{dt}$$

where K_{ij} is the capital requirement of the ith sector from the jth sector.
It is obvious that

$$(I - A)X = B\frac{dX}{dt}$$

is a matrix homogeneous differential equation with constant matrix coefficients. If B^{-1} exists — i.e., the rank of B is equal to its order — then, we will write

$$\frac{dX}{dt} = B^{-1}(I - A)X$$

or by substituting $B^{-1}(I - A) = D$, we have

$$\frac{dX}{dt} = DX$$

the solution of which for the initial condition $X(0) = C$ is

$$X = e^{Dt} \cdot C$$

so that the non-negativity of X depends on the non-negativity of $D = B^{-1}(I - A)$. The stability of this model will be taken up later on.[4]

Other Special Differential Equations.[5] So far, we have been discussing the vector homogeneous differential equations with constant coefficients. Now, we take

$$\frac{dX}{dt} = AX + W(t)$$

for $X(0) = C$ where the coefficients matrix is constant. The solution of the homogeneous part $\dfrac{dX}{dt} = AX$ is $X = e^{At} \cdot C$ for $X(0) = C$. However, by (9.2.17) through (9.2.20) of Chapter IX, e^{-At} is the integrating factor and the solution is

$$X = e^{At} \cdot C + \int_0^t e^{A(t-s)} \cdot W(s) \cdot ds.$$

If, however,

$$\frac{dX}{dt} = A(t)X + W(t)$$

the solution will be

$$X = X(t)C + \int_0^t X(t)X^{-1}(s)W(s) \cdot ds,$$

---

[4] For the economic applications of this model see the author's article in the *Indian Journal of Economics*, forthcoming.

[5] For the proofs and expanded versions of these cases see R. Bellman's *Stability Theory of Differential Equations*, 1953 pp. 11–12 and his *Introduction to Matrix Theory*, 1960, pp. 169–170.

where $X = X(t)$ is the solution of the equation

$$\frac{dX}{dt} = A(t)X$$

for $X(0) = I$. Finally, if

$$\frac{dX}{dt} = AX + XB$$

for the initial condition $X(0) = C$, the solution will be

$$X = e^{At}Ce^{Bt}.$$

Stability of Differential Equations.   The expressive and impressive term "stability" has recurred throughout this book many times. Let us imagine an economic system which operates under certain general conditions. Further, assume that the underlying conditions are slightly disturbed. What is the repercussion of this disturbance upon the system? The economic system is *stable* if the disturbance has no or little effect on it. If, however, the effect of the disturbance is considerable, the system is said to be *unstable*. To state it concretely, if the system after a disturbance converges to its original position or the neighborhood of the original position, the system is said to be stable. Otherwise, the system is unstable. Conventionally, the point of rest of a system is its *equilibrium* position.

Let us consider the dynamic system

(12.11.19) $$\frac{dX}{dt} = AX$$

for the initial condition $X(0) = C$ in the region Ω where Ω is the set of all non-negative or positive vectors. It is obvious that (12.11.19) for $X(0) = C$ has a solution

$$X = e^{At} \cdot C = X(t; C)$$

for all $t \geq 0$, which is continuous with respect to $X(0) = C$. A special property of (12.11.19) for all $t \geq 0$ in Ω is that $X(t; C) = 0$, which means that the point $X = C$ or $X - C = 0$ is a solution too. Such a point is called an *equilibrium*. Of course, depending on C there is a set of equilibria. If the origin is shown by $X^* = X - C = 0$, then the equilibrium point will be in the origin with $X(t; 0) = 0$ for $t \geq 0$ in Ω. Now, the vector X^* defines the fixed equilibrium point in the origin.

The dynamic system (12.11.19) is said to be *asymptotically stable* (sometimes referred to as *globally stable*[6]) if the solution $X(t; C)$ for any initial condition C in Ω tends to the origin as $t \to \infty$. The system is *stable* (sometimes referred to as *quasi-stable*[6]) if the solution $X(t; C)$ initiated at C is

---

[6] H. Uzawa, "The Stability of Dynamic Processes," *Econometrica*, 1961, p. 618.

bounded in the region ever after; *i.e.*, that the path starting at C never reaches the boundary sphere. Finally, the system (12.11.19) is *unstable* if there is always a solution initiating from the point, say, C, in the region, whose path through C reaches the boundary of sphere.

One of the most striking fundamental contributions to the discussion of dynamic analysis is *Liapunov's direct method*. Liapunov's stability theorems are the generalization and extension of the idea that if the energy near an equilibrium state of a dynamic process is always decreasing, then the equilibrium is stable. Thus, one can detect the stability of a system such as (12.11.19) from the properties of a Liapunov's function which are related, not to a knowledge of its solutions, but requires a knowledge of the system itself. A Liapunov's function $V(x)$ has the following properties:

1. $V(x)$ is positive definite,
2. $V(x)$ and all its first partials are continuous in the open spherical region Ω,
3. $V(0) = 0$,
4. $V(x)$ is non-negative and vanishes in the origin,
5. $\dfrac{dV(x)}{dt} \leq 0$.

Definition: *A real square matrix A is called stable if its characteristic roots all have negative real parts.*

Theorem of Stability: If a Liapunov function $V(x)$ exists in some neighborhood Ω of the origin of a system, then the origin of the system is *stable*.

Theorem of Asymptotical Stability: If a system in addition to what was required in the Theorem of Stability requires that $\dfrac{dV(x)}{dt}$ is negative definite, then the origin is asymptotically stable.

From the definition and the theorem of asymptotic stability we deduce the fact that the system $\dfrac{dX}{dt} = AX$ is asymptotically stable if and only when A is stable in the sense defined in the definition. When would matrix A be stable? This is a formidable question. The question is to seek a simple criterion with which to decide whether all roots of the polynomial

(12.11.20) $\qquad \varphi(\lambda) = |A - \lambda I| = p_0 + p_1\lambda + p_2\lambda^2 + \cdots + p_n\lambda^n = 0$

have *negative real part*. This question, which was raised by Maxwell and investigated by Routh, was solved elegantly by Hurwitz. Hurwitz's criterion is as follows:

All roots of equation (12.11.20) have negative real part if-and only when the n determinants

$$D_1 = p_0, \quad D_2 = \begin{vmatrix} p_1 & p_0 \\ p_3 & p_2 \end{vmatrix}, \quad D_3 = \begin{vmatrix} p_1 & p_0 & 0 \\ p_3 & p_2 & p_1 \\ p_5 & p_4 & p_3 \end{vmatrix}, \ldots,$$

$$D_n = \begin{vmatrix} p_1 & p_0 & \ldots & 0 \\ p_3 & p_2 & \ldots & 0 \\ \ldots & \ldots & \ldots & \ldots \\ p_{2n-1} & p_{2n-2} & \ldots & p_n \end{vmatrix}$$

are all positive with $p_0 > 0$.[7]

The indices of p's in each row of every determinant decrease by 1 and p_k for $k > n$ and the letters p's with negative indices are all replaced with zero. When $n = 2$ or

$$p_0 + p_1 \lambda + p_2 \lambda^2 = 0$$

the criterion $p_0 > 0$, $p_1 > 0$ and $p_2 > 0$ yields the two roots with negative real part. Let us apply the stability conditions to our input-output model:

(12.11.21)
$$\frac{dX}{dt} = DX$$

the solution of which for $X(0) = C$ was $X = e^{Dt} \cdot C$. If (12.11.21) is to be asymptotically stable, then D must be a stability matrix. And if D is to be a stability matrix, then it should satisfy Hurwitz's criterion.

Positive Matrices, Perron and Frobenius Theorems. The dynamic General Leontief's input-output system can be described by the following set of n linear differential equations

(12.11.22)
$$x_i(t) = \sum_{j=1}^{n} a_{ij}x_j(t) + \sum_{j=1}^{n} b_{ij}\frac{dx_j(t)}{dt} + y_j(t)$$

where $x_i(t)$ is the output of the ith good produced by the ith sector at time t, a_{ij} is the flow coefficient, b_{ij} is the stock coefficient and defines $k_{ij} = b_{ij}x_j$. If $y_j(t) = 0$, (12.11.22) is the "closed" system, and if $y_j(t)$ is positive the system is "open." Let us rewrite the "closed" system in matrix form

$$X - AX - B\frac{dX}{dt} = 0$$

(12.11.23)
$$(I - A)X - B\frac{dX}{dt} = 0$$

$$X - (I - A)^{-1}B\frac{dX}{dt} = 0.$$

---

[7] For the proof of this theorem see the elegant method of Schur in J. V. Uspensky's *Theory of Equations*, 1948, pp. 305–309.

It is assumed that B is a non-negative matrix, *i.e.*, that all its elements are non-negative. It is also assumed that A is non-negative. Thus if $(I - A)^{-1}$ is positive (non-negative), then $(I - A)^{-1}B$ will be non-negative and the characteristic matrix of the entire system

(12.11.24) $$I - (I - A)^{-1}B\hat{\lambda}$$

will be positive too. $\hat{\lambda}$ is a diagonal matrix, $I\lambda$, of identical elements representing the unknown root λ. It is obvious that the characteristic matrix of the entire system is positive. By a well-known theorem of Perron-Frobenius, which will be given without proof, the dominant root of a non-negative characteristic matrix is real and positive. It is also the only root with a characteristic vector whose elements have the same sign. It means that the outputs of the economy defined by (12.11.23) will, first, approach a steady growth rate and then "will expand at the same exponential rate equal to the single positive real root referred to above. The relative magnitudes of the individual sectoral outputs will at the same time approach aymptotically the relative magnitudes of corresponding elements of the dominant characteristic vector. This rate of growth and these proportions have sometimes been referred to as the equilibrium rate and the equilibrium proportions, while the system as a whole was called stable because both are independent of the particular combination of positive outputs described by the initial conditions."[8]

The Perron-Frobenius Theorem was first studied by Perron who stated the theorem for positive matrices but was extended by Frobenius who investigated non-negative matrices, the much more complicated case. We mention the names of both mathematicians that we may detract from the originality of neither.

The Theorem of Perron-Frobenius: If A is a non-negative matrix, A has a unique characteristic root (A) which has greatest absolute value. This root is positive and simple and is associated with a positive characteristic vector.[9]

---

[8] W. Leontief, "Lags and the Stability of Dynamic Systems," *Econometrica*, 1961, p. 660.

[9] For a proof of this theorem see O. Perron, "Zur Theorie der Matrizen," *Math. Ann.* (1907), pp. 248–263; G. Frobenius, "Uber Matrizen aus nicht-negatiren Elementen," *Sitzsbere der kgl. Preuss*, Akad. Wiss, 1912, pp. 456–477; G. Debreu and I. N. Herstein, "Non-negative Matrices," *Econometrica* 1957, pp. 597–607; A. Brauer, "A New Proof of Theorems of Perron- and Frobenius on Non-negative Matrices," *Duke Mathematical Journal* 1957, pp. 367–378; R. Bellman, *op. cit.*, pp. 278–284; H. Samelson "On the Perron-Frobenius Theorem," *Michigan Mathematical Journal* 1957, pp. 57–59; J. L. Ullman, "On a Theorem of Frobenius," *Michigan Mathematical Journal*, 1952, pp. 189–193.

EXERCISES 12

1. Discuss the uniqueness, consistency and inconsistency of the following systems:

$$\begin{cases} 2x_1 - 2x_2 + x_3 - x_4 = 2 \\ x_1 + x_2 + 3x_3 + x_4 = 3 \\ 3x_1 + 2x_2 - 4x_3 + 5x_4 = -1 \\ -x_1 + x_2 - 2x_3 + 3x_4 = 5. \end{cases}$$

$$\begin{cases} x_1 + x_2 + 2x_3 - 2x_4 = 3 \\ x_1 + 2x_2 - 3x_3 + x_4 = -2 \\ -x_1 - 3x_2 + x_3 + 4x_4 = 1 \end{cases}$$

$$\begin{cases} x_1 - x_2 - 5x_3 = 7 \\ -x_1 - 2x_2 + 4x_3 = 5 \\ 2x_1 - 3x_2 - 2x_3 = 12 \\ -3x_1 + 5x_2 + x_3 = 3 \end{cases}$$

$$\begin{cases} -x_1 + 7x_2 + 4x_3 = 1 \\ x_1 + x_3 = 3 \\ x_2 + 3x_3 = -5 \end{cases}$$

2. Show all preceding systems in matrix notation. What is the inverse and rank of each of the coefficient matrix? Discuss Hawkins-Simons conditions with respect to the above systems.

3. Determine as to whether or not the following vectors are linearly dependent:

$$\begin{bmatrix} 1 \\ -1 \\ 1 \end{bmatrix} \quad \begin{bmatrix} 1 \\ 2 \\ 2 \end{bmatrix} \quad \begin{bmatrix} 3 \\ 2 \\ 0 \end{bmatrix}$$

$$\begin{bmatrix} 3 \\ 5 \\ 6 \\ 3 \end{bmatrix} \begin{bmatrix} -1 \\ 2 \\ 3 \\ 4 \end{bmatrix} \begin{bmatrix} -3 \\ 4 \\ 2 \\ -1 \end{bmatrix} \begin{bmatrix} 1 \\ 2 \\ 4 \\ -4 \end{bmatrix} \begin{bmatrix} 1 \\ 3 \\ -1 \\ -3 \end{bmatrix}$$

4. Determine the characteristic roots and the associate characteristic vectors for the following matrices:

$$\begin{bmatrix} 2 & 1 & 4 \\ -1 & 2 & 1 \\ 2 & 3 & 1 \end{bmatrix} \begin{bmatrix} 1 & 0 & 0 \\ 0 & 2 & 0 \\ 0 & 0 & 4 \end{bmatrix} \begin{bmatrix} 0 & 2 & 1 \\ 0 & 1 & 2 \\ 2 & -3 & 4 \end{bmatrix} \begin{bmatrix} 3 & 4 & 5 & 6 \\ -1 & 2 & -3 & 1 \\ 0 & 1 & 0 & 2 \\ 2 & 2 & 3 & 1 \end{bmatrix}$$

$$\begin{bmatrix} a_1 & a_2 \cdots a_n \\ a_1 & a_2 \cdots a_n \\ \cdot & \cdot \cdot \cdot \cdot \cdot \\ a_1 & a_2 \cdots a_n \end{bmatrix}$$

5. Reduce the following by Lagrange's method

$$X' \begin{bmatrix} 3 & 2 & 4 \\ 2 & -1 & 2 \\ 4 & 2 & 2 \end{bmatrix} X \qquad X' \begin{bmatrix} i & 2 & -i \\ 2 & 1 & 1+i \\ -i & 1+i & 2 \end{bmatrix} X \qquad X' \begin{bmatrix} 0 & 0 & 1 & 1 \\ 0 & 2 & 3 & 4 \\ 1 & 3 & 4 & 2 \\ 0 & 4 & 2 & 1 \end{bmatrix} X.$$

6. Extend the method of non-linear investment programming to n variables and analyze the stability conditions.

13 THE SIMPLEX AND DUAL METHODS IN PROGRAMMING

13.1 Introduction

The recent revival of interest among economists in linear programming problems is the formal continuation and the practical application of the traditional preoccupation with the problems of maxima and minima in macroeconomics; *e.g.* maximum income and minimum employment. Also, the linear programming techniques have proved to be powerful tools for resource allocation where there are limitations on the supply of the factors.

Anyone, whether he be of Classical or Keynesian persuasion, who is at all acquainted with major economic questions, knows well that maximization and minimization have been the pillars of economic science since its inception. Adequate attention seems to have been paid to these questions, and indeed they have been fully explored from various possible angles. Usually, mathematical economists have provided the necessary tools and methods of systematic thinking for analyzing, and *ipso facto* elaborating of, economic theorems.

When economic theorems were based on, and derived from, the functioning of a single and homogeneous input, the conventional mathematical techniques of calculus could have been used to systematize economic thinking. When Adam Smith was occupied with the idea of scrutinizing the causes of, and reasons for, the augmentation and "maximization" of the "annual produce of nation," a mathematical economist could have summed up Smith's ideas and visions by a few differential equations. Likewise, the ideas entertained by David Ricardo concerning the maximization of "values" could have been demonstrated by the aid of a few basic theorems of differential calculus. The same could have been said for the later economists of the older tradition who indulged in the discussion of a single homogeneous input and output where the supply of factors or

338

other requirements are unlimited. Linear programming, a tool that has emerged from the generous contributions of the U.S. government agencies, is based on such a simplicity of assumptions as to have a slight edge over the conventional mathematical techniques, as far as economics is concerned. A typical firm, in aiming at its goals, is usually confronted with limited resources of all kinds; also it desires to have positive output, price, and profits at the same time. The linear programming gives a solution which is non-negative while it takes into consideration the availability of resources. Here is the edge. This superiority, as far as economics is concerned, is in one direction alone; *vide*, in all other directions it is used as a supplement to differential calculus. In mathematical economics, when one is engaged in the maximization of, let us say, output where there are n inputs one can use linear programming tools to find the optimum, *the best possible*, solution.

13.2 Linear Programming Problems

A linear programming problem should be formulated in systematic terms of: (1) an *objective function* which should be optimized, either maximized or minimized; and (2) a set of *constraints* which represent the limitations and extensions of the factors upon which the objective function is erected. A linear programming problem is related to optimization of an objective function. It usually deals with non-negative solutions to consistent systems of linear equations. Maximization and minimization are two sides of the same coin; *viz.*, if we want to maximize some target, *e.g.*, revenue, we at the same time want to minimize the negative, *e.g.* cost, of the objective or target function and vice versa.

We do not necessarily have to specify the nature and characteristics of an *objective function*, except that it is the given desideratum or datum to be optimized. Any businessman or economic theorist knows what to optimize in his own "laboratory." Keynes wished to have national employment and output maximized; an applied businessman wants to minimize costs, *et hoc genus omne*.

But we need to belabor some of the characteristics and nature of *constraints* which are sometimes called *side-relations*. First, constraints are the foundations of a linear programme; for without them one cannot pose and solve a programming problem. Secondly, as pointed out above, linear programming is, in one respect, superior to the conventional mathematical techniques used for, say, marginal analysis. Practically almost all business problems nowadays are posed with certain limitations. These limitations are expressed in terms of *inequalities* in contrast to equalities. So, in linear programming projects, we are usually confronted with inequalities of all kinds.

Tools of calculus are hard (one should not say impossible) to apply when the problem is blended with a set of inequalities; contrariwise, the tools of matrix algebra, from which the tools of linear programming are derived, are expeditiously labile and easily applicable. Also, in the economic and decision-making realm, one is faced with the non-negativity conditions. Programming techniques are formed and molded so that they can take care of inequality constraints and non-negativity requirements at the same time.

The non-negativity condition is of fundamental importance to an economist as well as a practical businessman. In the example given in the first chapter, we posed the problem of a firm with a certain revenue function desiring to maximize its revenue. Our answer was that the maximum revenue coincided with a negative output! This is not the sort of answer that a sane economist can offer as a sensible solution to a practical problem. No one can convince a businessman that he can maximize his revenue at a negative output! One is out by the door. This is the second reason why linear programming techniques for certain economic problems are superior to the conventional techniques for, say, marginal analysis. (One note is to be made in passing. We wish the reader would make a distinction between the content of the "profit-maximization" principle discussed so often in microeconomics and *maximization of profit* used in linear programming techniques. We wish to say that these terms are different and convey two distinct ideas. The "profit-maximization" principle of microeconomics means simply the equality of marginal cost and marginal revenue. While *maximization of profit* used in programming relates to the actual increase of profits and escalation of it.)

So much for justification! Accordingly, linear programming techniques are employed to analyze and realize the optimum solution of the economic problems with non-negative inequations. As a prelude, programming methods are a series of *trial and error* procedures which are followed according to a definite plan not similar to what once Taylor and Lange suggested for the allocative problem of a socialist economy.[1] Programming techniques are scientific in the sense that an analyst knows well (1) that there are certain steps and results which he should follow and obtain, (2) that each step and each result bring the analyst closer to the optimum solution, and finally, (3) that there are ways to overcome any bottleneck which has been called *degeneracy*.

13.3 Example and Geometry

An example can illustrate the topic more lucidly than anything else. Let us go back to our baby furniture company which gave us some charming delights in Chapter 11. Suppose that the company desires to produce two kinds of articles, that it knows the unit cost and profit of these articles, that it finally knows some limitations imposed on its production process. Having been mindful of these advance data, the company proceeds to

---

[1] See O. Lange and F. M. Taylor, *On the Economic Theory of Socialism*, 1938.

maximize its profits. Let us suppose that these articles are called x and y, we can construct the linear programming model of our firm in the following way:

Maximize total profits shown by

(13.3.1) $$z = 2x + y$$

subject to

(13.3.2)
$$
\begin{aligned}
2x - 3y + 9 &\geq 0 \quad \text{(capacity available)} \\
x + 3y - 18 &\leq 0 \quad \text{(machine time available)} \\
2x - y - 8 &\leq 0 \quad \text{(labor time available)} \\
-x - 5y + 15 &\leq 0 \quad \text{(misc. constraint)}
\end{aligned}
$$

and the non-negativity requirements

(13.3.3) $$x \geq 0, \qquad y \geq 0.$$

We give the following definitions:[2] A solution which satisfies (13.3.2) and (13.3.3) is called a feasible solution. A *feasible solution* which satisfies (13.3.1) is called an *optimum feasible solution*.

Since we have two commodities, the problem can be projected on a two-dimensional diagram. There is a problem, though. We cannot graph an inequality on a plane, an equation being the only one capable of being graphed on a plane. However, we do know that an equation demonstrates a curve and an inequation depicts an *area*. To solve the problem, we can set the inequalities equal to zero and then reject the areas which are not consistent with the inequalities since the inequality put equal to zero divides the plane into two areas: consistent and inconsistent. By setting (13.3.2) equal to zero we will have:

(13.3.4)
$$
\begin{cases}
2x - 3y + 9 = 0 \\
x + 3y - 18 = 0 \\
2x - y - 8 = 0 \\
-x - 5y + 15 = 0.
\end{cases}
$$

The graph of these equalities is given in Figure 13.1.

We notice that the graph of each equation divides the plane into two sections: one section is consistent with the corresponding inequality, while the other section is inconsistent. The consistent sections of the inequalities are shaded for recognition. The reader can easily find out the section which is consistent. The way to determine the relevant section is to try $x = 0$ and $y = 0$, and if the remaining values satisfy the inequality, then the side

---

[2] These definitions can be found in all texts on programming. See G. B. Dantzig, "Maximization of Linear Functions, . . . ," in Koopmans (ed.) *Activity Analysis of Production and Distribution*, New York: 1951, pp. 339–47.

which has the origin $(0, 0)$ is the consistent section. Let us take the first inequality. Set x and y equal to zero. We readily find that $9 > 0$, which is consistent. Thus, the shaded side of a and related to the first equation contains all points including the origin. And the half-plane of the side of the shaded section defines the inequality. So the consistent section of that inequality is the shaded section which is on the x-axis. The same procedure is used for all other inequalities.

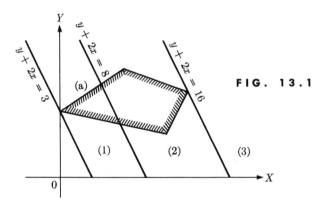

FIG. 13.1

There is one point which should be made clear before we proceed to other subjects and that is the fact that a curve (we pointed out above) depicts an equation, while an inequality represents an area. The *space* or section which satisfies our inequalities is encircled by the lines inside of the shaded area. A space, defined therefrom, which satisfies a set of inequalities is called the *solution space*.

Now, our main responsibility is to determine what point of this solution space can optimize the objective function. We give different values to the left-hand side of (13.3.1) and graph them on the diagram. We notice that in Figure 13.1, (1) is related to the minimum point of the solution space and that (2) is located where there are some points more and other points less than those of the intersection of the objective function and the solution space, but that (3) is consistent with the highest possible point of the solution space. When $y = 4$ and $x = 6$, our firm maximizes its profit. Moreover, the non-negativity requirements (13.3.3) are satisfied, too.

For a number of reasons, the reader should not rashly conclude that he can solve all the problems in the above manner. First of all, linear programming problems are not always capable of being projected on a two-dimensional diagram, since programming problems usually involve more than two variables. Secondly, there is the danger that the feasible solution space may happen to be wide open in one side or the other. The above geometrical presentation was only to facilitate the general comprehension of the topic.

13.4 Matrix Notation and Linear Programming

Our set of inequalities (13.3.2) can be rearranged and shown in the following way:

(13.4.1)
$$\begin{cases} 2x - 3y + 9 \geq 0 \\ -x - 3y + 18 \geq 0 \\ -2x + y + 8 \geq 0 \\ +x + 5y + 15 \geq 0. \end{cases}$$

Employing our matrix notation, (13.4.1) would be represented by the following

$$\begin{bmatrix} 2 & -3 \\ -1 & -3 \\ -2 & 1 \\ +1 & +5 \end{bmatrix} \begin{bmatrix} x \\ y \end{bmatrix} \geq \begin{bmatrix} -9 \\ -18 \\ -8 \\ -15 \end{bmatrix},$$

and if

$$\begin{bmatrix} 2 \\ -1 \\ -2 \\ +1 \end{bmatrix} = A_1 \qquad \begin{bmatrix} -3 \\ -3 \\ 1 \\ +5 \end{bmatrix} = A_2 \qquad \begin{bmatrix} -9 \\ -18 \\ -8 \\ -15 \end{bmatrix} = A_0$$

(13.4.1) can be simplified by the reduced form:

(13.4.2) $$A_1 x + A_2 y \geq A_0.$$

Thus, there are many ways in which one may represent a programming problem. We formulate a general linear programming problem with the aid of matrix notations. It can be said that a general linear programming problem consists in finding a set of solutions which optimizes (minimizes or maximizes) the *objective function:*

(13.4.3) $$z = c_1 x_1 + c_2 x_2 + \cdots + c_n x_n,$$

subject to the linear constraints

(13.4.4) $$x_j \geq 0,$$

and

(13.4.5)
$$\begin{cases} a_{11}x_1 + a_{12}x_2 + \cdots + a_{1n}x_n \geq b_1 \\ a_{21}x_1 + a_{22}x_2 + \cdots + a_{2n}x_n \geq b_2 \\ \cdot \quad \cdot \quad \cdot \quad \cdot \quad \cdot \quad \cdot \quad \cdot \quad \cdot \quad \cdot \quad \cdot \quad \cdot \quad \cdot \\ a_{m1}x_1 + a_{m2}x_2 + \cdots + a_{mn}x_n \geq b_m. \end{cases}$$

We may formulate the above problem in a simpler way:
Optimize

$$cX,$$

subject to

$$X \geq 0,$$

and

$$AX \geq B.$$

Here A is the coefficient matrix of (13.4.5) and B is the column vector of the inequalities. There is one more way to formulate the problem:
  Optimize

$$\sum_{j=1}^{n} c_j x_j,$$

subject to

$$x_j \geq 0,$$

and

$$\sum_{i=1}^{n} a_{ij} x_j \geq b_i.$$

Now we know that there are many ways that a programming problem can be represented. We advise the reader to take the easiest way. In the general problem, we have m equations and n unknowns.

  We give the following definitions: A feasible solution which has more than m (the number of equations or inequations) positive variables is called a *basic feasible solution*. A basic feasible solution which has exactly m positive variables, x_i, is called a *non-degenerate basic feasible solution*. An *optimum non-degenerate feasible solution* is the one which also optimizes the objective function.

  The "Simplex Method" is employed to obtain non-degenerate basic feasible solutions. Before we launch the Simplex Method, we wish to ask the reader to review the *Linear Independency of Vectors*, a topic of the preceding chapter which occupied such an important position. We give the reader a sort of recapitulation: If there are m equations and m (not n) unknowns, the condition which permits us to have unique solutions is that the vectors of the unknowns are *linearly independent*. We, intuitively, proved this theorem in the preceding chapter. If in

(13.4.6)
$$\begin{cases} a_{11}x_1 + a_{12}x_2 + a_{13}x_3 = b_1 \\ a_{21}x_1 + a_{22}x_2 + a_{23}x_3 = b_2 \\ a_{31}x_1 + a_{32}x_2 + a_{33}x_3 = b_3 \end{cases}$$

the rank of the coefficient matrix is equal to the number of unknowns, then the column vectors are linearly independent, and there are three unique solutions for (13.4.6) which will be called feasible solutions in a programming problem. In the light of this recapitulation and what the reader has deduced from the treatment of the linear independency, we can now proceed with the "Simplex Method."

13.5 The Simplex Method

Let us suppose that we have the following linear programming problem: Maximize

(13.5.1) $$z = c_1 x_1 + c_2 x_2 + \cdots + c_n x_n,$$

subject to

(13.5.2) $$x_j \geq 0,$$

and

(13.5.3) $$\begin{cases} a_{11}x_1 + a_{12}x_2 + \cdots + a_{1n}x_n \geq b_1 \\ a_{21}x_1 + a_{22}x_2 + \cdots + a_{2n}x_n \geq b_2 \\ \cdot \quad \cdot \quad \cdot \quad \cdot \quad \cdot \quad \cdot \quad \cdot \quad \cdot \quad \cdot \quad \cdot \quad \cdot \\ a_{m1}x_1 + a_{m2}x_2 + \cdots + a_{mn}x_n \geq b_m. \end{cases}$$

The first thing that we should do is to eliminate, somehow, the inequalities of (13.5.3). In order to explicate ourselves from the inequalities, we add something called "slack variables." If we add these slack variables to the left-hand side members of (13.5.3), the inequations will be transformed into equations:

(13.5.4) $$\begin{cases} a_{11}x_1 + a_{12}x_2 + \cdots + a_{1n}x_n + x_{n+1} = b_1 \\ a_{21}x_1 + a_{22}x_2 + \cdots + a_{2n}x_n + x_{n+2} = b_2 \\ \cdot \quad \cdot \quad \cdot \quad \cdot \quad \cdot \quad \cdot \quad \cdot \quad \cdot \quad \cdot \quad \cdot \quad \cdot \\ a_{m1}x_1 + a_{m2}x_2 + \cdots + a_{mn}x_n + x_{m+n} = b_m \end{cases}$$

where there are $m + n$ unknowns instead of n unknowns of (13.5.3). The first n unknowns have the coefficient matrix as their coefficient and the slack variables have unit vectors as their coefficients; *i.e.*

(13.5.5) $$\begin{bmatrix} a_{11} & a_{12} & \cdots & a_{1n} & 1 & 0 & \cdots & 0 \\ a_{21} & a_{22} & \cdots & a_{2n} & 0 & 1 & \cdots & 0 \\ \cdot & \cdot & \cdot & \cdot & \cdot & \cdot & \cdot & \cdot \\ a_{m1} & a_{m2} & \cdots & a_{mn} & 0 & 0 & \cdots & 1 \end{bmatrix}$$

is the coefficient matrix for all variables including the slack variables, where the first part of it is A while the second part constitutes an identity matrix both of which parts being expressible in the simple form

(13.5.6) $$A, I.$$

The addition of the slack variables has many advantages: (1) the inequalities are transformed into equations; (2) we have added a definite number of variables whose coefficient vectors are linearly independent. (Why are the vectors of an identity matrix linearly independent?) If the vectors of the coefficient matrix are linearly independent, we will have a whole set of equations whose vector coefficients are linearly independent and will give us, according to our theorem, a set of non-degenerate basic feasible solutions. This is an important result. We should always have a coefficient matrix which is linearly independent; and a programming problem which has a coefficient matrix with linearly independent vectors is called a *non-degenerate problem*.

The Simplex Method can be summarized as follows:

1. We first take an initial basic feasible solution; *i.e.* a solution which has as many unknowns as equations. (Remember that the vector coefficient of these unknowns should be linearly independent.) The unknowns included in any basic solution will be henceforth called *included variables* and those set equal to zero *excluded variables*.

2. Then, we include other variables, one by one; and with the included variables the value of the objective function will be evaluated. If there is any improvement by including one new variable and excluding one at the same time, the included variable is getting us closer to the optimum basic solution. If the included variable does not improve the condition, we will proceed with other variables.

3. Steps (1) and (2) are repeated and tried until the optimum solution is attained.

We would like to exemplify the above rule algebraically. Suppose the following problem is given:

Maximize

(13.5.7) $$z = c_1x_1 + c_2x_2 + c_3x_3 + c_4x_4 + c_5x_5 + c_6x_6,$$

subject to

(13.5.8) $$x_j \geq 0,$$

and

(13.5.9)
$$a_{11}x_1 + a_{12}x_2 + a_{13}x_3 + a_{14}x_4 + a_{15}x_5 + a_{16}x_6 = b_1$$
$$a_{21}x_1 + a_{22}x_2 + a_{23}x_3 + a_{24}x_4 + a_{25}x_5 + a_{26}x_6 = b_2$$
$$a_{31}x_1 + a_{32}x_2 + a_{33}x_3 + a_{34}x_4 + a_{35}x_5 + a_{36}x_6 = b_3$$
$$a_{41}x_1 + a_{42}x_2 + a_{43}x_3 + a_{44}x_4 + a_{45}x_5 + a_{46}x_6 = b_4.$$

Let us suppose that

$$\begin{bmatrix} a_{11} \\ a_{21} \\ a_{31} \\ a_{41} \end{bmatrix} = A_1, \quad \begin{bmatrix} a_{12} \\ a_{22} \\ a_{32} \\ a_{42} \end{bmatrix} = A_2, \quad \begin{bmatrix} a_{13} \\ a_{23} \\ a_{33} \\ a_{43} \end{bmatrix} = A_3,$$

$$\begin{bmatrix} a_{14} \\ a_{24} \\ a_{34} \\ a_{44} \end{bmatrix} = A_4, \quad \begin{bmatrix} a_{15} \\ a_{25} \\ a_{35} \\ a_{45} \end{bmatrix} = A_5, \quad \begin{bmatrix} a_{16} \\ a_{26} \\ a_{36} \\ a_{46} \end{bmatrix} = A_6,$$

are linearly independent. Let us suppose, again, that the first basic solution is $(x_1\, x_2\, x_3\, x_4\, 0\, 0)$. In here, we have included x_1, x_2, x_3, and x_4, and excluded x_5 and x_6 by setting them equal to zero. With this solution, (13.5.9) will be reduced to

(13.5.10)
$$\begin{aligned} a_{11}x_1 + a_{12}x_2 + a_{13}x_3 + a_{14}x_4 &= b_1 \\ a_{21}x_1 + a_{22}x_2 + a_{23}x_3 + a_{24}x_4 &= b_2 \\ a_{31}x_1 + a_{32}x_2 + a_{33}x_3 + a_{34}x_4 &= b_3 \\ a_{41}x_1 + a_{42}x_2 + a_{43}x_3 + a_{44}x_4 &= b_4. \end{aligned}$$

The last system of equations in four unknowns and four equations will give unique values for x_1, x_2, x_3, and x_4. These values of the variables x_1, x_2, x_3, x_4, and $x_5 = x_6 = 0$ should be substituted in the objective function and the values of z be obtained.

Next we try x_5 as a possible variable to be included at the expense of one of the previously included variables. To do so, we take the coefficients of the previously included variables and test them against the candidate variable; *viz.*

(13.5.11)
$$\begin{aligned} a_{11}x_{15} + a_{12}x_{25} + x_{13}x_{35} + a_{14}x_{45} &= a_{15} \\ a_{21}x_{15} + a_{22}x_{25} + a_{23}x_{35} + a_{24}x_{45} &= a_{25} \\ a_{31}x_{15} + a_{32}x_{25} + a_{33}x_{35} + a_{34}x_{45} &= a_{35} \\ a_{41}x_{15} + a_{42}x_{25} + a_{43}x_{35} + a_{44}x_{45} &= a_{45}. \end{aligned}$$

Multiply each element of (13.5.11) by e_5 and subtract element by element from (13.5.10) to yield

(13.5.12)
$$\begin{aligned} b_1 &= a_{15}e_5 + a_{11}(x_1 - e_5x_{15}) + a_{12}(x_2 - e_5x_{25}) \\ &\quad + a_{13}(x_3 - e_5x_{35}) + a_{14}(x_4 - e_5x_{45}) \\ b_2 &= a_{25}e_5 + a_{21}(x_1 - e_5x_{15}) + a_{22}(x_2 - e_5x_{25}) \\ &\quad + a_{23}(x_3 - e_5x_{35}) + a_{24}(x_4 - e_5x_{45}) \\ b_3 &= a_{35}e_5 + a_{31}(x_1 - e_5x_{15}) + a_{32}(x_2 - e_5x_{25}) \\ &\quad + a_{33}(x_3 - e_5x_{35}) + a_{34}(x_4 - e_5x_{45}) \\ b_4 &= a_{45}e_5 + a_{41}(x_1 - e_5x_{15}) + a_{42}(x_2 - e_5x_{25}) \\ &\quad + a_{43}(x_3 - e_5x_{35}) + a_{44}(x_4 - e_5x_{45}). \end{aligned}$$

From (13.5.11) the unique values of x_{15}, x_{25}, x_{35}, and x_{45} will be obtained. The value of the objective function for our basic solution is

(13.5.13)
$$z_0 = c_1x_1 + c_2x_2 + c_3x_3 + c_4x_4,$$

since $x_5 = x_6 = 0$. And the value of the objective function for e (including x_5) is

(13.5.14)
$$\begin{aligned} z(e) = c_1(x_1 - e_5x_{15}) + c_2(x_2 - e_5x_{25}) \\ + c_3(x_3 - e_5x_{35}) + c_4(x_4 - e_5x_{45}) + c_5e_5. \end{aligned}$$

(If $e_5 = 0$, $z(e) = z_0$; *i.e.* if x_5 is excluded and the basic solution is the original one with the included variables x_1, x_2, x_3, and x_4). Subtract (13.5.13) from (13.5.14) to yield

$$\textbf{(13.5.15)} \qquad z(e) - z_0 = e(c_5 - c_1 x_{15} - c_2 x_{25} - c_3 x_{35} - c_4 x_{45})$$
$$= e[c_5 - (c_1 x_{15} + c_2 x_{25} + c_3 x_{35} + c_4 x_{45})].$$

Let

$$\textbf{(13.5.16)} \qquad z_5 = (c_1 x_{15} + c_2 x_{25} + c_3 x_{35} + c_4 x_{45})$$

there will be

$$\textbf{(13.5.17)} \qquad z(e) - z_0 = e(c_5 - z_5)$$

where $(c_5 - z_5)$ is called the *simplex criterion*. The simplex criterion is of great importance because it indicates whether or not the inclusion of x_5 has made any improvement as far as the objective function is concerned. On the interpretation of the simplex criterion, two cases are in order:

1. $c_5 - z_5 > 0$ (and by and large $c_j - z_j > 0$). This means that the value of the objective function z has increased by including x_5, (and in general x_j) at the expense of one of the variables of the initial feasible solution ($x_1\ x_2\ x_3\ x_4\ 0\ 0$). That is, we should include x_5 (or x_j) and exclude one of the variables of the initial solution. The rule for exclusion is given by the following formula:

$$\textbf{(13.5.18)} \qquad e = \min \left(\frac{x_1}{x_{15}}, \frac{x_2}{x_{25}}, \frac{x_3}{x_{35}}, \frac{x_4}{x_{45}} \right)$$

or in general

$$\textbf{(13.5.19)} \qquad e = \min_{j} \left(\frac{x_j}{x_{jk}} \right)$$

where k in (13.5.19) refers to kth variable which is being tried. The numerator of the fraction that has the *smallest positive* value will be excluded, and the new variable which has shown and demonstrated improvement will be included instead.

2. $c_5 - z_5 \leq 0$ (and in general $c_j - z_j \leq 0$). In this case, x_5 (or x_j) does not make any improvement, and the initial solution with the combination of x_1, x_2, x_3, and x_4 is the best so far.

On the balance of what has been said, we can construct the following generalized table:

I.   THE SIMPLEX CRITERIA FOR MAXIMIZATION

	Conditions	Policies
If $c_j - z_j > 0$	j makes improvement in z,	j should be included.
If $c_j - z_j \leq 0$	j makes no improvement in z,	j should not be included.

I. THE SIMPLEX CRITERIA FOR MINIMIZATION

	Conditions	Policies
If $z_j - c_j \leq 0$	j does not make any improvement in z,	j should not be included
If $z_j - c_j > 0$	j makes improvement in z,	j should be included

The trial-error process of finding the optimum solution is called the *iteration process.*

13.6 The Basic Feasible Solution and Artificial Base

To the astute reader who may have taken us already to task for overlooking "a few points," we wish to say that the content of the preceding section was based on the assumption (an oversimplified one) that "all is going well" in the sense that a basic feasible solution exists without there being any "tie" in (13.5.18) or (13.5.19) so as to determine what variable should be included and what variable excluded. This latter problem is referred to in the programming literature as the *degeneracy* problem. And the first one is the problem of finding the initial *base* or what we have called an initial base solution. Again and again, here in this section we wish to rule out *degeneracy* problem and emphasize the hows of finding the initial base. The degeneracy problem will be taken up and treated fully in the following section, to satisfy our discerning reader.

How to Find the Initial Basic Solution. Remember! the vectors (column coefficients) of any feasible solution should, according to our definition, be linearly independent. Moreover, a feasible solution which has as many variables as there are equations or inequations is called a basic feasible solution. These two principles should be committed to memory.

There are cases where the initial basic solution can be written down at sight. Take the following problem:

Maximize

(13.6.1) $$z = c_1 x_1 + c_2 x_2 + \cdots + c_n x_n,$$

subject to

(13.6.2) $$x_j \geq 0,$$

and

(13.6.3)
$$a_{11}x_1 + a_{12}x_2 + \cdots + a_{1n}x_n + x_{n+1} = b_1$$
$$a_{21}x_1 + a_{22}x_2 + \cdots + a_{2n}x_n + x_{n+2} = b_2$$
$$\cdot \quad \cdot \quad \cdot \quad \cdot \quad \cdot \quad \cdot \quad \cdot \quad \cdot \quad \cdot \quad \cdot \quad \cdot \quad \cdot$$
$$a_{m1}x_1 + a_{m2}x_2 + \cdots + a_{mn}x_n + x_{n+m} = b_m.$$

This is the case involving a set of inequalities which must be transformed into a set of equalities by adding the slack variables, x_{n+1}, x_{n+2}, $\ldots$, x_{n+m}. Since the slack variables have the unit vector coefficient and since the unit vector coefficients are linearly independent, we can at sight spot them as our first initial solution. We may generalize the procedure set forth by stating that if there are as many variables (with unit vector column coefficient) as there are equalities (whether these variables are the slack ones added to replace inequalities by equalities or belong originally to a set of equations), these variables are to be used as our initial basic solution.

If the problem does not appear to have any variables which make up a unit vector solution with as many positive variables as equations, we shall follow, in that case, the neat device due to Dantzig. Take the following problem:

Minimize

(13.6.4)
$$z = c_1 x_1 + \cdots + c_n x_n,$$

subject to

(13.6.5)
$$x_j \geq 0,$$

and

(13.6.6)
$$\begin{aligned}
a_{11} x_1 + a_{12} x_2 + \cdots + a_{1n} x_n &= b_1 \\
a_{21} x_1 + a_{22} x_2 + \cdots + a_{2n} x_n &= b_n \\
\cdot \quad \cdot \quad \cdot \quad \cdot \quad \cdot \quad \cdot \quad \cdot \quad \cdot \quad \cdot \quad \cdot \quad \cdot \quad \cdot \quad & \\
a_{m1} x_1 + a_{m2} x_2 + \cdots + a_{mn} x_n &= b_m.
\end{aligned}$$

The reader may notice here that there exists no unit vector solution and that there are no inequalities to which we could add slack variables. In this case, following Dantzig, we set up the following auxiliary problem:
Find $x_1, \ldots, x_n, x_{n+1}, x_{n+2}, \ldots, x_{n+m}$ such that

(13.6.7)
$$z = x_{n+1} + \cdots + x_{n+m},$$

as small as possible and subject to

(13.6.8)
$$x_j \geq 0,$$

and

(13.6.9)
$$\begin{aligned}
a_{11} x_1 + a_{12} x_2 + \cdots + a_{1n} x_n + x_{n+1} &= b_1 \\
a_{21} x_1 + a_{22} x_2 + \cdots + a_{2n} x_n + x_{n+2} &= b_2 \\
\cdot \quad \cdot \quad \cdot \quad \cdot \quad \cdot \quad \cdot \quad \cdot \quad \cdot \quad \cdot \quad \cdot \quad \cdot \quad \cdot \quad & \\
a_{m1} x_1 + a_{m2} x_2 + \cdots + a_{mn} x_n + x_{n+m} &= b_m.
\end{aligned}$$

Since the constraints of this problem (13.6.9) are exactly the same as the (13.6.6), a basic feasible solution can be written down at sight $X =$

$(x_{n+1}, x_{n+2} \ldots x_{n+m})$. Also the minimum possible value of z here is zero, and this occurs when

$$x_{n+1} = x_{n+2} = \cdots = x_{n+m} = 0.$$

But when the last expression is zero, the above problem is the same as those before that; *viz.*, (13.6.4), (13.6.5) and (13.6.6). Thus, an optimum solution to the auxiliary problem is a feasible solution to the original problem.

In what follows, we will solve two examples: one related to the case where there are unit vector variables which can be written down at sight as the initial basic solution, and the other related to the setting up of the auxiliary problem.

Example 1. Let us call on our baby furniture company once again. Suppose the company is producing six articles $x_1, \ldots x_6$ where there are three commodities, x_3, x_4, and x_6 which do not come into the cost structure of the company. Given the available data, the company wishes to minimize its cost subject to capacity and other limitations. The problem can be formalized as follows:

Minimize the cost

(13.6.10)
$$z = 2x_1 - 4x_2 + 3x_5,$$

subject to

(13.6.11)
$$x_j \geq 0,$$

(13.6.12)
$$\begin{cases} 2x_1 + x_2 + x_3 + x_4 & = 8 \quad \text{(Raw material)} \\ -x_1 - 2x_2 + 3x_3 + x_5 & = 9 \quad \text{(Capacity)} \\ 4x_1 + 2x_2 - 2x_3 + x_6 & = 5 \quad \text{(Misc.)} \end{cases}$$

The reader can check the entries of the constraints. He can convince himself of the plausibility of this example by visualizing a company where some commodities are entered into some constraints and some are not. In (13.6.12), commodities x_5 and x_6 do not come into the raw material constraint. The same is true of other constraints.

Our first task is to find an initial basic solution. Since (13.6.12) is not a set of inequalities, we cannot add slack variables. But there are three variables, x_4, x_5 and x_6 which have unit vector coefficients. We can use them as our first basic solution by setting x_1, x_2, and x_3 equal to zero. With this background, we rewrite (13.6.12) so as to satisfy the basic solution; *i.e.*

(13.6.12')
$$\begin{cases} x_4 & = 8 \\ x_5 & = 9 \quad z = 27. \\ x_6 & = 5 \end{cases}$$

At this point, the objective function should be evaluated. Furthermore, the inverse matrices should be constructed, *i.e.*, other variables should be checked as to whether or not they improve the objective function. Following the procedure set forth before, the following set of equations are formed:

(13.6.13a)
$$\begin{cases} a_{14}x_{41} + a_{15}x_{51} + a_{16}x_{61} = 2 \\ a_{24}x_{41} + a_{25}x_{51} + a_{26}x_{61} = -1 \\ a_{34}x_{41} + a_{35}x_{51} + a_{36}x_{61} = 4, \end{cases}$$

(13.6.13b)
$$\begin{cases} a_{14}x_{42} + a_{15}x_{52} + a_{16}x_{62} = 1 \\ a_{24}x_{42} + a_{25}x_{52} + a_{26}x_{62} = -2 \\ a_{34}x_{42} + a_{35}x_{52} + a_{36}x_{62} = 2, \end{cases}$$

(13.6.13c)
$$\begin{cases} a_{14}x_{43} + a_{15}x_{53} + a_{16}x_{63} = 1 \\ a_{24}x_{43} + a_{25}x_{53} + a_{26}x_{63} = 3 \\ a_{34}x_{43} + a_{35}x_{53} + a_{36}x_{63} = -2, \end{cases}$$

and on substitution from (13.6.12) we obtain:

(13.6.14)
$$\begin{cases} x_{41} = 2 \\ x_{51} = -1 \\ x_{61} = 4, \end{cases} \quad \begin{cases} x_{42} = 1 \\ x_{52} = -2 \\ x_{62} = 2, \end{cases} \quad \begin{cases} x_{43} = 1 \\ x_{53} = 3 \\ x_{63} = -2, \end{cases}$$

and the simplex criterion for each variable is:

(13.6.15a)
$$\begin{cases} z_1 = c_4 x_{41} + c_5 x_{51} + c_6 x_{61} \\ = -3 \\ z_1 - c_1 = -3 - 2 = -5 < 0 \quad \text{(no improvement)}, \end{cases}$$

(13.6.15b)
$$\begin{cases} z_2 = c_4 x_{42} + c_5 x_{52} + c_6 x_{62} \\ = -6 \\ z_2 - c_2 = -6 + 4 = -2 < 0 \quad \text{(no improvement)}, \end{cases}$$

(13.6.15c)
$$\begin{cases} z_3 = c_4 x_{43} + c_5 x_{53} + c_6 x_{63} \\ = 9 \\ z_3 - c_3 = 9 - 0 = 9 > 0 \quad \text{(improvement)}. \end{cases}$$

According to our rule of the simplex criterion, x_1 and x_2 do not make any improvement, but only x_3 improves the condition, thus it can be included at the expense of one of the variables of our original feasible solution. The question of which one of x_4, x_5, or x_6 should be excluded depends, as it was said before, on

$$e = \min \left(\frac{x_4}{x_{43}}, \frac{x_5}{x_{53}}, \frac{x_6}{x_{63}} \right).$$

According to the rule, the numerator of the fraction which has the lowest positive value will be excluded and x_3 will replace it.

Collecting values from (13.6.12) and the third set of (13.6.14) which is related to the "inverse" of x_3, we have

$$\left(\frac{8}{1}, \frac{9}{3}, \frac{5}{-2} \right).$$

Whereas $\frac{9}{3}$ is the lowest positive fraction, the numerator of this fraction, x_5, is excluded and x_3 will be included in our new feasible solution inasmuch as the latter gives a better result than the former.

The new basic feasible solution, therefore, is

$$X = (x_3 \quad x_4 \quad x_6) \qquad \text{where} \qquad x_1 = x_2 = x_5 = 0.$$

We repeat exactly what we did before in the case of our first solution. We rewrite (13.6.12) to satisfy the conditions for the new basic solution:

(13.6.12″)
$$\begin{cases} x_3 + x_4 \quad\;\; = 8 \\ 3x_3 \qquad\;\;\; = 9 \\ -2x_3 \quad\;\; + x_6 = 5 \end{cases}$$

from which we obtain

$$x_3 = 3 \qquad x_4 = 5 \qquad x_6 = 11$$

and

$$z = 0.$$

We notice that with the new values of the solution, the value of the objective function is $z = 0$ which is an improvement over the previous cases where $z = 27$.

Further, the inverse matrices should now be constructed, that is, other variables ought to be brought to a "trial" and see whether or not they improve the objective function. The only variables that we should try are x_1 and x_2; we already know that x_5 could not make any improvement and for that reason was excluded. Thus, we write:

(13.6.16a)
$$\begin{aligned} a_{13}x_{31} + a_{14}x_{41} + a_{16}x_{61} &= 2 \\ a_{23}x_{31} + a_{24}x_{41} + a_{26}x_{61} &= -1 \\ a_{33}x_{31} + a_{34}x_{41} + a_{36}x_{61} &= 4 \end{aligned}$$

(13.6.16b)
$$\begin{aligned} a_{13}x_{32} + a_{14}x_{42} + a_{16}x_{62} &= 1 \\ a_{23}x_{32} + a_{24}x_{42} + a_{26}x_{62} &= -2 \\ a_{33}x_{32} + a_{34}x_{42} + a_{36}x_{62} &= 2, \end{aligned}$$

and on substitution from (13.6.12) we have

(13.6.17)
$$\begin{cases} x_{31} + x_{41} \quad\;\; = 2 \\ 3x_{31} \qquad\;\;\; = -1 \\ -2x_{31} \quad\; + x_{61} = 4 \end{cases} \qquad \begin{cases} x_{32} + x_{42} \quad\;\; = 1 \\ 3x_{32} \qquad\;\;\; = -2 \\ -2x_{32} \quad\; + x_{61} = 2 \end{cases}$$

On solving the systems of (13.6.17), we get

$$\begin{aligned} x_{31} &= -\tfrac{1}{3} & x_{32} &= -\tfrac{2}{3} \\ x_{41} &= \tfrac{7}{3} & x_{42} &= \tfrac{5}{3} \\ x_{61} &= \tfrac{10}{3} & x_{62} &= \tfrac{2}{3}, \end{aligned}$$

and the simplex criterion for each variable is:

(13.6.18a)
$$\begin{cases} z_1 = c_3 x_{31} + c_4 x_{41} + c_6 x_{61} \\ \quad = 0 \\ z_1 - c_1 = 0 - 2 < 0 \qquad \text{(no improvement)} \end{cases}$$

(13.6.18b)
$$\begin{cases} z_2 = c_3 x_{32} + c_4 x_{42} + c_5 x_{52} \\ z_2 = 0 \\ z_2 - c_2 = 0 + 4 > 0 \qquad \text{(improvement).} \end{cases}$$

Since the simplex criterion of x_2 is positive, that is to say, it makes an improvement by being included in the solution, we will investigate to find out what variable of the solution is to be excluded. Thus,

$$e = \min\left(\frac{x_3}{x_{32}}, \frac{x_4}{x_{42}}, \frac{x_6}{x_{62}}\right)$$
$$= \min\left(\frac{3}{-2/3}, \frac{5}{5/3}, \frac{11}{2/3}\right).$$

Since x_4 is the numerator of the fraction which has the lowest positive value, it should be excluded and replaced by x_2. On that basis, our new basic feasible solution is:

$$X = (x_2 \quad x_3 \quad x_6) \qquad \text{with} \qquad x_1 = x_4 = x_5 = 0.$$

Let us rewrite (13.6.12) to satisfy the new basic solution:

(13.6.12‴)
$$\begin{cases} x_3 + x_3 \qquad\quad = 8 \\ -2x_2 + 3x_3 \qquad = 9 \\ 2x_2 - 2x_3 + x_6 = 5, \end{cases}$$

which yields

$$x_2 = 3 \qquad x_3 = 5 \qquad x_6 = 9$$

and the value of the objective function is $z = -12$, which is an improvement over the previous case. We continue and repeat whatever we have done in the last two cases in order to find out if there exists any other solution which could improve the condition. Thus, we write

(13.6.19a)
$$\begin{cases} x_{21} + x_{31} \qquad\quad = 2 \\ -2x_{21} + 3x_{31} \qquad = -1 \\ 2x_{21} - 2x_{31} + x_{61} = 4 \end{cases}$$

(13.6.19b)
$$\begin{cases} x_{25} + x_{35} \qquad\quad = 0 \\ -2x_{25} + 3x_{35} \qquad = 1 \\ 2x_{25} - 2x_{35} + x_{65} = 0 \end{cases}$$

from which we get, respectively,

$$\begin{cases} x_{21} \qquad\qquad\quad = \tfrac{7}{5} \\ \qquad x_{31} \qquad\quad = \tfrac{3}{5} \\ \qquad\qquad x_{61} = \tfrac{12}{5}, \end{cases}$$

and

$$\begin{cases} x_{25} & = -\frac{1}{5} \\ \quad x_{35} & = \frac{1}{5} \\ \quad\quad x_{65} = \frac{4}{5}. \end{cases}$$

The simplex criterion in the light of our solutions is

(13.6.20a)
$$\begin{cases} z_1 = c_2 x_{21} + c_3 x_{31} + c_6 x_{61} \\ \quad = -\frac{28}{5} \\ z_1 - c_1 = -\frac{28}{5} - 2 < 0 \quad\quad \text{(no improvement)} \end{cases}$$

(13.6.20b)
$$\begin{cases} z_5 = c_2 x_{25} + c_3 x_{35} + c_6 x_{65} \\ \quad = \frac{4}{5} \\ z_5 - c_5 = \frac{4}{5} - 3 < 0 \quad\quad \text{(no improvement)} \end{cases}$$

Since neither x_1 nor x_5 would make any improvement, our basic solution (optimum solution) to the minimization problem posed is:

$$X = (x_2 \quad x_3 \quad x_6) \quad \text{with} \quad x_1 = x_4 = x_5 = 0.$$

Interpretation. The practical meaning of the formal solution obtained is that our baby furniture company should discontinue x_1, x_4, and x_5 articles and, instead, concentrate on the production of x_2, x_3, and x_6 articles. To be more concrete, if it desires to minimize its cost, on the basis of its production possibilities, it should only produce 3 units of x_2, 5 units of x_3, and 9 units of x_6 (3, 5 and 9 are the unique solutions of (13.6.12''')). This is the optimum production of our company as far as cost minimization is concerned.

Degeneracy Problem. Before we probe the degeneracy problem, a rather misplaced remark is in order. Sometimes, the results of the simplex method can be and have been condensed in what is called a "simplex criterion." In the following example, illustrating the degeneracy problem, the simplex tableau will be used.

Degeneracy is the case where there are *ties* in

$$e = \min \left(\frac{x_r}{x_{rk}} \right)$$

wherefrom we adopt the included variable which would improve an objective function. Here, there will exist two or more variables which have exactly the same lowest positive values, (most often it happens when the numerators are zero). In such a case or situation, there are two rules for *breaking* the ties: One is that we are to choose the variable which has the lowest subscript. The other is that we are to look in the table of random numbers and to exclude the variable whose subscript comes first in the random numbers. These two rules, however, do not prove effective in the case of degeneracy. The following alternative rule is due to Dantzig[3] and later to Charnes.[4] The rule follows:[5]

> The rule is perfectly general. Whenever degeneracy occurs, the vector to be eliminated and the vector to be retained in the basis may be determined by calculating the ratios x_{ij}/x_{ik} across the rows in which the *tie* occurs. Here x_{ik} refers to the elements in the ith rows (e.g. rows 1 and 2) of the *column* under A_k, the vector to be brought into the basis. x_{ij} refers to the other elements in the same rows. The two sets of elements are then examined, term by term, from left to right. At the first place where no equality holds (*i.e.* the *tie* is broken) between the ratios so calculated, a decision is reached. Remove the basis vector in the row with the (algebraically) smallest ratio. The same rule is applied in the extent of a *tie* between more than two vectors —multiple degeneracy. Moreover, a decision must always be reached, since the vectors in question, by virtue of being in the basis, must differ at least in one place. At the intersection with its own column the basis vector must have $x_{ij} = 1$. All other elements in that column must be zero.

We solve the following example[6] which is related to the problem of degeneracy. We should make an exploratory attempt to use the "simplex tableau" which the reader may find extremely useful and helpful in solving programming problems. Our programming problem now is:

Minimize the objective function

$$(13.6.21) \qquad Z = -\tfrac{3}{4}x_1 + 150x_2 - \tfrac{1}{50}x_3 + 6x_4$$

subject to

$$(13.6.22) \qquad\qquad\qquad x_j \geq 0$$

$$(13.6.23) \quad \begin{aligned} \tfrac{1}{4}x_1 - 60x_2 - \tfrac{1}{25}x_3 + 9x_4 + x_5 & = 0 \\ \tfrac{1}{2}x_1 - 90x_2 - \tfrac{1}{50}x_3 + 3x_4 &+ x_6 = 0 \\ x_3 &+ x_7 = 1 \end{aligned}$$

Let the coefficients of the variables and the constant terms be called

$$\begin{bmatrix} \tfrac{1}{4} \\ \tfrac{1}{2} \\ 0 \end{bmatrix} = A_1 \qquad \begin{bmatrix} -60 \\ -90 \\ 0 \end{bmatrix} = A_2 \qquad \begin{bmatrix} -\tfrac{1}{25} \\ -\tfrac{1}{50} \\ 1 \end{bmatrix} = A_3$$

---

[3] "Computational Algorithm of the Revised Simplex Method." Rand Report RM-1266, The Rand Corporation, Santa Monica, Calif. 1953.

[4] "Optimality and Degeneracy in Linear Programming," *Econometrics* XX, 1952.

[5] A. Charnes, W. W. Cooper, and A. Henderson, *An Introduction to Linear Programming*, (New York: Wiley, 1953) pp. 23–24.

[6] This problem is due to E. M. L. Beale designated in his "Cycling in the Dual Simplex Algorithm," *Naval Research Logistics Quarterly*, II, No. 4, 1955, where he discussed cycling and unresolubility of problems. See also S. I. Gass, *Linear Programming*, (New York: McGraw-Hill, 1958) pp. 106–108.

$$\begin{bmatrix} 9 \\ 3 \\ 0 \end{bmatrix} = A_4 \qquad \begin{bmatrix} 1 \\ 0 \\ 0 \end{bmatrix} = A_5 \qquad \begin{bmatrix} 0 \\ 1 \\ 0 \end{bmatrix} = A_6$$

$$\begin{bmatrix} 0 \\ 0 \\ 1 \end{bmatrix} = A_7 \qquad \begin{bmatrix} 0 \\ 0 \\ 1 \end{bmatrix} = A_0.$$

Since x_5, x_6 and x_7 form a basis with coefficient vectors which are linearly independent, we use them as our first basic solution. The first stage of the *simplex tableau* will appear as follows:

Basis	A_0	A_1	A_2	A_3	A_4	A_5	A_6	A_7
A_5	0	$\frac{1}{4}$	-60	$-\frac{1}{25}$	9	1	0	0
A_6	0	$\frac{1}{2}$	-90	$-\frac{1}{50}$	3	0	1	0
A_7	1	0	0	1	0	0	0	1
$z_j - c_j$	0	$\frac{3}{4}$	-150	$\frac{1}{50}$	-6	0	0	0

There are two points which should be made clear as far as the *first stage of the simplex tableau* is concerned. One is the explanation of the figures which appear in each column. The second point is the determination of the variables that are excluded from and included in the tableau.

As to the first point. By A_5, A_6, and A_7 under the *Basis* (the letters in the first column), we imply that x_5, x_6, and x_7 are the variables of the first basic solution. The values of the second column under A_0 are the values of (13.6.23) which satisfy the initial basic solution. It is exactly like (13.6.12''') of the preceding example. The values which appear under $A_1, A_2, \ldots A_7$ (disregarding the values of the last row) belong to "inverse" matrices when $x_1, x_2, \ldots x_7$ are tried. They are exactly like the values obtained from (13.6.17) and (13.6.18) for the preceding example. These values are obtained in the same manner and with the same techniques and entered into the respective column; i.e., the values for x_1 against x_5, x_6, and x_7 under A_1, and so forth. Concretely, $\frac{1}{4}$, $\frac{1}{2}$, and 0 under A_1 in the third column from left of the tableau are obtained from

$$\begin{cases} x_5 & = \frac{1}{4} \\ \quad x_6 & = \frac{1}{2} \\ \quad\quad x_7 = 0. \end{cases}$$

As we already know, the constants of the right-hand side of the above system are the coefficient of x_1 in the system of equations (13.6.23) which are the constraints. All other values are calculated similarly.

As to the second point on the determination of the excludable and includable variables, the values of the last row corresponding to $z_j - c_j$, which are the "simplex criteria" for different variables, represent the center of attraction. These values are computed exactly in the same way and with the same techniques that the simplex criteria of the preceding example were solved. We observe immediately that the values of the objective function for the initial basic solution is zero, and that the values of the objective function with x_1 included at the expense of one of the variables of the initial solution is $\frac{3}{4}$, and so forth. We offer the following rule: *Having arranged the values of the "simplex criteria" under their respective columns, we should include that variable whose "simplex criterion" has the largest positive value.* This follows from the law of simplex method.

The next step is to exclude one variable from the initial base to make room for the new variable. To exclude one variable from the original base, according to our rule, we should form

$$e = \min \left(\frac{x_r}{x_{rk}} \right).$$

That is to say, we should divide the values of A_0 by the corresponding values of A_1 and the one which has the smallest positive value is to be excluded. Now we know that the "simplex criterion" of x_1 which is $\frac{3}{4}$ is the highest positive value that appears in the row of simplex criteria. Thus, x_1 is to be included. For exclusion, we ought to divide the values of the column A_0 by the corresponding values of A_1, or

$$\frac{0}{\frac{1}{4}}, \frac{0}{\frac{1}{2}}, \frac{1}{0}.$$

As the reader notices, the results of x_5 and x_6 are zero and the last one will give infinity. Therefore, there is a "tie" between x_5 and x_6. A situation like this is called "degeneracy" for which we cited the rule for its resolution. In conformity with the rule of resolving the degeneracy, we should divide all the values of the first row related to A_5 by $\frac{1}{4}$, and all the values of the second row related to A_6 by $\frac{1}{2}$. Or, we write

$$A_5 \quad \frac{-60}{\frac{1}{4}} \quad \frac{-\frac{1}{25}}{\frac{1}{4}} \quad \frac{9}{\frac{1}{4}} \quad \frac{1}{\frac{1}{4}} \quad \frac{0}{\frac{1}{4}} \quad \frac{0}{\frac{1}{4}}$$

$$A_6 \quad \frac{-90}{\frac{1}{2}} \quad \frac{-\frac{1}{50}}{\frac{1}{2}} \quad \boxed{\frac{3}{\frac{1}{2}}} \quad \frac{0}{\frac{1}{2}} \quad \frac{1}{\frac{1}{2}} \quad \frac{0}{\frac{1}{2}}.$$

Then, we compare the pair of values in the same column from the left: the one of a pair which has the lowest value (positive) will be chosen and the variable of the same row corresponding to that value will be excluded. In the case presented above, the third pair have positive values, and the one which is circled is the lowest positive of the two. Thus, x_6 will be excluded and x_5 retained.

According to whatever we have done so far, the new basic feasible solution is

$$X = (x_1 \ x_5 \ x_7) \quad \text{with} \quad x_2 = x_3 = x_4 = x_6 = 0.$$

If we follow carefully the procedure explained thus far, our *second stage* of the simplex tableau will look as follows:

Basis	A_0	A_1	A_2	A_3	A_4	A_5	A_6	A_7
A_1	0	1	-180	$-\frac{2}{50}$	6	0	2	0
A_5	0	0	-15	$-\frac{3}{100}$	7.5	1	$-\frac{1}{2}$	0
A_7	1	0	0	①	0	0	0	1
$z_j - c_j$	0	0	-15	$\frac{1}{20}$	$-\frac{21}{2}$	0	$-\frac{3}{2}$	0

The reader observes that x_3 is to be included because its simplex criterion is the largest positive value. And the variable which is to be excluded is x_7 which is circled in the tableau.

Continuing the method, the third and the last stage of the tableau will appear as follows:

Basis	A_0	A_1	A_2	A_3	A_4	A_5	A_6	A_7
A_1	$\frac{1}{25}$	1	-180	0	6	0	2	$\frac{1}{25}$
A_3	1	0	0	1	0	0	0	1
A_5	$\frac{3}{100}$	0	-15	0	$\frac{15}{2}$	1	$-\frac{1}{2}$	$\frac{3}{100}$
$z_j - c_j$	$-\frac{1}{20}$	0	-15	0	$\frac{21}{2}$	0	$-\frac{3}{2}$	$-\frac{1}{20}$

The reader notices that *it does not pay* to change any variable because no simplex criterion can make any improvement and that the basic solution x_1, x_3, and x_5 is the optimum one.

There is a remark or precaution to be made in conclusion. Once one writes and arranges a simplex tableau, that arrangement should be kept to the end of the problem.

13.7 Duality Problem

Every mathematical linear programming model has another model which is closely related to it and called its *dual*. Sometimes the original programming model is called the *primal*. The primal and the dual are two sides of the same problem expressed in two forms. In economics, resource allocation and pricing (and a few other examples) are the dual and the primal of the same issue.

Let us suppose that our primal is: Find a column vector X which minimizes the linear functional

(13.7.1)
$$z = \sum_{j=1}^{n} p_j x_j, \quad (j = 1, \ldots n)$$

subject to

(13.7.2)
$$x_j \geq 0,$$

and

(13.7.3)
$$\sum_{i=1}^{m} a_{ij}x_j = b_i.$$

The dual problem of the above primal is: Find a column vector W which maximizes the linear functional

(13.7.4)
$$z' = \sum_{i=1}^{m} b_i w_i,$$

subject to

(13.7.5)
$$a_{11}w_1 + a_{21}w_2 + \cdots + a_{m1}w_m \leq p_1$$
$$a_{12}w_1 + a_{22}w_2 + \cdots + a_{m2}w_m \leq p_2$$
$$\cdots \cdots \cdots \cdots \cdots \cdots$$
$$a_{1n}w_1 + a_{2n}w_2 + \cdots + a_{mn}w_m \leq p_n.$$

From the preceding discussion, it is noticed readily that

1. If the primal is a maximizing problem, its dual will be a minimizing one; vice versa, the dual of a minimizing problem is a maximizing one.

2. The dual is constructed so that the constant terms of the primal are the coefficients of the objective function of the dual and, conversely, the coefficients of the objective function (in our example p_j) of the primal are the constants of the constraints of the dual.

3. The number of the variables of the dual is the same as the number of constraints of the primal.

4. Since the primal and the dual are two expressions for the same problem, the computational method used for primal and discussed before, ought to be used for computing the dual. The simplex method which was suggested to be used for solving a linear programming problem is the method for computing the dual.

5. Therefore, if there is a primal, the dual can be constructed from the rules set forth above.

The following theorem is, in conclusion, given without proof:

Duality Theorem: If there is an optimum solution for the primal problem, there will be an optimal solution for its dual too; conversely, when there exists an optimal solution for the dual, the primal has also the optimal solution. The solution which optimizes the primal also optimizes the dual of the same problem, and vice versa. If the optimal solution of the primal is infinite, the dual's final basic solution is infinite also.

EXERCISES 13

1. Consider the system: $3x + y = \min$ subject to

$$4x + 3y \geq 19$$
$$-x + 3y \geq 2$$
$$4x - y \leq 26$$
$$x + 3y \leq 26$$
$$x - 2y \geq -11$$
$$x \geq 0, \quad y \geq 0.$$

(a) Draw the convex set defined by the inequalities.
(b) Find the optimal solution graphically.

2. Consider the system: $1.5x + y = \max.$ subject to

$$-2x + y \leq 0$$
$$-x + 3y \leq 10$$
$$2x - y \leq 5$$
$$3x - 8y \leq 1$$
$$x + 2y \geq 5$$
$$x \geq 0, \quad y \geq 0$$

(a) Draw the convex set defined by the inequalities.
(b) Find the solution graphically.
(c) Use the simplex method to find the solution.

3. Consider the system: $y + 4x = \min.$ subject to

$$6x - y \leq 2$$
$$2x + y \leq 6$$
$$\tfrac{1}{2}x + y \leq 3$$
$$\tfrac{1}{4}x + y \leq 2$$
$$x \geq 0, \quad y \geq 0.$$

(a) Draw the convex set defined by the inequalities.
(b) Find the solution graphically.
(c) Use the simplex method to find the solution.

14

LINEAR PROGRAMMING
AND ACTIVITY ANALYSIS

This chapter deals with a new technique of analysis for solving problems of production and allocation. This technique will be formed in contrast to the traditional tools of marginal analysis, even though both apparatus offer pretty much the same results. We begin with a few "loose" sections, but in the last sections we shall tie all the "loose" ends together.

14.1 Production Function*

The concept of a production function has occupied the central place in the literature on production and resource allocation. A production function had long embodied technical relations between input and outputs which lie behind the cost curves of a firm. Further, it was assumed and taken for granted that an economy was the aggregate of the firms comprising it. So, the production function, at a macroscopic level, was assumed to have the same shape and form as the one for the "representative firm." This latter assumes the validity of the Say's Law of Markets, *i.e.*, given the effective demand the analysis of economic growth[1] and general economic equilibrium[2] are contingent upon the way in which the production function is formulated. One is always confronted with two types of formulation of the production function in the literature. Now, for the sake of clarity, we make the distinction between these two formulations. One of these may be called a *continuous production function* for reasons which will be eluci-

---

*This section is based on T. C. Koopmans' "Analysis of Production as an Efficient Combination of Activities," in Koopmans' (Ed.) *Activity Analysis of Production and Allocation*, ch. III, pp. 33–97.

[1] J. E. Meade, *A Neo-Classical Theory of Economic Growth*, 1961.

[2] W. W. Leontief, *The Structure of American Economy, 1919–39*, 1951. See also, J. Von Neumann, "A Model of General Economic Equilibrium," *Review of Economic Studies*, Vol. 13, pp. 1–9, English translation of an earlier (1937) article in German.

dated below. The second type will be referred to as a "transformation function" to borrow Koopmans' phraseology.[3]

14.2 A Continuous Production Function

Under "pure competition" where factor payments are equal to the value of their marginal products, constant returns to scale are consequential.[4] The condition

(14.2.1)
$$w = p \frac{\partial Q}{\partial N},$$

where w is the money-wage rate, Q the output, and N the labor input presupposes the neo-classical production function

(14.2.2)
$$Q = Q(K, N),$$

where K is an "index-number" of the stock of capital.[5] From (14.2.1) and (14.2.2) the hereunder condition can be deduced

(14.2.3)
$$Q \equiv \frac{\partial Q}{\partial K} K + \frac{\partial Q}{\partial N} N.$$

Expression (14.2.3) is Euler's Theorem applied to production analysis of a firm, and it conveys

$$\lambda Q = Q(\lambda K, \lambda N).$$

From (14.2.1), (14.2.2), and (14.2.3) we can further deduce

(14.2.4)
$$Q = AK^a N^b$$

where

$$A = e^{-c}, \quad a = \frac{\partial(\log Q)}{\partial(\log K)}, \quad b = \frac{\partial(\log Q)}{\partial(\log N)}.$$

The expression (14.2.4) is the Cobb-Douglas production function which makes the sum of partial elasticities of output with respect to an "index-number" of the stock of capital and labor equal to one with the elasticities of substitution between K and N in the production of Q:

(14.2.5)
$$\frac{\left(\frac{\partial Q}{\partial N}\right)\left(\frac{\partial Q}{\partial K}\right)}{Q \frac{\partial^2 Q}{\partial N \, \partial K}}.$$

---

[3] Koopmans, *op. cit.*, p. 35.

[4] See pp. 150–152 and 168–172. It should also be noted in passing that the assumption of the constant returns to scale implies the prevalence of pure competition wherein factor payments are equal to the value of their marginal products.

[5] D. Champrenowne, *The Theory of Capital*, Hague (Ed.), 1961, p. 223.

Equations (14.2.1)–(14.2.5) describe the production function which is homogeneous of degree one; that is to say, $\dfrac{dQ}{d\lambda}$ is constant so that there are constant returns to scale, and this happens when output Q increases in proportion to the use of the factors. The validity of the above discussion is based on the assumption that there are continuous partial derivatives all along the production related to the firm. *In extenso*, we can gather the following results: The production function (14.2.2) relates to a firm. If it is to be applied to the whole economy, the latter should be thought of as the sum of "representative firms." Some may, in a heretical dialogue, question the validity and applicability of the "representative firm" and constant returns to scale as realistic.[6] Production function (14.2.2) assumes continuous substitution between inputs and output. This may not appear to be *prima facie* a shortcoming of this production function.[7] Let us project production function (14.2.2) on a two-dimensional diagram where Q's indicate constant product curves as in Figure 14.1. Each curve is

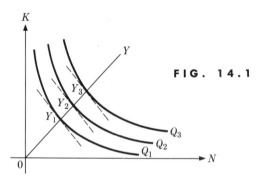

FIG. 14.1

negatively inclined and the slope of the tangent to the curve at any point measures the marginal rate of substitution of the ratio of the marginal products and is numerically equal to $-\dfrac{dK}{dN} = \dfrac{\partial Q/\partial N}{\partial Q/\partial K}$. Since the assumption of constant returns to scale is behind (14.2.2), the distance between Q_1 and Q_2 is in the same ratio as the ratio which increases the inputs. If there are three points such as Y_1, Y_2, and Y_3 at which the tangents have the same slopes, these points are on the same line which goes through the origin like $0Y$.

There is one question which is fundamental and should be raised: Why should pure competition and its consequential constant returns to scale be assumed as many economists nowadays tend to do? The answer is rather

---

[6] P. Sraffa, "The Laws of Returns Under Competitive Conditions," *Economic Journal*, Vol. XXXVI (1926), pp. 535–550.

[7] P. A. Samuelson, *Foundations of Economic Analysis*, pp. 70–73.

simple.   The assumptions of pure competition and constant returns to scale determine all the variables of the system and make the system altogether consistent, as the reader can infer from the formal proof given above.   That is to say, given the money-wage rate, the level of output will be determined by equations (14.2.1) and (14.2.2).   The output, having been determined in this manner, will determine the rate of change of capital accumulation and economic growth, at the macroscopic level, via (14.2.4), with capital and labor-output ratios determined by (14.2.5). Needless to say, given income distribution, *viz.*, the money-wage rate, (assuming that wages are functional and profits are residual) the growth rate of output is determined.

All this, as we pointed out before,[8] presupposes that factors of production are continuously substitutable in the production of a homogeneous output. The "differentiated" features of monopolistic competition and oligopoly do not conform to the requirements and foundation of the *continuous production function*. There is another alternative, strangely enough, which is classical in content and revolutionary in form, and which endeavors to account for the elements of "differentiated" outputs of different firms of all industries. This production function is a consequence of "input-output analysis." We wish to call this production function a "transformation function" because it demonstrates the transformation of inputs into the outputs of a heterogeneous nature.

A Transformation Function.   The following analysis can be applied to micro-problems, but since it has been employed for the anatomy of macro-problems, we will follow the convention.

Let us suppose that the economy is composed of n heterogeneous outputs $X_1, X_2, \ldots X_n$ of n industries. Each output is to be composed of m inputs x_{ij} for $i = 1, \ldots m$. If the input-output coefficients (which sometimes are called *technical* coefficients) are assumed to be constant for the production of the outputs of the economy, we can write:

(14.2.6)
$$\begin{cases} x_{11} = a_{11}X_1 & x_{12} = a_{12}X_2 \ldots x_{1n} = a_{1n}X_n \\ x_{21} = a_{21}X_1 & x_{22} = a_{22}X_2 \ldots x_{2n} = a_{2n}X_n \\ \cdot \quad \cdot \quad \cdot \quad \cdot \quad \cdot \quad \cdot \quad \cdot \quad \cdot \quad \cdot \quad \cdot \quad \cdot \quad \cdot \quad \cdot \quad \cdot \\ x_{m1} = a_{m1}X_1 & x_{m2} = a_{m2}X_2 \ldots x_{mn} = a_{mn}X_n \end{cases}$$

or

(14.2.7)
$$x_{ij} = a_{ij}X_j$$

where a_{ij} is the amount of the ith input used in the production of a unit of the jth output, so that the total usages are:

$$x_1 = \sum_{j=1}^{n} x_{ij}, \ldots, x_m = \sum_{j=1}^{n} x_{mj}.$$

---

[8] See Chapter 7, Section 7.4 pp. 168–172.

(14.2.6) or (14.2.7) is our transformation function which represents the transformation of inputs of the economy into the outputs. (14.2.6) demonstrates the analysis of the production of the whole economy. It assumes a constant and fixed technical coefficient, and thus production varies with constant returns to scale. The convenience of formulation (14.2.6) is that it can be used to represent the production function of a "firm." Since the discussion is related to microeconomics, we would like to apply the above analysis to a firm which has a single output X and two inputs x_1 and x_2 with technical coefficients a_1 and a_2 which determine the amounts of the two inputs per unit of output. Then, the transformation function of the firm is

(14.2.8) $$x_1 \geq a_1 X \quad \text{and} \quad x_2 \geq a_2 X.$$

(14.2.8) is and can be viewed as a special form of

$$X = f(x_1, x_2)$$

which is based on the assumption that factors are to be used in the ratio

$$x_1 : x_2 = a_1 : a_2$$

and in no other way. Any excess of one input or the other is just wasted, no increase in the output being obtained. The constant product curves then take the special form of Figure 14.2, output being in effect limited to combinations of inputs on the radius $0P$. The production function is also subject to constant returns to scale; if x_1 and x_2 are increased in proportion λ, output will also increase in proportion λ. That is to say; $Q_1 : Q_2 : Q_3 : \ldots$ $= 0P_1 : 0P_2 : 0P_3 : \ldots$ as in Figure 14.2. Then, on the assumption that the production function is homogeneous and linear, the technical relations are $x_1 = a_1 X$ and $x_2 = a_2 X$ where the direction of $0P$ is fixed by the ratio $a_1 : a_2$. In this case there is no reason why only one pair of fixed technical

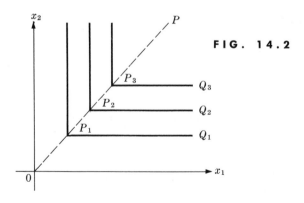

FIG. 14.2

coefficients, or one radius $0P$ across the constant product map, should be taken. A finite number of alternative technical coefficients can be taken:

$$\begin{array}{lll} x_{11} = a_{11}X; & \text{or} \quad x_{12} = a_{12}X \quad \text{or} \quad \ldots & x_{1n} = a_{1n}X \\ \text{and} & \text{and} & \ldots & \text{and} \\ x_{21} = a_{21}X; & x_{22} = a_{22}X & & x_{2n} = a_{2n}X. \end{array}$$

(14.2.9)

Each of these technical alternatives can be called a *production* process, a way of getting the product X from a particular fixed combination of inputs x_1 and x_2. Then, $x_{ij} = a_{ij}X$, with a_{ij} as a fixed technical coefficient, indicated the use of the ith input (for $i = 1, 2, \ldots m$) in the production of X in the jth process. In Figure 14.1 of the previous section, each process corresponds to a single radius like $0P$ across the constant product curves of a linear homogeneous production function. The assumption of technical conditions (14.2.9) for a firm implies the linear homogeneous case (constant returns to scale) and a choice between a finite number of processes. Indeed, a further step can be taken by assuming that production can proceed by two or more processes simultaneously and the results added.

The production function (14.2.9) is not as rigid as (14.2.2). Flexibility is obtained by combining (by addition) different processes. When extended, in an obvious way, to include many factors and products, this concept of a set of different processes, to be used singly or in combination, is the basis of "linear programming" or "activity analysis" of the firm, to be developed. It is a real alternative to a continuous production function (14.2.2) mentioned and explained above. For example, in the one-product-two-input case, the product may be obtained by use of four different types of machinery, each with its corresponding labor requirements. There are then four processes, with fixed technical coefficients (labor per machine ratios), between which the firm is of form (14.2.9), with four pairs of coefficients, and the decisions of the firm become an exercise in "linear programming."

Let us carry the above example for exposition.[9] Let us assume that the technical conditions (of a firm producing output Q with inputs K and N for capital and labor, respectively) are limited to five processes. Assuming constant returns to scale (a consequence of fixed technical coefficients), the production function of the firm will be of the type:

(14.2.10)

$$N_{11} = a_{11}Q, N_{12} = a_{12}Q, N_{13} = a_{13}Q, N_{14} = a_{14}Q, N_{15} = a_{15}Q$$
$$K_{21} = a_{21}Q, K_{22} = a_{22}Q, K_{23} = a_{23}Q, K_{24} = a_{24}Q, K_{25} = a_{25}Q$$

There are five processes, and each process is represented by a vector of three elements; *i.e.* $(1, -a_{1j}, -a_{2j})$ for the jth process, where, by convention, 1 indicates a unit output and $-a_{1j}, -a_{2j}$ the corresponding inputs of

---

[9] This example is taken from and based on R. Dorfman's "Mathematical or 'Linear' Programming: A Non-Mathematical Exposition," *American Economic Rev.* December 1953, pp. 794–808.

*j*th process. "Negative coefficients a_{nk} indicate that the commodity involved is used up by the activity (input of the process); contrariwise,
positive coefficients indicate that the commodity is produced (that the
commodity is an output). A value $a_{nk} = 0$ indicates that the *n*th commodity is not involved in the *k*th activity."[10] The whole set of technical
relations of the firm is represented by the "matrix"

(14.2.11)
$$\begin{bmatrix} 1 & 1 & 1 & 1 & 1 \\ -a_{11} & -a_{12} & -a_{13} & -a_{14} & -a_{15} \\ -a_{21} & -a_{22} & -a_{23} & -a_{24} & -a_{25} \end{bmatrix}$$

where the columns show the processes or "activities" of the firm. Such a
matrix has been called the *technology matrix* or, briefly, the *technology* of
the firm.[11] Or if there are *k*th processes, the *technology* will be:

$$\begin{bmatrix} 1 & 1 & 1 & \cdots & 1 \\ -a_{11} & -a_{12} & -a_{13} & \cdots & -a_{1k} \\ \cdot & \cdot & \cdot & \cdot & \cdot \\ -a_{m1} & -a_{m2} & -a_{m3} & \cdots & -a_{mk} \end{bmatrix}.$$

Our firm has five choices, activities, and these activities can be used singly or in combination under a linear homogeneous production function. The
diagrammatic representation of the activity analysis of the firm is shown
in Figure 14.3. It is assumed from the outset that the number of processes
is finite, that within a process the relevant factors are used in fixed proportions, and that output varies directly with inputs. The last two assumptions are based on and inferred from the constant returns to scale if the
production function is presumed. In Figure 14.3, the line $0A$ illustrates
the proportion in which K and N should be used and combined in the

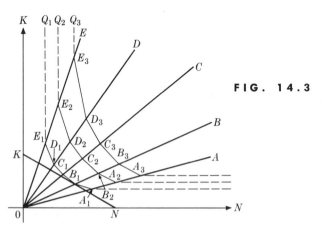

FIG. 14.3

---

[10] Koopmans, *op. cit.*, p. 36.
[11] *Ibid.*, p. 37.

process A, according to the technical coefficient of that activity. Also, $0B$ indicates the proportion in which K and N must be combined in the process B subject to the technical condition of that activity. Figure 14.3 shows that the output of Q produced by the combination of K and N denoted by A_1 on $0A$ is the same as that produced by B_1 on $0B$ and ... is the same promised by E_1 on $0E$. Likewise, the output Q_2 is the same for A_2, B_2, C_2, D_2, and E_2. The output for the level of subscripts 2 is higher than the one promised by 1's. Since the broken line $A_3B_3C_3D_3E_3$ is on a higher level than the ones before that, Q_3 belongs to a higher output in contrast to Q_2 and Q_1. This is roughly analogous to the typical one of indifference curve analysis.

In Figure 14.3 constant product curves are not "continuous" in the sense that they are not smooth as those of Figure 14.1. It indicates that processes can be combined. If the processes are both independent and efficient in the sense that they could be chosen for use alone, then the five points $A_1B_1C_1D_1E_1$ or $A_iB_iC_iD_iE_i$ are to be convex to the origin of the axes as illustrated in Figure 14.3. For efficient production we can only combine adjacent points representing adjacent activities. That is to say, for an efficient production we can combine A_1 and B_1; we cannot combine A_1 and C_1 or C_1 and E_1. Further, any combination of inputs represented by points within the *cone* identified by $0A$, $0B$, ... $0E$ is a possible combination of the activities but not a combination outside this *cone*.

The formation of the *technology* of a firm, thus understood, is of great importance because it defines the range of possibilities and processes whereby certain outputs can be created with given inputs. And the mapping of the activities of the firm against the price structure of inputs (the price-line or the budget constraint), similar to indifference curve analysis, determines the optimum allocation of inputs for a desired level of output. Let us suppose that the firm can purchase at constant prices unlimited quantities of K and N, as shown by the price line KN on Figure 14.3. The price-line passes through all activities. For optimization purposes, the firm would have to obtain K units of capital and N units of labor with the relevant activity $0B$ for production of a definite commodity. Here, we are assuming, *inter alia*, that there are finite number of activities and that the proportions in which the appropriate factors are to be employed are *not* continuously variable. The reason for the latter case is that different activities are combined into discrete "kinked" lines AE's, in contrast to the marginal analysis which assumes, *a la* calculus of continuous variation, that variables are continuously substitutable for each other.

There is one more point to be noted as far as this example is concerned. In the marginal analysis of the continuous production function, the supply of factors is unlimited while the prices of factors are fixed. In the discontinuous production of activity analysis, on the other hand, special attention is paid to the situation where there are factors which can be purchased at given prices up to a fixed quantity. Let us suppose that $0N$ and $0K$ are the quantities of labor and capital which are available at fixed prices. Then, accordingly, M denotes the output that the firm can produce, and this output is the optimum which can be produced with a combination of C and B, as shown in Figure 14.4.

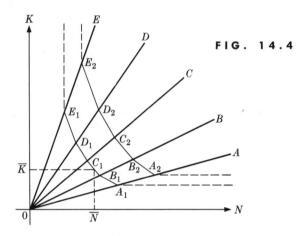

FIG. 14.4

14.3 The Technology, Commodities, and Activities; Basic Concepts of Activity Analysis

We have made a casual acquaintance with activity analysis through the example discussed in the previous section. The meaning of activity analysis *in its relation to linear programming* can be understood clearly and explicitly if the basic concepts of activity analysis — commodities, technology and activity — are defined.

Technology. The technology of a firm is the sum of its "activities." The sum of the activities put together into a matrix form is usually shown by the following matrix

$$A = \begin{bmatrix} a_{11} & a_{12} & \cdots & a_{1n} \\ a_{21} & a_{22} & \cdots & a_{2n} \\ \cdot & \cdot & \cdots & \cdot \\ a_{m1} & a_{m2} & \cdots & a_{mn} \end{bmatrix}.$$

The jth activity is shown by

$$A^{(j)} = \begin{bmatrix} a_{1j} \\ a_{2j} \\ \vdots \\ a_{mj} \end{bmatrix} = \{a_{1j}\}.$$

We are assuming *inter alia* that the basic activities are finite. Each activity is composed of commodities to be defined later on. The a's are given constants and commodities. Each positive a is the output of that process. There may be many positive a's in a process (activity). If there are negative a's, they identify inputs of the activity. The a's not appearing for an item in an activity are zero. This classification is made according to convention.

There are two assumptions which are incorporated into the notion of an activity: *divisibility* and *additivity*. Divisibility implies the continuous expansion or reduction of each activity in the process of production. This assumption in turn implies constant returns to scale. On the other hand, additivity signifies that activities can be combined without modifying their structural coefficients by which they are defined. The two assumptions can be simplified by

(14.3.1) $$\lambda A^{(j)} = \{\lambda a_{ij}\}$$

(14.3.2) $$A^{(j)} + A^{(t)} = \{(a_{ij} + a_{it})\}.$$

Assumptions (14.3.1) and (14.3.2), taken together, denote the combination of p activities:

(14.3.3) $$\sum_{j=1}^{p} \lambda_j A^{(j)} = \sum_{j=1}^{p} \lambda_j \{a_{ij}\} = \left\{ \left(\sum_{j=1}^{p} \lambda_j a_{ij} \right) \right\}$$

where $(\lambda_j \geq 0)$. The sum is itself an activity. Therefore, any activity can be written in the form of (14.3.3).

Commodity. "Each commodity is assumed to be homogeneous qualitatively and continuously divisible quantitatively. Commodities include *primary factors* of production, such as labor of various kinds, the use of land of various grades, including land giving access to mineral resources; *intermediate products.* such as coal, pig iron, steel; and *final products,* the production of which is the objective of the economy under study."[12] Accordingly, activity analysis is the study of the methods of control of the organization of production to attain that objective.

Technical Transformation and Convex Cones. If we have

		Outputs From Industries				Total Output of Industries
Inputs	x_{11}	x_{12}	x_{13}	$\ldots$	x_{1n}	Y_1
to	x_{21}	x_{22}	x_{23}	$\ldots$	x_{2n}	Y_2
Indus-	.	.	.	. . . .		. . . . .
tries	x_{m1}	x_{m2}	x_{m3}	$\ldots$	x_{mn}	Y_m
(14.3.4)	X_1	X_2	X_3	$\ldots$	X_n	

---

[12] *Ibid.,* p. 35.

we can form our technical transformation by

(14.3.5) $$x_{ij} = a_{ij}X_j$$

or

(14.3.6) $$\sum_{j=1}^{n} x_{ij} = Y_i \qquad (i = 1, 2, \ldots m)$$

where

$$\sum_{i=1}^{m} x_{i1} = X_1 \qquad \sum_{j=1}^{n} x_{1j} = Y_1$$

$$\sum_{j=1}^{n} X_j = \sum_{i=1}^{m} Y_i$$

with the coefficient matrix

(14.3.7)
$$\begin{bmatrix} a_{11} & a_{12} & \cdots & a_{1n} \\ a_{21} & a_{22} & \cdots & a_{2n} \\ \cdot & \cdot & \cdot & \cdot \\ a_{m1} & a_{m2} & \cdots & a_{mn} \end{bmatrix}.$$

If we take (14.3.6) for our transformation, each column of (14.3.7) will denote one activity. As we pointed out before, the elements of each activity might be negative, positive, or zero if the commodity is consumed, produced, or not used at all. We assume that there is at least one primary factor which is consumed by all activities where $a_{mj} < 0$ and $x_m < 0$.

The technical possibilities emanating from technical transformation (14.3.6) are composed of two *spaces:* (1) *activity space* of m dimensions each of which represents a particular combination of activities; (2) *commodity space* of n dimensions each of which represents a particular set of outputs.

In order to illustrate the activity and commodity spaces, we take a very simple example made up of three commodities and two activities. We make two assumptions at the outset. There is one commodity (here known as labor) which is used as an input of all activities and called hereafter a primary factor. There is, at least, one commodity which is *not* used as a primary factor and is for use outside of the system. This commodity is used as an input in any activity. Table (1) denotes our input-output coefficients.

TABLE 1

		Output			Final Demand	Total Output
	a_{11}	a_{12}	a_{13}	a_{14}	D_1	Y_1
Input	a_{21}	a_{22}	a_{23}	a_{24}	D_2	Y_2
	a_{31}	a_{32}	a_{33}	a_{34}		Y_3
	X_1	X_2	X_3	X_4		

Here we have three commodities and four activities. Our technology is

$$A = \begin{bmatrix} a_{11} & a_{12} & a_{13} & a_{14} \\ a_{21} & a_{22} & a_{23} & a_{24} \\ a_{31} & a_{32} & a_{33} & a_{34} \end{bmatrix}$$

and our four activities are

$$A_1 = \begin{bmatrix} a_{11} \\ a_{21} \\ a_{31} \end{bmatrix} \qquad A_2 = \begin{bmatrix} a_{12} \\ a_{22} \\ a_{32} \end{bmatrix} \qquad A_3 = \begin{bmatrix} a_{13} \\ a_{23} \\ a_{33} \end{bmatrix} \qquad A_4 = \begin{bmatrix} a_{14} \\ a_{24} \\ a_{34} \end{bmatrix}$$

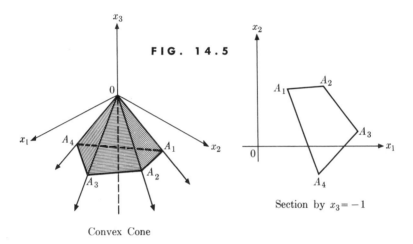

FIG. 14.5

Convex Cone

Section by $x_3 = -1$

If we put $a_{31} = a_{32} = a_{33} = a_{34} = -1$ and $a_{11}, a_{12}, a_{13}, a_{14};$ $a_{21},$ $a_{22}, a_{23}, a_{24} \geq 0$, the graphic representation of our activity analysis is: All *feasible points* $x = Ay$ lie in or on the boundary of the *cone* $0A_1A_2A_3A_4$ illustrated in Figure 14.5. This is analogous to the feasible solution space of the linear programming. $0x_1x_2x_3$ is called the *commodity space*, and the convex cone $0A_1A_2A_3A_4$ is called the *activity space* of our analysis. In order to obtain the activity space, we plot the points $A_1 = (a_{11}, a_{21}, -1)$, $A_2 = (a_{12}, a_{22}, -1)$, $A_3 = (a_{13}, a_{23}, -1)$ and $A_4 = (a_{14}, a_{24}, -1)$ on the three dimensional commodity space $0x_1x_2x_3$. The four points $A_1 \ldots A_4$ in the commodity space $0x_1x_2x_3$ and on the section by the plane $x_3 = -1$ make up a polygon in two-dimensional space $0x_1x_2$ as shown above. The polygon $A_1A_2A_3A_4$ should be located, according to assumptions, to the right of x_2 axis. It should be remembered that any point A_i cannot be on the line-segment between the other two points. Should this happen, A_i cannot be a basic activity.

14.4 Efficiency and Allocation

If $x = Ay$ defines the technical transformation of a system and if A is composed of A_i's activities, the whole convex cone (A) is denoted by A_i's activities and the technical transformation $x = Ay$. Further, as we pointed out before, the efficient allocation of resources should be obtained on the *boundary* of the convex cone (A). A boundary is composed of *facets* with dimensions not exceeding the number of commodities minus one. A *facet* of a boundary represents all possible allocations of a method using only specific number of activities. For instance, in the example of the preceding section, which consisted of 3 commodities and 4 activities, the facet $0A_1A_2$ is obtained from the two activities A_1 and A_2. Thus, the facet $(F) = 0A_1A_2$ is identified by

$$x = Fy \text{ where } y > 0 \text{ and } F = \begin{bmatrix} a_{11} & a_{12} \\ a_{21} & a_{22} \\ a_{31} & a_{32} \end{bmatrix}.$$

If the basic activities A_1 and A_2 are included in the facet, the facet is called closed and written (F); otherwise, it is called open and written $)F($. One more definition is in order. This definition is perhaps unrelated to the preceding section but relevant to the putting together of the loose ends later.

Definition: Efficient feasible resource allocation: *Efficient resource allocation is "an addition to the total net output of one of the desired commodities which does not entail a reduction in the net output of any other desired commodity." That is to say, the "efficiency criterion will prescribe maximization of the (negative) net output, or what is equivalent, minimization of the (positive) net input."*[13]

The net conclusion is that a feasible resource allocation is called efficient if the final output cannot be increased unless some other output is decreased or the primary factor is increased. Thus, efficiency is to be analyzed on two grounds: (1) where there is no limitation on the primary factor, (2) where there is a certain limitation on the primary factor.

The Efficiency Condition with No Limitation on Primary Inputs. We assume that our *technology* is:

(14.4.1)
$$A = \begin{bmatrix} a_{11} & a_{12} & a_{13} & a_{14} \\ a_{21} & a_{22} & a_{23} & a_{24} \\ a_{31} & a_{32} & a_{33} & a_{34} \end{bmatrix}$$

from the example of the preceding section. From the technology, we can deduce facets of different dimensions. If there is such a vector $P = (p_1, p_2, p_3)$ that:

(14.4.2)
$$p_1 a_{11} + p_2 a_{21} + p_3 a_{31} = 0$$
$$p_1 a_{12} + p_2 a_{22} + p_3 a_{32} \leq 0$$
$$p_1 a_{13} + p_2 a_{23} + p_3 a_{33} \leq 0$$
$$p_1 a_{14} + p_2 a_{24} + p_3 a_{34} \leq 0$$

---

[13] *Ibid.*, pp. 38–39.

then, the one-dimensional facet $0a_1$ is an efficient one. If

(14.4.3)
$$
\begin{aligned}
p_1 a_{11} + p_2 a_{21} + p_3 a_{31} &= 0 \\
p_1 a_{12} + p_2 a_{22} + p_3 a_{32} &= 0 \\
p_1 a_{13} + p_2 a_{23} + p_3 a_{33} &\leq 0 \\
p_1 a_{14} + p_2 a_{24} + p_3 a_{34} &\leq 0
\end{aligned}
$$

then, the two-dimensional facet $0A_1A_2$ is an efficient facet, and so on. A vector such as p in (14.4.2) and (14.4.3), which is positive, is at a right angle to the cone (A) on x. Such a vector is called *normal*. Thus, the practical problem of efficiency is to find the positive vector p which is *normal*. We can generalize the above results in the form of the following conditions: For a technology

(14.4.4)
$$
A = \begin{bmatrix}
a_{11} & a_{12} & \cdots & a_{1n} \\
a_{21} & a_{22} & \cdots & a_{2n} \\
\cdot & \cdot & \cdots & \cdot \\
a_{m1} & a_{m2} & \cdots & a_{mn}
\end{bmatrix}
$$

composed of m commodities and n activities, the necessary and sufficient condition that an open or closed facet of $i = 1, 2, \ldots n$ dimensions is efficient is that there exists a positive vector $p = (p_1, p_2, \ldots p_m)$ satisfying

(14.4.5)
$$
p'F = 0 \qquad p'A \leq 0
$$

where

$$
F = \begin{bmatrix}
a_{1j} \\
a_{2j} \\
a_{3j} \\
\vdots \\
a_{mj}
\end{bmatrix}
$$

j being the dimension of the facet while

$$
p'F = (p_1\ p_2 \ldots p_m) \begin{bmatrix}
a_{1j} \\
a_{2j} \\
\vdots \\
a_{mj}
\end{bmatrix} = 0
$$

and

$$
p'A = \begin{cases}
p_1 a_{11} & + p_2 a_{21} & + \cdots + p_m a_{m1} & = 0 \\
p_1 a_{12} & + p_2 a_{22} & + \cdots + p_m a_{m2} & = 0 \\
\cdot & \cdot & \cdots & \cdot \\
p_1 a_{1j} & + p_2 a_{2j} & + \cdots + p_m a_{mj} & = 0 \\
\cdot & \cdot & \cdots & \cdot \\
p_1 a_{1,j+1} & + p_2 a_{2,j+1} & + \cdots + p_m a_{m,j+1} & \leq 0 \\
\cdot & \cdot & \cdots & \cdot \\
p_1 a_{1n} & + p_2 a_{2n} & + \cdots + p_m a_{mn} & \leq 0
\end{cases}
$$

(The proof of the above conditions is given by Koopmans.)[14] Therefore, *feasible allocations* of resources for production are denoted by $x = Ay$ and the *efficient allocations* by the points of efficient facets of the convex cone (A) and the necessary and sufficient conditions (14.4.5) given above.

Efficiency Condition with Limitation on Primary Inputs. In the above case where there is no limitation on the primary factor, we can find one activity or combination of activities which would give us an efficient allocation. Stated concretely, there are certain facets of the convex cone (A) which are efficient. If we bring in prices of the factors and outputs, then our efficiency criterion will be judged by profitability; that is to say, those activities which yield profits are efficient and those which do not yield profits are inefficient.

The following section gives the analysis of the efficiency condition for allocation with a limited primary factor.[15] This analysis is not essentially different from the preceding one. We suppose that there are two sets of commodities: (1) final products such that net output

$$x_{\text{fin}} \geq 0$$

and (2) primary factors not desired in themselves with net output

$$x_{\text{pri}} \leq 0.$$

All intermediate products are ignored. Let us suppose that the amount of available primary factors from outside the system can be denoted by η_{pri}. If $x_{\text{pri}} = -\eta_{\text{pri}}$, all available resources are utilized and the prices of the primary factors will be set. But if $x_{\text{pri}} > -\eta_{\text{pri}}$, there are some parts of the primary factor which are utilized and the remainder which is unutilized.

Let us take the example that we had before. There are four activities, two final products, and one primary factor x_3. If we assume units for the primary factor, the technology matrix will appear as follows:

$$A = \begin{bmatrix} a_{11} & a_{12} & a_{13} & a_{14} \\ a_{21} & a_{22} & a_{23} & a_{24} \\ -1 & -1 & -1 & -1 \end{bmatrix}.$$

Since we do not have any intermediate products in the example, all available a's in the technology are positive. Figure 14.5 depicts the case where there are no limitations on x_3 except that all the facets in the positive quadrant of $0x_1x_2$. But if there is a limitation on one of the factors, say $x_3 = -1$, the *attainable cone* is simply the truncated cone at $x_3 = -1$,

---

[14] *Ibid.*, pp. 64–65.
[15] *Ibid.*, pp. 79–95.

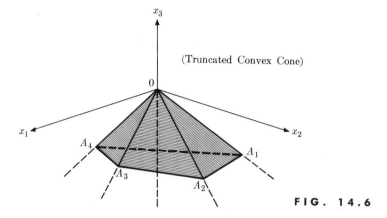

(Truncated Convex Cone)

FIG. 14.6

of the original cone.[16] And attainable allocations are checked and obtained from the truncated (attainable) cone. The new efficient points or facets of the attainable cone are deduced, again, according to the definition of efficiency given above; that an increase in the output of one final product is only attainable at the expense of a decrease in the output of another final product. Further, the maximum condition

$$\pi = \sum_{i=1}^{2} p_i x_i = \text{max},$$

or, in general

$$\pi = \sum_{i=1}^{n} p_i x_i = \text{max}$$

where π is the receipts from the outputs of final products at the (accounting) prices, should be maximized. p_i, the (accounting) prices, constitute the column vector of (14.4.5) and interpreted as a normal to an efficient facet of the cone representing $X = FY$.

The general results, developed more completely in Koopmans' aforementioned article for a technology of any order, are now obvious. The scale of production and price level are inferred hereunder.

The functions of the (accounting) prices is that they are used as rates of substitution and also determine the relative level of profits in various activities. This widens the scope of relative importance of the price system. These (accounting) prices will be identical with market prices if there is a competitive market condition which would equate rates of substitution

---

[16] C. Hildreth and S. Reiter have applied this approach to the problem of the selection of a crop rotation plan by an individual farmer. See "On the Choice of a Crop Rotation Plan," Chapter XI of Koopmans' *Activity Analysis of Production and Allocation*, pp. 177–188.

with the given market prices. However, as Taylor and Lange once suggested in a different context, these (accounting) prices are available to the central board of a planned economy as given data for resource allocation and efficient management of the economy.

We have emphasized that the efficient allocation constitutes a number of activities, located on those parts of the boundary of a truncated cone which also satisfy the attainment of the limits of one or more primary factors. Moreover, (accounting) prices eliminate unprofitable allocations, taking into account the maximum condition $\pi = \sum_{i=1}^{n} p_i x_i$, where π is the proceeds from the outputs of final products evaluated at the (accounting) prices. One final point should be made in passing. The number of scarce primary factors is equal to the number of activities, where the primary factors are not desired in themselves.

15 LINEAR PROGRAMMING AND THE THEORY OF GAMES

Robinson Crusoe, who dwelt on an island without any population and uninhabited by anything and moved and motivated by the desire to maximize the quantity of products which he could acquire from Mother Nature, has for many years and decades been the sole "subject-matter" of economic analysis: The entrepreneur who is confronted with nothing except nature and the limitations of nature, the consumer who has nothing in mind except pursuing his happiness. The odd thing is that our dear Robinson Crusoe does not have to worry about anything like "collusion," "ignorance," "imperfect mobility," etc. This does not, and should not, convey the suggestion that an economic analysis contingent upon Robinson Crusoe proviso is totally unrealistic; *econterario*, an analysis which abstracts from institutional assumptions possesses the quality of universal validity. However, for many years it was not disclosed that Robinson-Crusoe-type analysis was erected upon certain assumptions as though it was inclusive of all sorts of conditions and situations.

The recent revival of interest among academic economists in questions of resource allocation and economic growth under certain restrictions and frictions (lack of knowledge, imperfect mobility, collusion, etc.), seems to have stemmed on the formal side from the study of market structure and the behavior of the elements composing the market. Recent theories of resource allocation and growth in vogue among academic economists are interwoven with mathematical theories of linear programming and games. Mention has been made that linear programming has helped economists to formulate their theories of growth and allocation. On the other hand, the theory of games has been used in allocative problems.

In a one-man society of Robinson Crusoe, unique problems emerge. But in a society with two or more members, new problems may appear which may not be foreseen from the analysis of one-man society. Mathematically, if there are n x's which have the same properties, one can analyze, for instance x_i for $i = 1, 2, \ldots n$. Then, for the aggregate result, we may sum up the acquired information. This is the approach which we select with the "representative firm." Many economists, nowadays, question the relevancy of the "representative firm"-approach to our present complex world. It was through this bottleneck that John von Neumann, the mathematician, was preoccupied with the thought, over the past two decades, that perhaps economics could be viewed as a parlor game rather than a one-man society. The application of the theory of games to economics has been carried out in these days by economists as well as mathematicians. It has been applied to oligopoly and duopoly rather extensively.

In order to gain a clear understanding of the games theory, we first give the following definitions, terminologies, and expressions.

15.1 Definitions and Terminologies

The following definitions and terminologies are all drawn from J. C. C. McKinsey's *Introduction to the Theory of Games*, (McGraw-Hill) 1952, Chapter 1, pages 3–6.

A *game* is a set of rules, regulations, and conventions for play. *Play* is a particular possible realization of the rules of a game. *Move* is a point in a game at which one of the players picks out an alternative from some set of alternatives. *Choice* is the alternative picked out from some set of alternatives. A game with a finite number of moves, each of which involves only a finite number of alternatives, is called a *finite game*. Other games are called *infinite games*. The set of rules and conventions that one player alone employs to maximize his gains (or to minimize his losses) is called a *one-person game*. Here, the player assumes, *inter alia*, that he is confronted with those rules and conventions to pursue his interests. An example of this is the case of Robinson Crusoe involving the sort of economic analysis in which one individual alone, by employing infinite number of moves, is confronted and struggles against nature. In the theory of games, a one-person game is dull and drab and presents no intellectual difficulty. An *n-person game* is the case where the rules of the game are such that the players fall into n mutually exclusive sets in such a way that the people within each set have identical interests. The returns to the participants of a game determined by the rules of the game are called the *payments*.

If p_i is the payment to P_i of an n-person, $P_1, P_2, \ldots P_n$ game and if

(15.1.1)
$$\sum_{i=1}^{n} p_i = 0$$

the play is called "zero-sum." The zero-sum play assumes away the incentive to collude because, according to (15.1.1), the joint payment is constant irrespective of the choice of strategies. All parlor games are zero-sum, for in such a play a certain sum of money is transferred from one hand to another. Hence, additional wealth cannot be created or destroyed. In reality, all economic games from one to n-person games are non-zero sum, for all participants will always "gain" from a game.

A particular case of n-person zero-sum game is a two-person game such as duopoly. Two-person zero-sum games are also called *rectangular games*. In this special case, there are m plays open to one player and n plays at the disposal of his "antagonist." We assume that whatever is chosen by one cannot be known to the other. Suppose that there are two players; one called P_1 has three cards marked 1, 2, 3, and his "antagonist" called P_2 has four cards marked 1, 2, 3, and 4. There are three choices, *strategies*, open to P_1 and four choices, *strategies*, open to P_2. P_1 draws a card (it is either 1, 2, or 3). Also P_2, without having known P_1's strategy, draws a card. Let us suppose, for the sake of argument, that P_2 pays P_1 according to the following table:

TABLE 1

P_1 \ P_2	1	2	3	4
1	1	3	5	6
2	-1	0	2	3
3	-5	-4	-3	-2

That is, if P_1 draws the card marked "2" and P_2 draws the card marked "1," then P_2 will pay P_1 $-\$1$; that is, P_2 will receive \$1 from P_1. Or, if P_1 draws the card marked "1" and P_2 draws "4," P_2 must pay \$6 to P_1. Table 1, and any table formed accordingly, is called a "*payoff matrix*," and the above game, and any game formed therefrom, is called a *rectangular* or *two-person zero-sum* game. In general, we can form a rectangular game with m by n *pure strategies* open to P_1 and P_2 as follows:

TABLE 2

P_1 \ P_2	1	2	$\ldots$	n
1	a_{11}	a_{12}	$\cdots$	a_{1n}
2	a_{21}	a_{22}	$\cdots$	a_{2n}
$\vdots$	.	.	.	.
m	a_{m1}	a_{m2}	$\cdots$	a_{mn}

with the *payoff matrix*

$$A = \begin{bmatrix} a_{11} & a_{12} & \cdots & a_{1n} \\ a_{21} & a_{22} & \cdots & a_{2n} \\ . & . & . & . \\ a_{m1} & a_{m2} & \cdots & a_{mn} \end{bmatrix}.$$

We mentioned *strategy* in the preceding section. By a "strategy" for player P_i, $(i = 1, 2, \ldots n)$ we mean a function which is defined for each information set corresponding to P_i and whose value for each such information set is one of the alternatives available to P_i; thus a strategy tells the player what to do for every possible state of his knowledge. Suppose that, in a game of chess, one player P_1 always starts, from among all the alternatives open to him, with an "indian" opening, and that his "antagonist" opens a "counter-indian" from among all the alternatives open to him at each and every play. If player P_1 repeats one and the same strategy from among a set of strategies open to him, his strategy is called a *pure strategy*. But if he selects a different strategy, from among all possible strategies at his disposal, he is employing a *mixed strategy*.

15.2 Saddle Points and Minimax

Let us suppose that

(15.2.1)
$$Z = f(x, y)$$

where

(15.2.2)
$$1 \geqq x, \qquad y \geqq 0.$$

Let us also assume that the surface of $Z = f(x, y)$ is as in Figure 15.1 below, where there is a saddle-point at C. We are assuming *a la* (15.2.2) that x and y are continuous over their ranges.

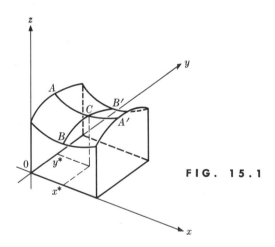

FIG. 15.1

For a given x, $f(x, y)$ changes with y and the maximum of Z, written as $\max_y f(x, y)$, will be on the ridge line $A\overset{\bullet}{A}'$. The ridge line AA' is the sum of all maxima derived therefrom. The minimum of the maxima

$$\min_x \max_y f(x, y)$$

is at point C. Likewise, for a given y, Z changes with x and the minimum of Z, $\min\limits_{x} f(x, y)$, is on the trough line BB'. BB' is the sum of minima derived therefrom. The maximum possible point of the minimum points

$$\max_{y} \min_{x} f(x, y)$$

is at point C. Then, intuitively point C has, corrsponding to specific x^* and y^* dimensions, the property

(15.2.3) $\min\limits_{x} \max\limits_{y} f(x, y) = \max\limits_{y} \min\limits_{x} f(x, y) = F(x^*, y^*).$

Point C is related to a minimax problem, namely, minimizing a set of maximum values and conversely maximizing a set of minimum values. Expression (15.2.3) is usually referred to as "Fixed" and "Existence" Theorems, and demonstrates a saddle point.

Figure 15.1 can illustrate a two-person zero-sum game with expectations $Z = f(x, y)$. Let us suppose that there are two players P_1 and P_2. P_1 assumes strategies from 0 to 1 of y, and that P_2 takes strategies 0 to 1 of x. P_1 can choose any strategy of his own choice. Let us say that he is very conservative and selects that value of y which is related to the worst choice of x made by P_2. That is to say, P_1 assumes that P_2 is clever enough to make the minimum possible mistake, namely,

$$\min_{x} f(x, y)$$

which is on the trough line BB'. Then, P_1 will select that y strategy which will give him the maximum value of all $\min\limits_{x} f(x, y)$ on BB', in other words, P_1 will choose that y which will offer him

$$\max_{y} \min_{x} f(x, y)$$

at C on BB'. No matter how P_2 plays, P_1 cannot get less than the amount shown by the height of the surface at C. Or, the trough line BB' shows the combination of the minima for P_2, no matter what value of y is taken by P_1. The object of P_1 is, and should be, to maximize the minimum points of the trough line BB'; i.e., to get to C. On the other hand, P_2's worst choice, if he plays wild, will position him over the ridge line AA'; he has to minimize his maximum choices, viz., to bring down the maximum to point C on the ridge line, no matter what y's are played by P_1; or

$$\min_{x} \max_{y} f(x, y).$$

That is, player P_2 figures out the worst choice (to him) that he may make, then to be on the safe side he will endeavor to minimize his worst choice.

Having based the example on the rational behavior of both players, one can deduce that both players aim at the point C related to

(15.2.4) $f(x^*, y^*) = \min_x \max_y f(x, y) = \max_y \min_x f(x, y).$

At this very point, the strategies are consistent and stable. It is in this sense that a game has a *stable* and *consistent* solution. Conversely, if there is a point like C for $f(x^*, y^*)$ such that (15.2.4) holds, it is the saddle point which yields a *stable* and *consistent* solution. If $f(x, y)$ does not possess any saddle point, within the considered range of variables, the game may or may not have any solution.

15.3 Two-Person Zero-Sum Games with Saddle Points

Let us consider the payoff matrix

$$A = \begin{bmatrix} a_{11} & a_{12} & \cdots & a_{1n} \\ a_{21} & a_{22} & \cdots & a_{2n} \\ \cdot & \cdot & \cdot & \cdot \\ a_{m1} & a_{m2} & \cdots & a_{mn} \end{bmatrix}$$

where $A = (a_{ij})_{(m,n)}$ is a real-valued function $f(i, j)$ such that $f(i, j)$ is defined by $f(i, j) = a_{ij}$.

Theorem 15.1.   Let us suppose that $\max_i \min_j f(i, j)$ and $\min_j \max_i f(i, j)$ exist, then we have

$$\max_i \min_j f(i, j) \leq \min_j \max_i f(i, j).$$

Proof. We can write

$$f(i, j) \leq \max_i f(i, j),$$

$$\min_j f(i, j) \leq f(i, j),$$

or

$$\min_j f(i, j) \leq \max_i f(i, j).$$

Since the left-hand side of the last expression is independent of i and the right-hand side of that expression is also independent of j, it can be written as

$$\max_i \min_j f(i, j) \leq \min_j \max_i f(i, j)$$

which completes the proof.

Definition.   *The saddle point $f(i^*, j^*)$ of $f(i, j)$ exists if the following conditions are met:*

$$f(i, j^*) \leq f(i^*, j^*) \leq f(i^*, j).$$

Theorem 15.2. Minimax Theorem. If both

$$\max_i \min_j f(i, j),$$

$$\min_j \max_i f(i, j)$$

exist; also, if there is a point $f(i^*, j^*)$ such that

$$f(i^*, j^*) = \max_i \min_j f(i, j) = \min_j \max_i f(i, j),$$

$f(i^*, j^*)$ is necessarily and sufficiently a saddle point of $f(i, j)$.

Proof. Let us suppose that $f(i^*, j^*)$ is a saddle point of $f(i, j)$. According to the definition given above,

$$f(i, j)^* \leqq f(i^*, j^*) \leqq f(i^*, j)$$

or

$$\max_i f(i, j^*) \leqq f(i^*, j^*) \leqq \min_j f(i^*, j),$$

since

$$\max_i f(i, j^*) \leqq f(i^*, j^*),$$

$$\min_j f(i^*, j) \geqq f(i^*, j^*).$$

Also, since

$$\min_j \max_i f(i, j) \leqq \max_i f(i, j^*),$$

$$\max_i \min_j f(i, j) \geqq \min_j f(i^*, j),$$

we can write

$$\min_j \max_i f(i, j) \leqq f(i^*, j^*) \leqq \max_i \min_j f(i, j).$$

According to Theorem 15.1, the first term of the last expression cannot be less than the third element of that expression; hence it should be concluded that all terms are equal. This is the sufficient condition; it is also the necessary condition.

From the Minimax Theorem the following corollary can be deduced.

Corollary 15.3. The necessary and sufficient condition that a game, the payoff matrix of which

$$A = \begin{bmatrix} a_{11} & a_{12} & \cdots & a_{1n} \\ a_{21} & a_{22} & \cdots & a_{2n} \\ \cdot & \cdot & \cdot & \cdot \\ a_{m1} & a_{m2} & \cdots & a_{mn} \end{bmatrix}$$

is a real-valued function of two variables i and j and defined by $f(i, j) = a_{ij}$, possesses a saddle point is given by

$$\max_i \min_j f(i, j) = \min_j \max_i f(i, j).$$

That is to say, the payoff matrix contains a pair of integers (i^*, j^*) such that $a_{i^*j^*}$ is simultaneously the minimum of its row and the maximum of its column. If (i^*, j^*) is that saddle point of A, then

$$a_{i^*j^*} = \max_i \min_j a_{ij} = \min_j \max_i a_{ij}.$$

The *optimal strategies* for the players, P_i for i and P_2 for j, are these: P_1 plays the row in which $a_{i^*j^*}$ is and P_2 plays the column in which $a_{i^*j^*}$ is.

Example 1. The payoff matrix

$$\begin{bmatrix} 2 & 1 & 3 \\ 4 & -1 & -2 \end{bmatrix}$$

has a saddle point at $(1, 2)$ because 1 is in the first row and is the minimum value of that row and in the second column and the maximum value of that column.

Example 2. The payoff matrix

$$\begin{bmatrix} 2 & 5 & 2 \\ 1 & 4 & -1 \end{bmatrix}$$

has two saddle points: one at $(1, 1)$ and the other one at $(1, 3)$.

Example 3. The payoff matrix

$$\begin{bmatrix} 2 & 5 & 2 \\ 1 & 4 & 3 \end{bmatrix}$$

has only one saddle point at $(1, 1)$.

Example 4. The payoff matrix

$$\begin{bmatrix} 1 & -1 \\ -1 & 1 \end{bmatrix}$$

does not possess any saddle point because there is not any element which is simultaneously the minimum of a row and the maximum of a column.

Example 5. The payoff matrix

$$\begin{bmatrix} 10 & 0 & 2 & -2 \\ 5 & 1 & 4 & 3 \\ -3 & 0 & -1 & -1 \end{bmatrix}$$

has one saddle point at $(2, 2)$ because 1 is concurrently the minimum value of the second row and the maximum value of the second column. The value of the game is 1. In other words, the optimal strategy for P_1 is to select his second strategy where the minimum feasible value that he gets is 1. Player P_2's optimal strategy should be his second column; this is the lowest price that he can pay on the basis of assuming complete rationality for both players. Since P_1 already has chosen the second row, P_2 may pay more, for instance 5, 4, and 3 if he plays wild. Thus the value of the game, the payoff at which both are settled, is 1.

The optimal strategy should not convey the suggestion that the *wisest* action and strategy for P_1 is to select his second strategy. No! If P_1 acquires the information that P_2 will choose his first strategy, then the wisest action for P_1 is his first strategy because then he can get 10 from P_2 in contrast to 1 of the *optimal* strategy. Or, conversely, if P_2 finds out that P_1 will choose his (own) first strategy, P_2 will select his fourth strategy whereby he pays P_1 the amount equal to -2, meaning that he will receive 2 from P_1.

(That is why the belligerent nations at *war* employ spies in order to acquire proper information on each other's strategies without the other one's knowing it.)

15.4 The Fundamental Theorems for Two-Person Zero-Sum Games

We noticed before that the two-person zero-sum game, the payoff matrix of which was

$$\begin{bmatrix} 1 & -1 \\ -1 & 1 \end{bmatrix},$$

did not have a saddle point. Similarly, the game whose payoff matrix is

(15.4.0)
$$\begin{bmatrix} 3 & 5 \\ 6 & 4 \end{bmatrix}$$

does not have a saddle point. The question remains: What are the optimum strategies which are not *strictly determined*, i.e., the optimum strategies for a game which has not an obvious saddle point? To explore this question, let us take (15.4.0).

If player P_1 plays 1, there is 50 per cent probability that P_2 may play 1 too, so that the net gain of P_1 is 3 rather than 5. But if P_1 plays 2 and P_2 finds this out, P_2 can play 2 to bring about 4 gain for P_1 rather than 6. Here there is no optimum way, so far, to say who plays what. For a single play of the game there is no difference between the two strategies as long as one's strategy is not conjectured by the other.

Next, let us consider that the game is played several times. Again player P_1 should not play 1 or 2 all the time. Since in either case P_2 will profit by it and will try to reduce his losses. Then, how should P_1 play the game? He may find a coin in his pocket and toss it; if it is heads, he will play the first row, and if it is tails, he will play the second row. This method will give him a *mixed strategy*.

Let us perform our mixed strategy in a general way. Suppose that P_1 has a chance device which can assign probabilities to the various choices. Suppose that P_1 plays 1 with probability x and 2 with probability $1 - x$ where $1 \geq x \geq 0$. Also, P_2 plays 1 with probability y and 2 with probability $1 - y$ where $1 \geq y \geq 0$. Further, if we assume that there is no association between the choices taken by P_1 and P_2, we will have the following pairs of strategies

$$\begin{bmatrix} 3xy & 5x(1-y) \\ 6(1-x)y & 4(1-x)(1-y) \end{bmatrix}.$$

Then, the average amount received by P_1; *i.e.*, the mathematical expectation of P_1, is

(15.4.1)
$$E(x, y) = 3xy + 5x(1-y) + 6(1-x)y$$
$$+4(1-x)(1-y)$$
$$E(x, y) = -4(x - \tfrac{1}{2})(y - \tfrac{1}{4}) + \tfrac{9}{2}.$$

In general, if we write our probability distribution of the strategies as

$$\begin{bmatrix} xyN & x(1-y)N \\ (1-x)yN & (1-x)(1-y)N \end{bmatrix},$$

for the payoff matrix

$$\begin{bmatrix} a_{11} & a_{12} \\ a_{21} & a_{22} \end{bmatrix},$$

our mathematical expectation will be

$$E(x, y) = a(x - b)(y - c) + d$$

where

$$a = a_{11} - a_{12} - a_{21} + a_{22} \neq 0$$
$$b = \frac{a_{22} - a_{21}}{a_{11} - a_{12} - a_{21} + a_{22}},$$
$$c = \frac{a_{22} - a_{12}}{a_{11} - a_{12} - a_{21} + a_{22}},$$

and

$$d = \frac{a_{11}a_{22} - a_{12}a_{21}}{a_{11} - a_{12} - a_{21} + a_{22}}.$$

As far as our specific example is concerned, if $x = \tfrac{1}{2}$, P_1 will be ensured that his mathematical expectation is $\tfrac{9}{2}$. P_1 cannot be sure that his expectation will be more than $\tfrac{9}{2}$, for P_2 by choosing $y = \tfrac{1}{4}$ can ensure that the mathematical expectation of P_1 is exactly $\tfrac{9}{2}$ and no more. Expressing (15.4.1) in a different form, we have:

(15.4.2)
$$E(x, \tfrac{1}{4}) \leq E(\tfrac{1}{2}, \tfrac{1}{4}) \leq E(\tfrac{1}{2}, y)$$

which, of course, implies that point $(\frac{1}{2}, \frac{1}{4})$ is a saddle point, according to our definition of the preceding section.

Condition (15.4.1) can be expressed in a general way. (This is the intuitive proof of the definition of the saddle point given above.) If the probabilities for playing 1 and 2 by P_1 are, respectively, x and $1 - x$, and for P_2 to play 1 and 2 are y and $1 - y$ respectively, then X^* for P_1 and Y^* for P_2 are optimal probabilities if

(15.4.3) $E(x, Y^*) \leqq E(X^*, Y^*) \leqq E(X^*, y),$

where

$$1 \geqq x \geqq 0 \quad \text{and} \quad 1 \geqq y \geqq 0.$$

If there is a game, the payoff matrix of which is

$$A = \begin{bmatrix} a_{11} & a_{12} & \cdots & a_{1n} \\ a_{21} & a_{22} & \cdots & a_{2n} \\ \cdot & \cdot & \cdot & \cdot \\ a_{m1} & a_{m2} & \cdots & a_{mn} \end{bmatrix}$$

and we suppose that the probabilities whereby P_1 plays are $x_1, \ldots x_i, \ldots x_m$ while those whereby P_2 plays are $y_1, \ldots y_i, y_{i+1}, \ldots y_n$ where

$$\sum_{i=1}^{m} x_i = 1,$$

$$\sum_{j=1}^{n} y_j = 1,$$

the mathematical expectation of P_1 is given by the bilinear form

(15.4.4) $E(x, y) = x'Ay = \sum_{j=1}^{n} \sum_{i=1}^{m} a_{ij} x_i y_j.$

If

(15.4.5) $E(x, Y^*) \leqq E(X^*, Y^*) \leqq E(X^*, y)$

where X^* and Y^* belong to the sets m-tuple $(x_1, \ldots, x_m)$ and n-tuple $(y_1, \ldots, y_n)$, the ordered point (X^*, Y^*) is called the solution or the *strategic saddle-point* of the game; and X^* and Y^* are the *mixed* or *optimal* strategies for P_1 and P_2, respectively.

This is called the fundamental or minimax theorem for two-person (rectangular) games. The following theorems without proofs are deduced from the fundamental theorem.

Theorem 15.4. Let the payoff matrix of a game be

$$A = \begin{bmatrix} a_{11} & a_{12} & \cdots & a_{1n} \\ a_{21} & a_{22} & \cdots & a_{2n} \\ \cdot & \cdot & \cdot & \cdot \\ a_{m1} & a_{m2} & \cdots & a_{mn} \end{bmatrix}.$$

And let the bilinear form

$$E(x, y) = \sum_{i=1}^{m} \sum_{j=1}^{n} a_{ij} x_i y_j = x' A y$$

define the expectation function $E(x, y)$ for $X = (x_1, \ldots x_m)$ and for $Y = (y_1, \ldots y_n)$. Then, we can have

(15.4.6) $$\max_{x \in X} \min_{y \in Y} E(x, y) = \min_{y \in Y} \max_{x \in X} E(x, y)$$

and, both exist (the symbol $\in$ means "belong").

Theorem 15.5. Let E be the expectation function of a payoff matrix $X = (a_{ij})_{(m,n)}$ whose value is v. The condition

(15.4.7) $$v \leqq E(X^*, y)$$

for every member of Y, is necessary and sufficient that X^*, a member of $X = (x_1, \ldots x_m)$, be an optimum strategy for P_1.
  Likewise, for every member of X, the condition

(15.4.8) $$v \geqq E(x, Y^*)$$

is necessary and sufficient so that Y^*, a member of $Y = (y_1, \ldots y_n)$, be an optimum strategy for P_2.
  If we substitute $E(i, y)$ for $E(X_i, y)$ and $E(x, Y_j)$, the condition

(15.4.9) $$E(i, Y^*) \leqq v \leqq E(X^*, j)$$

for $m \geqq i \geqq 1$ and $n \geqq j \geqq 1$, is necessary and sufficient that X^* and Y^* be optimal strategies for P_1 and P_2, respectively, and that v be the value of the game. Also, we have

(15.4.10) $$\max_{m \geqq i \geqq 1} E(i, Y^*) = \min_{n \geqq j \geqq 1} E(X^*, j).$$

Theorem 15.6. This theorem sums up the theorems stated before. Let us suppose that E is the expectation function of a two-person zero-sum (rectangular) game of m by n dimensions, and that X^* and Y^* are members of $X = (x_1, \ldots x_m)$ and $Y = (y_1, \ldots y_n)$, respectively. Then, the following conditions are all equivalent:
  (1) X^* and Y^* are optimal strategies for P_1 and P_2 respectively;
  (2) For X a member of vector X_i and Y of vector Y_j, the following condition holds

$$E(X, Y^*) \leqq E(X^*, Y^*) \leqq E(X^*, Y);$$

  (3) If i and j are any integers belonging to $m \geqq i \geqq 1$ and $n \geqq j \geqq 1$, then

$$E(i, Y^*) \leqq E(X^*, Y^*) \leqq E(X^*, j).$$

Theorem 15.7. Let X^* and Y^* be optimal strategies for an m by n two-person zero-sum game, whose value is v, with the expectation function P such that

$$E(i, Y^*) < v,$$
$$E(X^*, j) > v$$

for any $m \geq i \geq 1$ and $n \geq j \geq 1$, we have, respectively

$$X_i^* = 0$$

and

$$Y_j^* = 0.$$

Example 6. We wish to find the value and optimal strategies for the players of a two-person zero-sum game, the payoff matrix of which is:

$$\begin{bmatrix} 1 & -3 & 1 \\ -1 & 1 & 2 \\ 1 & 1 & -1 \end{bmatrix}.$$

According to condition (15.4.9) of Theorem 15.5, we should find numbers x_1, x_2, x_3, y_1, y_2, y_3 and v which satisfy the following conditions:

(15.4.11)
$$\begin{cases} 1 \geq x_1 \geq 0 \\ 1 \geq x_2 \geq 0 \\ 1 \geq x_3 \geq 0, \end{cases} \quad \begin{cases} 1 \geq y_1 \geq 0 \\ 1 \geq y_2 \geq 0 \\ 1 \geq y_3 \geq 0, \end{cases}$$

(15.4.12) $x_1 + x_2 + x_3 = 1, \quad y_1 + y_2 + y_3 = 1,$

and

(15.4.13)
$$\begin{cases} x_1 - x_2 + x_3 \geq v \\ -3x_1 + x_2 + x_3 \geq v \\ x_1 + 2x_2 - x_3 \geq v \end{cases} \quad \begin{cases} y_1 - 3y_2 + y_3 \leq v \\ -y_1 + y_2 + 2y_3 \leq v \\ y_1 + y_2 - y_3 \leq v. \end{cases}$$

Our problem constitutes systems containing inequalities as well as equalities. One way to solve (15.4.13), which can also satisfy (15.4.11) and (15.4.12), is to put (15.4.13) equal to v, *i.e.*, we replace all of the inequalities of (15.4.13) by equalities. By doing so, we obtain:

(15.4.14)
$$\begin{cases} x_1 - x_2 + x_3 = v \\ -3x_1 + x_2 + x_3 = v \\ x_1 + 2x_2 - x_3 = v \end{cases} \quad \begin{cases} y_1 - 3y_2 + y_3 = v \\ -y_1 + y_2 + 2y_3 = v \\ y_1 + y_2 - y_3 = v, \end{cases}$$

subject to (15.4.12). The set of equations (15.4.14) has the following solutions:

(15.4.15)
$$\begin{cases} x_1 = \tfrac{1}{6} \quad x_2 = \tfrac{2}{6} \quad x_3 = \tfrac{3}{6} \\ y_1 = \tfrac{3}{6} \quad y_2 = \tfrac{1}{6} \quad y_3 = \tfrac{2}{6} \end{cases}$$
$$v = \tfrac{2}{6}.$$

Since the set of solutions (15.4.15) also satisfy (15.4.12), it is a set of solutions for our original equations and inequations. An optimal strategy for P_1 to play this game is to choose the numbers 1, 2, 3 with respective probabilities $\frac{1}{6}$, $\frac{2}{6}$, and $\frac{3}{6}$; and for P_2 is to choose the numbers 1, 2, and 3, with respective probabilities $\frac{3}{6}$, $\frac{1}{6}$, and $\frac{2}{6}$. The value of the game is $\frac{2}{6}$; *i.e.*, P_2 should play in such a way as to make sure that P_1 will gain at least $\frac{2}{6}$, while P_1 can play in such a way as to make certain of not gaining more than $\frac{2}{6}$. This is a very strange game.

There are times when the set of equations corresponding to the six equations above turn out to be inconsistent or to have no solutions in the interval $(0, 1)$. We take the following example, which illustrates this difficulty, from McKinsey's *Introduction to the Theory of Games* (pp. 44–46).

Example 7. We find the value and optimal strategies for the two players of the two-person zero-sum game, the payoff matrix of which is:

$$\begin{bmatrix} 3 & -2 & 4 \\ -1 & 4 & 2 \\ 2 & 2 & 6 \end{bmatrix}$$

According[1] to the properties of Theorem 15.5, we have to find numbers x_1, x_2, x_3, y_1, y_2, y_3, and v which satisfy the following conditions:

(15.4.16)
$$\begin{cases} 1 \geq x_1 \geq 0 \\ 1 \geq x_2 \geq 0 \\ 1 \geq x_3 \geq 0 \end{cases} \quad \begin{cases} 1 \geq y_1 \geq 0 \\ 1 \geq y_2 \geq 0 \\ 1 \geq y_3 \geq 0 \end{cases}$$

also,

(15.4.17) $x_1 + x_2 + x_3 = 1 \qquad y_1 + y_2 + y_3 = 1$

and

(15.4.18)
$$\begin{cases} 3x_1 - x_2 + 2x_3 \geq v \\ -2x_1 + 4x_2 + 2x_3 \geq v \\ 4x_1 + 2x_2 + 6x_3 \geq v \end{cases} \quad \begin{cases} 3y_1 - 2y_2 + 4y_3 \leq v \\ -y_1 + 4y_2 + 2y_3 \leq v \\ 2y_1 + 2y_2 + 6y_3 \leq v. \end{cases}$$

If we replace all inequalities with equalities, as we did in the preceding example, there will be no solution for the system of equations. But we can utilize the unique property of Theorem 15.7 and just replace one or two of inequalities with equalities at a time. In this process of probing, we finally find the following case:

$$\begin{cases} 3x_1 - x_2 + 2x_3 = v \\ -2x_1 + 4x_2 + 2x_3 = v \\ 4x_1 + 2x_2 + 6x_3 > v \\ x_1 + x_2 + x_3 = 1. \end{cases} \quad \begin{cases} 3y_1 - 2y_2 + 4y_3 < v \\ -y_1 + 4y_2 + 2y_3 = v \\ 2y_1 + 2y_2 + 6y_3 = v \\ y_1 + y_2 + y_3 = 1. \end{cases}$$

---

[1] This example has been set and solved by J. C. C. McKinsey in *Introduction to the Theory of Games*, 1952, pp. 44–46.

The inequalities $4x_1 + 2x_2 + 6x_3 > v$ and $3y_1 - 2y_2 + 4y_3 < v$ imply that $y_3 = 0$ and $x_1 = 0$, respectively. Thus, we are to solve the equations

$$\begin{cases} -x_2 + 2x_3 = v \\ 4x_2 + 2x_3 = v \\ x_2 + x_3 = 1 \end{cases} \qquad \begin{cases} -y_1 + 4y_2 = v \\ 2y_1 + 2y_2 = v \\ y_1 + y_2 = 1. \end{cases}$$

This set of equations is found to have the following solution

$$x_2 = 0 \qquad x_3 = 1 \qquad y_1 = \tfrac{2}{5} \qquad y_2 = \tfrac{3}{5} \qquad v = 2.$$

We now substitute the values

$$\begin{cases} x_1 = 0, \quad x_2 = 0 \quad x_3 = 1 \\ y_1 = \tfrac{2}{5} \quad y_2 = \tfrac{3}{5} \quad y_3 = 0 \end{cases}$$
$$v = 2$$

into the original set of inequalities and notice that they are all satisfied. Thus, the vector $(0 \quad 0 \quad 1)$ is an optimal strategy for the first player, $(\tfrac{2}{5} \quad \tfrac{3}{5} \quad 0)$ is the optimal strategy for the second player, and finally the value of the game is 2.

15.5 Linear Programming and the Theory of Games

In this section we wish to show that an arbitrary two-person zero-sum game is equivalent to a linear programming problem. This section is based on J. Dantzig's[2] and D. H. Gale, H. W. Kuhn, and A. W. Tucker's[3] articles and proofs. It was J. von Neumann who first mentioned that a game problem could be reduced to a programming problem. He, however, conjectured that the converse reduction was possible.

Let there be given a two-person zero-sum game, the payoff matrix of which is $A = (a_{ij})_{(m,n)}$. Let us further assume that the player P_1 is engaged in a mixed strategy, $x_1, \ldots x_n$. Then, the expected payoff for P_1 is given by:

(15.5.0) $$Z = \min \sum_{j=1}^{n} a_{ij}x_j,$$

where, of course, $\sum x_j = 1$, and $x_j \geq 0$. Moreover, by virtue of a theorem due to von Neumann, the value of x_j which maximizes Z gives the optimal mixed strategy. Thus, we should seek the largest value of Z which satisfies the set of inequalities

(15.5.1) $$Ax \geqq Z.$$

---

[2] "A Proof of the Equivalence of the Programming Problem and the Game Problem," in Koopmans (Ed.) *op. cit.*, pp. 330–335.

[3] "Linear Programming and the Theory of Games," *Ibid.*, pp. 317–29.

We may rewrite (15.5.1) in an equation system by adding "slack" variables to the set of inequalities

(15.5.2)
$$a_{11}x_1 + a_{12}x_2 + \cdots + a_{1n}x_n - z_1 = Z,$$
$$a_{21}x_1 + a_{22}x_2 + \cdots + a_{2n}x_n - z_2 = Z,$$
$$\cdots \cdots \cdots \cdots$$
$$a_{m1}x_1 + a_{m2}x_2 + \cdots + a_{mn}x_n - z_m = Z,$$
$$x_1 + x_2 + \cdots + x_n = 1,$$

where $z_i \geqq 0$ and $x_j \geqq 0$.

Let us subtract the first equation of (15.5.2) from the second, third, etc.; the resulting system is equivalent to the linear programming problem of maximizing a linear form of non-negative variables subject to a system of linear restrictions, that is,

(15.5.3)
$$a_{11}x_1 + \cdots + a_{1n}x_n \qquad\qquad - z_1 \qquad\qquad = Z = \max,$$
$$(a_{21} - a_{11})x_1 + \cdots + (a_{2n} - a_{1n})x_n - (z_2 - z_1) = 0$$
$$\cdots \cdots \cdots \cdots \cdots$$
$$(a_{m1} - a_{11})x_1 + \cdots + (a_{mn} - a_{1n})x_n - (z_m - z_1) = 0$$
$$x_1 + \cdots + x_n \qquad\qquad\qquad = 1,$$

where $z_j \geqq 0$ and $x_j \geqq 0$.

It is obvious that solutions to (15.5.3) do exist and that the maximum of Z in (15.5.0) is equal to the maximum of Z of (15.5.1). Thus, a game is reduced to a linear programming problem.

Conversely, a linear programming problem can be reduced to its associated game problem. Let us consider the linear programming problem

(15.5.4)
$$AX \geqq B,$$

where $A = (a_{ij})_{(m,n)}$, $X = (x_1, \ldots x_n)$ and $B = (b_1, \ldots b_m)$. The set of solutions which satisfies (15.5.4) is called the feasible solution of (15.5.4). Let us suppose that the objective function

(15.5.5)
$$c_1x_1 + c_2x_2 + \cdots + c_nx_n \geqq Z,$$

is given. The feasible solution for (15.5.4) which satisfies (15.5.5) is called an optimum feasible solution. Now we write the dual for (15.5.4) and (15.5.5) to obtain

(15.5.6)
$$a_{11}y_1 + \cdots + a_{m1}y_m \leqq c_1$$
$$\cdots \cdots \cdots \cdots$$
$$a_{1n}y_1 + \cdots + a_{mn}y_m \leqq c_n,$$

and

(15.5.7)
$$b_1y_1 + \cdots + b_my_m \leqq Z',$$

where Z' is a maximum of the linear form (15.5.7) and $y_i \geqq 0$. Then we can, by virtue of a lemma proved by J. Farkas (1901) and Weyl (1950), find a set of feasible solutions y_i satisfying (15.5.7). Let us multiply the first inequality of (15.5.4) by y_1, the second one by y_2, and finally, the last one by y_m, then add them up to have:

(15.5.8) $$b_1 y_1 + \cdots + b_m y_m \leqq \left(\sum_{i-1}^{m} a_{i1} y_i \right) x_1 + \cdots + \left(\sum_{i=1}^{m} a_{in} y_i \right) x_n,$$

or

(15.5.9) $$b_1 y_1 + \cdots + b_m y_m \leqq c_1 x_1 + \cdots + c_n x_n,$$

and, according to the Lemma mentioned above, we will have

$$Z = Z'.$$

Now we wish to reduce the problem to a game problem. Consider the game problem given by the inequalities

$$a_{11} x_1 + \cdots + a_{1n} x_n - b_1 z \geqq Z,$$
$$\cdot \quad \cdot \quad \cdot \quad \cdot \quad \cdot \quad \cdot \quad \cdot \quad \cdot \quad \cdot \quad \cdot \quad \cdot \quad \cdot$$
$$a_{m1} x_1 + \cdots + a_{mn} x_n - b_m z \geqq Z,$$

(15.5.10)
$$\cdot \quad \cdot \quad \cdot \quad \cdot \quad \cdot \quad \cdot \quad \cdot \quad \cdot \quad \cdot \quad \cdot \quad \cdot$$
$$-(a_{11} y_1 + \cdots + a_{m1} y_m - c_1 z) \geqq Z,$$
$$\cdot \quad \cdot \quad \cdot \quad \cdot \quad \cdot \quad \cdot \quad \cdot \quad \cdot \quad \cdot \quad \cdot \quad \cdot$$
$$-(a_{1n} y_1 + \cdots + a_{mn} y_m - c_n z) \geqq Z,$$
$$-(c_1 x_1 + \cdots + c_n x_n) + (b_1 y_1 + \cdots + b_m y_m) \geqq Z,$$

where Z is a maximum. The payoff matrix associated with (15.5.10) is skew symmetric and can be written as

(15.5.11)
$$\begin{bmatrix} 0 & A & -b \\ -A' & 0 & c \\ b' & -c' & 0 \end{bmatrix}.$$

It is clear that a solution to (15.5.10) can be obtained if there is a solution to (15.5.4) and (15.5.6), with $Z = 0$. It is also shown that there is always a solution for (15.5.11), not necessarily with $z > 0$. But if there exists a solution for (15.5.11) with $z > 0$, we can obtain a solution to (15.5.4) and (15.5.6). Thus, a linear programming problem can be reduced to an associated game problem.

Answers to
Selected Exercises

The following answers to Selected Exercises of Chapters
1–12 are provided as a study guide for the student.

Exercises 1, page 20

1. a. $A = A(a)$; $A = a^2$.
    c. $V = V(a)$; $V = a^3$.
    e. $I = I(t)$; $I = 100 \times 0.03 \times t$.
    g. $R = R(x)$; $R = 2x$.
    h. $f(3) = 31, f(5) = 69, f(6) = 94$.
    m. $H(x + x) - H(x) = \dfrac{-3\,\Delta x}{(2x + 2\,\Delta x - 1)(2x - 1)}$.

9. Identity, identity, equation, identity, equation.
11. for $(5, -2)$ $x^2 - 3x - 10 = 0$,
    for $(3, 2)$ $x^2 - 5x + 6 = 0$,
    for $(10, -1)$ $x^2 - 9x - 10 = 0$,
    for $(-3, -1)$ $x^2 + 4x + 3 = 0$,
    for $(1, 3)$ $x^2 - 4x + 3 = 0$.

Exercises 2, page 46

1. $\log_4 64 = 3$, $\log_3 9 = 2$.
3. $\log_8 64 = 2$, $\log_{25} 125 = \frac{3}{2}$.
5. $x = e^{2y}$, $x = e^{\log_a y}$, $x = \dfrac{(2y + 1) \pm \sqrt{8y + 1}}{2}$

    $x = \dfrac{\log_e a - \log_e y}{b}$, $x = \log_d \left(1 - \dfrac{y - dy}{a}\right)$.
7. \$132.00.
9. \$9,380.00.
11. \$1,000.00.
13. $x = \dfrac{\pi}{2}$, $x = \cos^{-1}(-0.8)$.
15. 17, 22, 217.
23. $(-1)^{n-1} \dfrac{x^{2n-2}}{(2n - 2)!}$,

    $(-1)^{n-1} \dfrac{x(x - 1) \ldots (x - n + 1)}{n!}$.

25. $\dfrac{1}{2n}$ and 0,

   $-\dfrac{1}{2n}$ and 0.

Exercises 3, page 74

3.   Normal exponential.
7. $p = \frac{10}{11}$ and $S \equiv D = \frac{195}{11}$
   Since the slope of the supply curve is larger than the numerical value of the slope of the demand curve, the system is stable in both Marshallian and Walrasian senses.
9. $p = .0631$, $S \equiv D = 87.10$.
11. $p_b = -326.6971$, $p_c = 20.3786$, $p_h = -28.0637$, $p_o = 29.6815$.

Exercises 4, page 93

3. $\{0\}$, $\{a\}$, $\{b\}$, $\{c\}$, $\{a, b\}$, $\{b, c\}$ $\{a, c\}$, $\{a, b, c\}$.
7. $4 > -3$, $-\frac{1}{3} < \frac{5}{6}$.
15.   a. (-6).
   b. (15).
   e. (2).
21.   For $f(x) = 4x^2 - 3$.
   $f'(1) = 8$, $f'(-3) = -24$, $f'(3) = 24$, $f'(7) = 56$.
   For $f(x) = x - \dfrac{2}{3x}$
   $f'(1) = \frac{5}{3}$, $f'(-3) = \frac{29}{27}$, $f'(3) = \frac{29}{27}$, $f'(7) = \frac{149}{147}$.

Exercises 5, page 128

1.   a. $dy/dx = 3x^2 - 2x + 2$.
   b. $dy/dx = 2(2x + 2)(x^2 + 2x - 3)$.
   f. $dy/dx = \frac{1}{2}(x - 1)^{-1/2} + \frac{1}{2}(x + 2)^{-1/2}$.
   i. $dy/dx = 2\left(3x^2 + 2 - \dfrac{1}{x^2}\right)\left(x^3 + 2x - 3 + \dfrac{1}{x}\right)$.
   k. $dy/dx = \dfrac{-6x}{(x^2 + 6)^2}$.
   m. $dy/dx = \frac{1}{3}(9x^2 - 2x - 3)(1 - 3x - x^2 + 3x^3)^{-2/3}$.
3.   a. $dy/dx = \dfrac{3}{x - 3}$.
   c. $dy/dx = \frac{1}{2}(3 + x)^{-1/2} - \dfrac{2}{3 + x} + \dfrac{4}{x}$.
   d. $dy/dx = 3e^{3x} + \dfrac{3}{2x^2}\, e^{3/2x}$.
   i. $dy/dx = 0$.

5. a. $y' = 2e^{3x} + 6xe^{3x},$
        $y'' = 12e^{3x} + 18xe^{3x},$
        $y''' = 54e^{3x}(1 + x).$

    c. $y' = \dfrac{2a - x^2}{(2a + x^2)^2},$
        $y'' = \dfrac{2x^3 - 12ax}{(2a + x^2)^3},$
        $y''' = \dfrac{-6(x^4 - 12ax^2 + 4a^2)}{(2a + x^2)^4}.$

    e. $y' = \dfrac{x^2}{4} + 3, \quad y'' = \dfrac{x}{2}, \quad y''' = \dfrac{1}{2}.$

7. a. No extreme on the real axes.
    b. Min at $x = \sqrt{2}$, and Max. at $x = -\sqrt{2}$.
    e. Min at $x = e$.
    g. No extreme on the real axes.

9. 8 and 8.
11. $\sqrt{150} + 2.$
13. 210.
15. 1266.66.

Exercises 6, page 153

1. a. $\dfrac{\partial z}{\partial x} = 4x, \quad \dfrac{\partial z}{\partial y} = -9y^2, \quad \dfrac{\partial^2 z}{\partial x\, \partial y} = 0, \quad \dfrac{\partial^2 z}{\partial x^2} = 2,$
        $\dfrac{\partial^2 z}{\partial y^2} = -18y.$

    c. $\dfrac{\partial z}{\partial x} = e^x \sin y, \quad \dfrac{\partial z}{\partial y} = e^x \cos y, \quad \dfrac{\partial^2 z}{\partial x\, \partial y} = e^x \cos y,$
        $\dfrac{\partial^2 z}{\partial x^2} = e^x \sin y, \quad \dfrac{\partial^2 z}{\partial y^2} = -e^x \sin y.$

    e. $\dfrac{\partial z}{\partial x} = 0, \quad \dfrac{\partial z}{\partial y} = 2e^{2y}, \quad \dfrac{\partial^2 z}{\partial x\, \partial y} = 0, \quad \dfrac{\partial^2 z}{\partial y^2} = 4e^{2y}.$

    h. $\dfrac{\partial z}{\partial x} = 2e^{3x} \cos 3y + 6xe^{3x} \cos 3y,$
        $\dfrac{\partial z}{\partial y} = -6xe^{3x} \sin 3y,$
        $\dfrac{\partial^2 z}{\partial x\, \partial y} = -6e^{3x} \sin 3y - 18xe^{3x} \sin 3y,$
        $\dfrac{\partial^2 z}{\partial x^2} = 12e^{3x} \cos 3y + 18xe^{3x} \cos y,$
        $\dfrac{\partial^2 z}{\partial y^2} = -18xe^{3x} \cos 3y.$

3. a. $2x^2 - 4x + 3y^2 - z^2 - 2z = 0.$
    c. $8x^2 - 17x - 3y - z + 10 = 0.$
    e. $4x^2 - 5x - 8y^2 - 23y - 2z^2 + 9z - 7 = 0.$

7   $x = 1.18, \; y = -0.07, \; z = -0.52.$

Exercises 7, page 172

1.   a. $dz = 4x\,dx - 3x\,dy + 2y\,dy,$
             $d_x z = 4x\,dx - 3y\,dx,$
             $d_y z = -3x\,dy + 2y\,dy.$

    c. $dz = e^{-y^2}\cos x\,dx - 2ye^{-y^2}\sin x\,dy,$
             $d_x z = e^{-y^2}\cos x\,dx,$
             $d_y z = -2ye^{-y^2}\sin x\,dy.$

    g. $dz = \dfrac{3dx - 4y\,dy}{2(3x - 2y^2)},$

            $d_x z = \dfrac{3dx}{2(3x - 2y^2)},$

            $d_y z = \dfrac{-4y\,dy}{2(3x - 2y^2)}.$

    j. $dz = \dfrac{-2x}{(x^2 + y^2)^2}\,dx - \dfrac{2y}{(x^2 + y^2)^2}\,dy,$

            $d_x z = \dfrac{-2x}{(x^2 + y^2)^2}\,dx,$

            $d_y z = \dfrac{-2y}{(x^2 + y^2)^2}\,dy.$

3.   a. $\dfrac{dy}{dx} = \dfrac{-4y}{x}.$

    c. $\dfrac{dy}{dx} = \dfrac{5 - 4x}{9y^2}.$

    e. $\dfrac{dy}{dx} = \frac{1}{2}(x^{-1/2} + x^{-3/2}).$

    g. $\dfrac{dy}{dx} = \dfrac{-x^2}{y^2}.$

    i. $\dfrac{dy}{dx} = \dfrac{3}{4}x^{-1/4}.$

Exercises 8, page 203

1.   a. $x - x^2 + \frac{1}{12}x^4 + C.$

    c. $\dfrac{x^2}{2} - 2x + C.$

    e. $\dfrac{x^2}{2} + 2x + 4\log(x - 2) + C.$

3.   a. $\dfrac{-1}{2}\cos(3 + 2x) + C.$

    c. $-\frac{1}{3}e^{2x} + x - \frac{11}{18}\log(1 - 3e^{2x}) + C.$

    e. $\frac{1}{3}e^{3x} - \cos(x^2 + 4) + C.$

    g. $\frac{1}{3}e^{3x} + \dfrac{x^5}{5} + \frac{3}{2}e^{2x} + C.$

5.   a. $x\sin^{-1}3x + \frac{1}{6}\sqrt{1 - 9x^2} + C.$
    c. $x^3\log(x)^2 - \frac{2}{3}x^3 + C.$
    e. $x\log(3x + 1) - \frac{1}{3}x + \frac{1}{3}\log(3x + 1) + C.$

7. Total cost $= \dfrac{x^2}{4} + 6$.
9. Total cost $= \frac{2}{3}x^3 - \frac{187}{6}x + \frac{159}{2}$.
11. $Y_{10} = 570(\frac{57}{45})^2$.
13. a. $\frac{16}{3}$,
    c. no area.
15. a. $1 > x > -1$ for x^n.
    c. $\{x \in R : x < 0\}$ for e^{nx}.
    e. $\{x \in R : |x| > 1\}$ for $\dfrac{(-1)^n}{x^n}$.
    g. $\{0\}$ for $n!x^n$.
    i. $1 \geq x \geq -1$ for $\dfrac{x^n}{n(n+1)}$.

Exercises 9, page 248

1. a. second.
   c. first.
   e. fourth.
3. a. not exact.
   c. exact.
5. a. $y^2 + 4y - 3x^2 = C$.
   c. $y^2 - 2ye^x = C$.
   e. $4e^{-y} + 6xe^{2x} - 3e^{2x} = C$.
7. a. $3y^{-1} + x^4 = Cx$.
   c. $xy + x\cos x - \sin x = C$.
   e. $x = y(C + \log x)$.
9. a. $x^2 = (C + y)y$.
   c. $x^3 = 3y^3(\log Cy)$.
   e. $x + 2y = Cxy^3$.
11. a. $y = C_1 e^{2x} + C_2 e^{-2x}$.
    c. $y = C_1 e^{5x} + C_2 e^{3x}$.
    e. $y = C_1 e^{8x} + C_2 e^{2x}$.

Exercises 10, page 273

1. a. $y_t = y_0(-4)^t + \frac{7}{5}$.
   c. $y_t = y_0 4^t - 1$.
   e. $y_t = y_0(\frac{3}{4})^t + \frac{2}{7}$.
3. a. $y_t = C_1(\sqrt{2})^t + C_2(-\sqrt{2})$.
   c. $y_t = C_1 3^t + C_2 2^t$.
   e. $y_t = C_1\left(\dfrac{1 + \sqrt{11}\,i}{2}\right)^t + C_2\left(\dfrac{1 - \sqrt{11}\,i}{2}\right)^t$.

Exercises 11, page 295

1. a. $\begin{bmatrix} 5 & -6 & 9 & 10 & 11 \\ 30 & -3 & 26 & 36 & 45 \\ 15 & -12 & 11 & 11 & 16 \\ 6 & 14 & 4 & 14 & -1 \end{bmatrix}$.

  c. $\begin{bmatrix} 9 & 6 & 3 & 12 \\ 6 & 4 & 2 & 8 \\ 3 & 2 & 1 & 4 \\ -6 & -4 & -2 & -8 \end{bmatrix}$.

  e. -20.

Exercises 12, page 336

1. a. unique and consistent.
  c. inconsistent
3. a. linearly independent.

A Selected
Bibliography

AITKEN, A. C. *Determinants & Matrices*, Interscience, 1954.

ALBERT, A. A. *Modern Higher Algebra*, University of Chicago Press, 1937.

ALLEN, R. G. D. *Mathematical Analysis for Economists*, Macmillan, 1936.

———. *Mathematical Economics*, Macmillan, 1960.

AMERICAN ECONOMIC ASSOCIATION. *Readings in Cycle Theory*, Blakiston, 1944.

———. *Readings in Monetary Theory*, Blakiston, 1951.

———. *Readings in Price Theory*, Irwin, 1952.

ARROW, K. AND OTHERS. *Studies in Linear and Non-linear Programming*, Stanford University Press, 1958.

ARROW, K.; S. KARLIN. *Studies in the Mathematical Theory of Inventory and Production*, Stanford University Press, 1958.

ARROW, K; S. KARLIN; P. SUPPES. *Mathematical Methods in the Social Sciences*, Stanford University Press, 1959.

BAUMOL, W. J. *Economic Dynamics*, Macmillan, 1951.

———. "Activity Analysis in One Lesson," *American Economic Review*, 1958.

BEACH, E. F. *Economic Models*, Wiley, 1957.

BELLMAN, R. *Introduction to Matrix Analysis*, McGraw-Hill, 1960.

———. *Stability Theory of Differential Equations*, McGraw-Hill, 1953.

BELLMAN, R.; K. L. COOKE. *Differential-Difference Equations*, Academic Press, 1963.

BIRKHOFF, G.; S. MACLANE. *A Survey of Modern Algebra*, Macmillan, 1953.

BOCHER, M. *Introduction to Higher Algebra*, Macmillan, 1907.

BUSHAW, D. W.; R. W. CLOWER. *Introduction to Mathematical Economics*, Irwin, 1957.

CHARNES, A.; COOPER, W. W.; A. HENDERSON. *An Introduction to Linear Programming*, Wiley, 1953.

CHIPMAN, J. "Computational Problems in Linear Programming," *Review of Economics and Statistics*, 1953.

CISSELL-BRUGGEMAN. *Mathematics for Business and Economics*, Houghton Mifflin, 1962.

CODDINGTON, E. A.; N. LEVINSON. *Theory of Ordinary Differential Equations*, McGraw-Hill, 1955.

COOKE, R. G. *Matrix Calculus*, Interscience, 1956.

DANTZIG, G. B. "The Programming of Independent Activities: Mathematical Model," *Econometrica*, 1949.

403

DEBREU, G. *Theory of Value*, Wiley, 1959.

DEBREU, G., I. N. HERSTEIN. "Non-negative Square Matrices," Econometrica, 1953.

DICKSON, L. E. *New First Course in the Theory of Equations*, Wiley, 1960.

DOBB, M. H. *Economic Growth and Planning*, Monthly Review Press, 1960.

DOMAR, E. *Essays in the Theory of Economic Growth*, Oxford University Press, 1957.

DORFMAN, R. *Application of Linear Programming to the Theory of the Firm*, University of California Press, 1951.

DORFMAN, R.; P. A. SAMUELSON; R. SOLOW. *Linear Programming and Economic Analysis*, McGraw-Hill, 1958.

DUESENBERRY, J. S. *Business Cycles and Economic Growth*, McGraw-Hill, 1958.

DWYER, D. S. *Linear Computations*, Wiley, 1951.

EVANS, G. C. *Mathematical Introduction to Economics*, McGraw-Hill, 1930.

FRAZER, R. A.; W. J. DUNCAN; A. R. COLLAR. *Elementary Matrices and Some Applications to Dynamic and Differential Equations*, Cambridge University Press, 1950.

GALE, D. *The Theory of Linear Economic Model*, McGraw-Hill, 1960.

GARVIN, W. W. *Introduction to Linear Programming*, McGraw-Hill, 1960.

GASS, S. *Linear Programming*, McGraw-Hill, 1958.

GOLDBERG, S. *Introduction to Difference Equations*, Wiley, 1960.

GOLDBERGER, A. S. *Econometric Theory*, Wiley, 1964.

GOLOMB, M.; M. SHANKS. *Elements of Ordinary Differential Equations*, McGraw-Hill, 1953.

GOODWIN, R. M. "Dynamical Coupling with Special Reference to Markets Having Production Lags," *Econometrica*, 1947.

GUILLEMAN, E. A. *The Mathematics of Circuit Analysis*, Wiley, 1949.

HAAVELMO, T. *A Study in the Theory of Investment*, University of Chicago Press, 1960.

HADLY, G. *Linear Algebra*, Addison-Wesley, 1961.

HAHN, W. *Theory and Application of Liapunov's Direct Method.* (Trans. by S. H. Lehnigh and H. H. Hosenthien), Prentice-Hall, 1963.

HARDY, G. H. *A Course of Pure Mathematics*, Cambridge University Press, 1960.

HARROD, R. *Dynamic Economics*, Macmillan, 1948.

HAUSDORFF, F. *Set Theory*, (Trans. by John R. Aumann), Chelsea Press, 1957.

HAWKINS, D.; H. A. SIMON. "Some Conditions of Macroeconomic Stability," *Econometrica*, 1949.

HENDERSON, J. M.; E. QUANDT. *Microeconomic Theory*, McGraw-Hill, 1958.

HICKS, J. R. *A Contribution to the Theory of Trade Cycles*, Oxford University Press, 1950.

———. *Value and Capital*, Oxford University Press, 1960.

———. "Mr. Keynes and the Classics," *Econometrica*, 1937.

HILDEBRAND, F. B. *Introduction to Numerical Analysis*, McGraw-Hill, 1956.

HOOTEN, F. G. "Risk and the Cobweb Theorem," *Economic Journal*, 1950.

HOUTHAKKER, H. S. "The Present State of Consumption Theory: A Survey Article," *Econometrica*, 1961.

JAEGER, J. C. *Laplace Transformation*, Wiley, 1959.

JEVONS, W. S. *Theory of Political Economy*, Macmillan, 1888.

JOHNSTON, J. *Econometric Methods*, McGraw-Hill, 1963.

KALDOR, N. "Alternative Theories of Distribution," *Review of Economic Studies*, 1955–56.

KALECKI, M. "A Macrodynamic Theory of Business Cycles," *Econometrica*, 1935.

KEMENY, J. G.; J. L. SNELL; G. L. THOMPSON. *Finite Mathematics*, Prentice-Hall, 1957.

KEMKE, E. *Theory of Sets*, (Trans. by F. Bagemihl), Dover Press, 1950.

KEYNES, J. M. *General Theory*, Hartcort, 1936.

KLEIN, L. *A Textbook of Econometrics*, Row, Peterson, 1956.

―――. *An Introduction to Econometrics*, Prentice-Hall, 1962.

KOOPMANS, T. C. (Editor). *Activity Analysis of Production and Allocation*, Wiley, 1951.

KOOROS, A. "Aggregate Supply Function, A Comment," *Economic Journal*, 1961.

KOYCK, L. M. *Distributed Lags and Investment Analysis*, North-Holland Press, 1954.

KRASOVSKII, N. N. *Stability of Motion*, (Trans. by J. L. Brenner), Stanford University Press, 1963.

KUHN, H. W.; A. W. TUCKER. *Linear Inequalities and Related Systems*, Princeton University Press, 1956.

KUNZ, K. S. *Numerical Analysis*, McGraw-Hill, 1957.

KURIHARA, K. K. *Macroeconomics and Programming*, Allen and Unwin, 1964.

LANCZOS, C. *Applied Analysis*, Prentice-Hall, 1956.

LANGE, O. "Say's Law: A Restatement and Criticism," in *Studies in Mathematical Economics and Econometrics*, University of Chicago Press, 1942.

―――. *Price Flexibility and Employment*, Principia Press, 1944.

―――. *Introduction to Econometrics*, Pergamon Press, 1959.

LA SALLE, J.; S. LEFSCHETZ. *Stability By Liapunov's Direct Method*, Academic Press, 1961.

LEFSCHETZ, S. *Differential Equations, Geometric Theory*, Interscience Press, 1957.

LEONTIEF, W. W. *The Structure of the American Economics*, Oxford University Press, 1951.

―――. *Studies in the Structure of the American Economy*, Oxford University Press, 1953.

LUTZ, F. A. (Editor). *The Theory of Capital*, St. Martin's Press, 1961.

MARSHALL, ALFRED. *Principles of Economics*, Macmillan, 1922.

MCKINSEY, J. C. C. *Introduction to the Theory of Games*, McGraw-Hill, 1952.

MEADE, J. E. "A Simplified Model of Keynes' System," *Review of Economic Studies*, 1936.

―――. *A Neo-Classical Theory of Economic Growth*, Oxford University Press, 1961.

METZLER, L. A. "The Nature and Stability of Inventory Cycles," *Review of Economics and Statistics*, 1941.

———. "Stability of Multiple Markets: The Hicks Conditions," *Econometrica*, 1945.

MILLER, F. H. *Partial Differential Equations*, Wiley, 1941.

MIRSKY, L. *An Introduction to Linear Algebra*, Oxford University Press, 1961.

MORGENSTERN, O. *Economic Activity Analysis*, Wiley, 1954.

NEELKY, J. H.; J. TRACEY. *Differential and Integral Calculus*, Macmillan, 1939.

NEGISHI, T. "The Stability of a Competitive Equilibrium: A Survey Article," *Econometrica*, 1962.

NEUMANN, J. VON; O. MORGENSTERN. *Theory of Games and Economic Behavior*, Princeton University Press, 1954.

PATINKEN, D. *Money, Interest and Prices*, Row, Peterson, 1956.

PERLIS, S. *Theory of Matrices*, Addison-Wesley, 1958.

RICHARDSON, C. H. *An Introduction to the Calculus of Finite Differences*, Van Nostrand, 1960.

SAMUELSON, P. A. *Foundations of Economic Analysis*, Harvard University Press, 1947.

———. "Dynamic Process Analysis," *Survey of Contemporary Economics*, Irwin, 1948.

———. "Simple Mathematics of Income Determination," *Income, Employment, & Public Policy: Essays in Honor of Alvin H. Hansen.*, Norton, 1948.

SCHULTZ, H. *The Theory and Measurement of Demand*, University of Chicago Press, 1938.

SOLOW, R. "A Note on Dynamic Multipliers," *Econometrica*, 1951.

SPITZBART, A.; R. H. BARDELL. *College Algebra and Plane Trigonometry*, Addison-Wesley, 1961.

SPIVEY, A. *Linear Programming*, Macmillan, 1963.

STIGLER, G. J. *The Theory of Price*, Macmillan, 1952.

STOLL, R. F. *Linear Algebra and Matrix Theory*, McGraw-Hill, 1952.

TAYLOR, A. E. *Calculus with Analytic Geometry*, Prentice-Hall, 1959.

———. *Advanced Calculus*, Ginn & Co., 1955.

TINBERGEN, J.; H. C. BOS. *Mathematical Models of Economic Growth*, McGraw-Hill, 1962.

USPENSKY, J. V. *Theory of Equations*, McGraw-Hill, 1948.

VAJDA, S. *The Theory of Games and Linear Programming*, Methuen, 1956.

WALRAS, L. *Elements of Pure Economics*, (Trans. by W. Jaffe), Irwin, 1954.

WATSON, D. *Price Theory and Its Uses*, Houghton Mifflin, 1963.

YAMANE, T. *Mathematics for Economists*, Prentice-Hall, 1962.

Index